Collins
revision guides

TotalRevision

GCSEScience

Chris Sunley and Mike Smith

Series editor: Jayne de Courcy

CONTENTS AND REVISION PLANNER

ABOUT THIS BOOK

Exams are about much more than just repeating memorized facts, so we have planned this book to make your revision as active and effective as possible.

How?

- by breaking down the content into manageable chunks (Revision Sessions)

- by testing your understanding at every step of the way (Check Yourself Questions)

- by providing extra information to help you aim for the very top grade (A* Extras)

- by listing the most likely exam questions for each topic (Question Spotters)

- by giving you invaluable examiner's guidance about exam technique (Exam Practice)

  Revision Sessions

- Each topic is divided into a number of **short revision sessions**. You should be able to read through each of these in no more than 30 minutes. That is the maximum amount of time that you should spend on revising without taking a short break.

- Ask your teacher for a copy of your own exam board's **GCSE Science syllabus**. Tick off on the Contents list each of the revision sessions that you need to cover. It will probably be most of them.

 ## CHECK YOURSELF QUESTIONS

- At the end of each revision session there are some **Check Yourself Questions**. By trying these questions, you will immediately find out whether you have understood and remembered what you have read in the revision session. **Answers** are at the back of the book, along with **extra hints and guidance**.

- If you manage to answer all the Check Yourself Questions for a session correctly, then you can confidently tick off this topic in the box provided in the Contents list. If not, you will need to tick the 'Revise again' box to remind yourself to return to this topic later in your revision programme.

⚡ A* EXTRA

These boxes occur in each revision session. They contain some **extra information** which you need to learn if you are aiming to achieve the very top grade. If you have the chance to use these additional facts in your exam, it could make the difference between a good answer and a very good answer.

💡 QUESTION SPOTTER

It's obviously important to revise the facts, but it's also helpful to know how you might need to use this information in your exam.

The authors, who have been involved with examining for many years, know the sorts of questions that are most likely to be asked on each topic. They have put together these Question Spotter boxes so that they can help you to **focus your revision**.

Exam Practice

- This unit gives you **invaluable guidance on how to answer exam questions well**.

- It contains some sample students' answers to typical exam questions, followed by examiner's comments on them, showing where the students lost and gained marks. Reading through these will help you get a very clear idea of what you need to do in order to score **full marks** when answering questions in your exam.

- There are also some **typical exam questions** for you to try answering. Model answers are given at the back of the book for you to check your own answers against. There are also examiner's hints, highlighting **how to achieve full marks**.

- Working through this unit will give you an excellent grounding in exam technique. If you feel you want further exam practice, look at *Do Brilliantly GCSE Science*, also published by Collins Educational.

About your GCSE Science course

Does this book match my course?

This book has been written to support all the double and single-award Science GCSE syllabuses produced by the four Exam Boards in England and Wales. These syllabuses include content from the three main areas of Biology, Chemistry and Physics and are based on the National Curriculum Key Stage 4 Programmes of Study. This means that although different syllabuses may arrange the content in different ways, they must all cover the same work.

The double-Science courses lead to the award of two GCSE Science grades. The single-Science courses result in a single GCSE grade. The content of the single award syllabuses is taken from the double award. Ask your teacher whether you are following a single or double-award course.

Foundation and Higher Tier papers

In your GCSE science exam you will be entered for either the Foundation Tier exam papers or the Higher Tier exam papers. The Foundation exams allow you to obtain grades from G to C. The Higher exams allow you to obtain grades from D to A*.

What will my exam questions be like?

The exam questions will be of a type known as structured questions. Usually these are based on a particular topic and will include related questions. Some of these questions will require short answers involving a single word, phrase or sentence. Other questions will require a longer answer involving extended prose. You will have plenty of practice at both types of questions as you work through this book.

Short answer questions

These are used to test a wide range of knowledge and understanding quite quickly.

They are often worth one mark each.

Extended prose questions

These are used to test how well you can link different ideas together. Usually they ask you to explain ideas in some detail. It is important to use the correct scientific terms and to write clearly.

They may be worth four or five marks and sometimes more.

How should I answer exam questions?

- Look at the number of marks. The marks should tell you how long to spend on a question. A rough guide is a minute for every mark. The number of marks will indicate how many different points are required in the answer.

- Look at the space allocated for the answer. If only one line is given, then only a short answer is required, e.g. a single word, a short phrase or a short sentence. Some questions will require more extended writing and so four or more lines will be allocated.

- Read the question carefully. Students frequently answer the question they would like to answer rather than the one that has actually been set! Circle or underline the key words. Make sure you know what you are being asked to do. Are you choosing from a list? Are you using the Periodic Table? Are you completing a table? Have you been given the formula you will need to use in a calculation? Are you describing or explaining?

UNIT 1: LIFE PROCESSES AND CELLS

 ■ Characteristics of living things

☐ What is biology?

■ Biology is the study of living things. An individual living thing is called an **organism**. The two main types of organism are **animals** (which includes us) and **plants**.

■ Although there is a huge variety of organisms, they have many things in common. This includes the way they are built and how they work.

☐ Cells

■ Most living things are made up of building blocks called **cells**. Most cells are so small that they can only be seen with a microscope.

■ There are many different types of cells, which all have different jobs, such as nerve cells, muscle cells and blood cells. However, most cells have certain features in common.

■ Plant cells have features that are not found in animal cells. The diagrams show a typical animal cell and a typical plant cell.

Animal cell

cell membrane

mitochondrion

cytoplasm

nucleus

Plant cell

cell wall

cytoplasm

mitochondrion

cell membrane

nucleus

vacuole

chloroplast

☐ What do the different parts of a cell do?

■ The **cell membrane** holds the cell together and controls substances entering or leaving the cell.

■ The **cytoplasm** is more complicated than it looks. This is where many different chemical processes happen.

■ The **nucleus** contains **chromosomes** and **genes**. These control how a cell grows and works. Genes also control the features that can be passed on to offspring.

■ The **mitochondria** (singular: mitochondrion) are the parts of the cell where energy is released from food in the process known as **respiration**.

 A* EXTRA

The chemical reactions that take place in the cytoplasm are controlled by enzymes (biological catalysts).

- Plants have a **cell wall** as well as a cell membrane. It is much more rigid than the cell membrane and gives the cell shape and support.

- The plant cell's **vacuole** contains a liquid called cell sap, which is water with various substances dissolved in it. In a healthy plant the vacuole is large and helps support the cell.

- Plants also contain **chloroplasts**. These contain the green pigment **chlorophyll**, which absorbs the light energy that plants need to make food in the process known as **photosynthesis**.

Similarities	Differences	
Most cells contain	**Animal cells**	**Plant cells**
Cell membrane	No cell wall	Have a cell wall
Cytoplasm	No large vacuole (although there may be small ones)	Usually have a large vacuole
Nucleus	No chloroplasts	Green parts of a plant contain chloroplasts
Mitochondria	Many irregular shapes	Usually have a regular shape

QUESTION SPOTTER

▸ You will often be asked to label the outside layer of a cell.
▸ Whether it is the cell membrane or the cell wall depends on what type of cell it is.

Organisation of cells

- Many cells are not 'typical' cells like the ones just described. They are **specialised** – they have special features that allow them to carry out different jobs.

- Cells of the same type form **tissue**. Different tissues may make up an **organ**. Organs that work together make up an **organ system**.

- For example, the circulatory system includes the heart organ, which contains muscle tissue and nervous tissue, which are made of muscle cells and nerve cells.

CHECK YOURSELF QUESTIONS

Q1 Look at the diagram of an onion cell.

  a How is the onion cell different from a typical plant cell?
  b Explain the reason for this difference.
  c How is the onion cell different from an animal cell?

Q2 Name which part of a cell does the following:
  a Releases energy from food.

  b Allows oxygen to enter.
  c Contains the genes.
  d Contains cell sap.
  e Stops plant cells swelling if they take in a lot of water.

Q3 For each of the following say whether it is a cell, a tissue, an organ, a system or an organism:
  a oak tree
  b human egg
  c brain, spinal cord and nerves
  d leaf
  e stomach lining
  f kidney.

Answers are on page 226.

Transport into and out of cells

☐ How do substances enter and leave cells?

■ It's not only whole organisms that take in or give out in substances (for example when animals eat and breathe or when they excrete) – each cell in a body has to take in and give out different things. All of these things will have to pass through the **cell membrane**.

■ There are three main ways substances enter and leave cells:

1 diffusion

2 osmosis

3 active transport.

☐ Diffusion

■ Substances like water, oxygen, carbon dioxide and food are made of particles. You will find out more about particles in Unit 8.

■ In liquids and gases the particles are constantly moving around. This means that they will tend to spread themselves out evenly. For example, if you dissolve sugar in a cup of tea, even if you do not stir it, the sugar will eventually spread throughout the tea because the sugar molecules are constantly moving around, colliding with and bouncing off other particles. This is an example of **diffusion**.

diffusion is net movement from a region of high concentration to a region of low concentration.

 water molecules

 sugar molecules

The sugar molecules are concentrated in one area.

The sugar molecules are spreading out because they are constantly moving and colliding.

The sugar molecules are now evenly concentrated throughout.

SUMMARY OF DIFFUSION

■ Diffusion occurs when there is a difference in concentration. The greater the difference in concentration the faster the rate of diffusion.

■ Particles diffuse from regions of high concentration to regions of low concentration. They move along the **concentration gradient**.

■ Diffusion stops when the particles are evenly concentrated. But this does not mean that the particles themselves stop moving.

■ Diffusion happens because particles are constantly and randomly moving. It does not need an input of energy from a plant or animal.

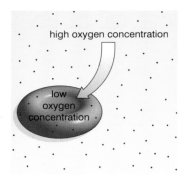

A high concentration gradient leads to diffusion. Red blood cells low in oxygen will soak it up from more oxygen-rich surroundings.

DIFFUSION IN CELLS

- Substances can enter and leave cells by diffusion. If there is a higher concentration on one side of the membrane than the other and the substance can move through the membrane, then it will.

- For example, red blood cells travel to the lungs to collect oxygen. There is a **low** oxygen concentration in the cells (because they have given up their oxygen to other parts of the body) but a **high** oxygen concentration in the air spaces in the lungs. Therefore oxygen diffuses into the red blood cells.

- Other examples of diffusion are oxygen and carbon dioxide moving in and out of plant leaves, and digested food in the small intestine entering the blood. You can read more about diffusion in Unit 8.

⸢⸤Osmosis

- Osmosis is a special example of diffusion where **only water** moves into or out of cells. It occurs because cell membranes are **partially permeable** – they allow some substances (such as water) to move through them but not others.

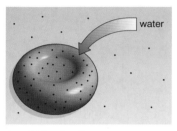

A red blood cell in pure water.

- Water will diffuse from a place where there is a high concentration of water molecules (such as a dilute sugar solution) to where there is a low concentration of water molecules (such as a concentrated sugar solution).

A red blood cell in in a concentrated solution.

- Many people confuse the concentration of the solution with the concentration of the water. Remember, it is the **water that is moving**, so we must think of the **concentration of water in the solution** instead of the concentration of substance dissolved in it.
  - A low concentration of dissolved substances means a high concentration of water.
  - A high concentration of dissolved substances means a low concentration of water. So the water is still moving from a high concentration (of water) to a low concentration (of water), even though this is often described as water moving from a low-concentration **solution** to a high-concentration **solution**.

The water is less concentrated on the right and more concentrated on the left. The water diffuses to the right. This sort of diffusion is known as osmosis.

- One important example of osmosis is water entering the roots of plants.

- If animal cells such as blood cells are placed in different-strength solutions they will shrink or swell up (and even burst) depending on whether they gain or lose water via osmosis.

⊏⊐ Active transport

- Sometimes cells need to absorb substances **against a concentration gradient** – from a region of low concentration to a region of high concentration.

- For example, root hair cells may take in nitrate ions from the soil even though the concentration of these ions is higher in the plant than in the soil. The way that the nitrate ions are absorbed is called **active transport**. Another example of active transport is dissolved ions being actively absorbed back into the blood from kidney tubules.

- Active transport occurs when special **'carrier proteins'** on the surface of a cell pick up particles from one side of the membrane and transport them to the other side. You can see this happening in the diagram below.

- Active transport uses energy that the cells release during respiration.

? CHECK YOURSELF QUESTIONS

Q1 An old-fashioned way of killing slugs in the garden is to sprinkle salt on them. This kills slugs by drying them out. Explain why this would dry them out.

Q2 Which of the following are examples of: diffusion, osmosis or neither?
   a Carbon dioxide entering a leaf when it is photosynthesising.
   b Food entering your stomach when you swallow.

   c Tears leaving your tear ducts when you cry.
   d A dried out piece of celery swelling up when placed in a bowl of water.

Q3 Why would you expect plant root hair cells to contain more mitochondria than other plant cells?

Answers are on page 226.

UNIT 2: HUMAN BODY SYSTEMS

 REVISION SESSION I

 Respiration

⊏⊐ What is respiration?

- The energy that our bodies need to keep us alive is released from our food. Releasing the energy is called **respiration** and happens in every cell of our body. The food is usually **glucose** (sugar) but other kinds of food can be used if enough glucose is not available.

- Respiration usually involves **oxygen**. This kind of respiration is called **aerobic respiration**. Water and carbon dioxide are produced as waste products.

- Aerobic respiration can be summarised by a word equation:

  glucose + oxygen → water + carbon dioxide + energy

- It can also be written as a chemical equation:

  $$C_6H_{12}O_6 + 6O_2 \rightarrow 6H_2O + 6CO_2 + \text{energy}$$

- The energy released is used for all the processes of life: movement, sensitivity, growth, reproduction, excretion and nutrition (feeding). Eventually most of the energy is lost as heat.

- Aerobic respiration provides most of the energy we need. If we need to release more, for example if we are exercising, then aerobic respiration increases. For this to happen the cells involved, in this case the muscle cells, need more glucose and oxygen. Breathing gets faster and deeper to take in more oxygen and the heart beats faster to get the oxygen and glucose to the muscles more quickly.

⊏⊐ Anaerobic respiration

- There is a limit to how fast we can breathe and how fast the heart can beat. This means that the muscles might not get enough oxygen. In this case another kind of respiration is used that does not need oxygen. This is called **anaerobic respiration**.

- Anaerobic respiration is shown by the word equation:

  glucose → lactic acid + energy

- Although anaerobic respiration may be happening to a small extent a lot of the time, it really only happens to a great extent when aerobic respiration can not provide all the energy needed.

- There are other kinds of anaerobic respiration in other organisms that produce different substances. For example, yeast respires anaerobically, converting sugar directly into ethanol and carbon dioxide, releasing energy.

Differences between aerobic and anaerobic respiration	
Aerobic respiration	**Anaerobic respiration**
Uses oxygen	Does not use oxygen
Does not make lactic acid	Makes lactic acid
Makes carbon dioxide	Does not make carbon dioxide
Makes water	Does not make water
Releases a large amount of energy	Releases a small amount of energy

⊡ The oxygen debt

- The lactic acid that builds up during anaerobic respiration in humans is poisonous. It causes muscle fatigue (tiredness) and makes muscles ache.

- Lactic acid has to be broken down, and oxygen is needed to do this. This is why you continue to breathe quickly even after you have finished exercising. You are taking in the extra oxygen you need to remove the lactic acid. This is sometimes called **'repaying the oxygen debt'**.

- Only when all the lactic acid has been broken down do your heart rate and breathing return to normal.

QUESTION SPOTTER

- You can expect to get at least one question on respiration in your exam.
- A key to answering most questions is remembering the equations. For example, you may be asked why your breathing rate increases during exercise. In your answer include the need for an increased oxygen supply so the muscles can release more energy, and the need to get rid of the extra carbon dioxide produced.

CHECK YOURSELF QUESTIONS

Q1 Why do living things respire?

Q2 Where does respiration happen?

Q3 a Why is aerobic respiration better than anaerobic respiration?

b If aerobic respiration is better, why does anaerobic respiration sometimes happen?

Answers are on page 227.

Blood and the circulatory system

⌑ What are the functions of the blood?

■ Blood is the body's **transport system**, carrying materials from one part of the body to another. Some of the substances transported are shown in the table below:

Substance	Carried from	Carried to
Food (glucose, amino acids, fat)	Small intestine	All parts of the body
Water	Intestines	All parts of the body
Oxygen	Lungs	All parts of the body
Carbon dioxide	All parts of the body	Lungs
Urea (waste)	Liver	Kidneys
Hormones	Glands	All parts of the body (different hormones affect different parts)

■ The blood also plays a part in **fighting disease** and in **controlling body temperature**. You can find out more about these in Unit 3.

Parts of the blood	Job
Plasma (pale yellow liquid making up most of the blood)	Transports food, carbon dioxide, urea, hormones, antibodies and other substances all dissolved in water. Heat is also redistributed around the body
Red blood cells	Carry oxygen (and some carbon dioxide)
White blood cells	Defend body against disease. (See Unit 3)
Platelets	Involved in blood clotting

red blood cells

platelets

white blood cells

Blood is mostly water, containing cells and many dissolved substances.

A✳ EXTRA

▸ In the lungs, haemoglobin combines with oxygen to form oxyhaemoglobin.
▸ In other organs and tissues oxyhaemoglobin splits up into oxygen and haemoglobin.

Red blood cells

■ Red blood cells are specialised to carry oxygen.

Feature of red blood cells	How it helps
'Biconcave' disc shape (flattened with a dimple in each side)	Large surface area for oxygen to enter and leave
No nucleus	More room to carry oxygen
Contains haemoglobin (red pigment)	Haemoglobin combines with oxygen to form oxyhaemoglobin. The oxygen is released when the cells reach tissues that need it.
Small	Can fit inside the smallest blood capillaries. Small cells can quickly 'fill up' with oxygen as it is not far for the oxygen to travel right to the centre.
Flexible	Can squeeze into the smallest capillary
Large number	Can carry a lot of oxygen

In this micrograph you can see the distinctive 'biconcave' shape of red blood cells.

The circulatory system

■ Blood flows around the body through **arteries**, **veins** and **capillaries**. The **heart** pumps to keep the blood flowing.

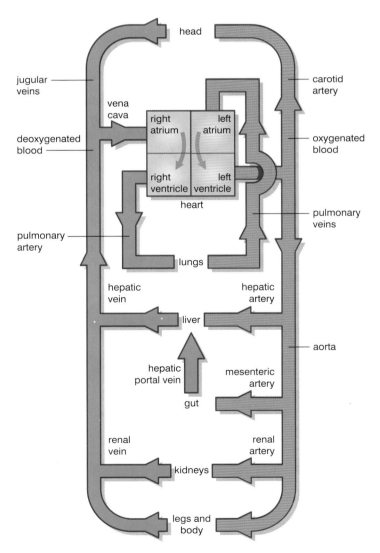

The heart

- The heart is a muscular bag that pumps blood by expanding in size, filling with blood, and then contracting, forcing the blood on its way.

- The heart is two pumps in one. The right side pumps blood to the lungs to collect oxygen. The left side then pumps the **oxygenated blood** around the rest of the body. The **deoxygenated** (without oxygen) blood then returns to the right side to be sent to the lungs again.

- The heart contains several valves and four chambers, two called atria (singular: atrium) and two called ventricles. The **atria** have thin walls. They collect blood before it enters the ventricles. The **ventricles** have thick muscular walls that contract, forcing the blood out. The **valves** allow the blood to only flow one way, preventing it flowing back the way it has come from.

Blood vessels

- Blood leaves the heart through **arteries** and returns through **veins**. **Capillaries** connect the two. (Remember, **a** for **a**rteries that travel **a**way from the heart. Ve**in**s carry blood **in**to the heart.)

- Arteries, veins and capillaries are adapted to carry out their different jobs.

Blood vessel	Job	Adaptations	Explanation
Arteries	Carry blood away from heart.	Thick muscular and elastic wall.	Blood leaves the heart under high pressure. The thick wall is needed to withstand and maintain the pressure. The elastic wall gradually reduces the harsh surge of the pumped blood to a steadier flow.
Veins	Carry blood back to the heart.	Thinner walls than arteries.	Blood is now at a lower pressure so there is no need to withstand it.
		Large lumen (space in the middle).	Provides less resistance to blood flow.
		Valves.	Prevent back flow which could happen because of the reduced pressure.
Capillaries	Exchange substances with body tissues.	Thin, permeable wall (may only be one cell thick).	Substances such as oxygen and food can enter and leave the blood through the capillary walls.
		Small size.	Can reach inside body tissues and between cells.

normal blood flow

veins have valves to stop the blood flowing backwards

open

closed

The valves in the veins prevent backflow.

⌂ Double circulation

- In humans (but not all animals) the blood travels through the heart twice on each complete journey around the body. This is a **double circulation**.

- By the time the blood has been pushed through a system of capillaries (in either the lungs or the rest of the body) it is at quite a low pressure. The pressure required to push the blood through the lungs and then the rest of the body in one go would be enormous and could damage the blood vessels. A double circulation system maintains the high blood pressure needed for efficient transport of materials around the body.

- The double circulation also allows for the fact that the pressure needed to push blood through the lungs (a relatively short round trip) is much smaller than the pressure needed to push blood around the rest of the body. This is why the left half of the heart is much more muscular than the right half.

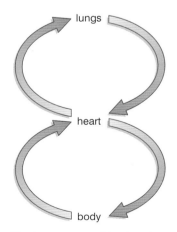

lungs

heart

body

The heart pumps blood to the lungs and back, then to the body and back. This is a double circulation.

Q1 Small organisms, like *Amoeba*, a single-celled animal, do not need a transport system. So why do bigger organisms need them?

Q2 This equation shows the reversible reaction between oxygen and haemoglobin.

oxygen + haemoglobin $\rightleftharpoons$ oxyhaemoglobin

a Where in the body would oxyhaemoglobin form?

b Where in the body would oxyhaemoglobin break down?

c People who live at high altitudes, where there is less oxygen, have more red blood cells per litre of blood than people who live at lower altitudes. Suggest why.

Q3 **a** In the heart, the ventricles have thicker walls than the atria. Why is this?

b Why does the left ventricle have a thicker wall than the right ventricle?

Q4 **a** List three ways that veins differ from arteries.

b Substances such as oxygen and food enter and leave the blood through the capillary walls. Why not through the walls of arteries and veins?

Answers are on page 227.

Breathing

Breathing is *not* respiration

- Breathing is the way that oxygen is taken into our bodies and carbon dioxide removed. Sometimes it is called **ventilation**.

- Do not confuse breathing with respiration. Respiration is a chemical process that happens in every cell in the body. Unfortunately, the confusion is not helped when you realise that the parts of the body responsible for breathing are known as the **respiratory system**!

How we breathe

- When we breathe, air is moved into and out of our lungs. This involves different parts of the respiratory system inside the thorax (chest).

- When we **breathe in**, air enters though the nose and mouth. In the nose the air is moistened and warmed.

- The air travels down the **trachea** (windpipe) to the lungs. Tiny hairs called **cilia** help to remove dirt and microbes. (You can find out more about the cilia in Unit 3.)

- The air enters the lungs through the **bronchi** (singular: bronchus), which branch and divide to form a network of **bronchioles**.

- At the end of the bronchioles are air sacs called **alveoli** (singular: alveolus) which are covered in tiny blood capillaries. This is where oxygen enters the blood and carbon dioxide leaves the blood.

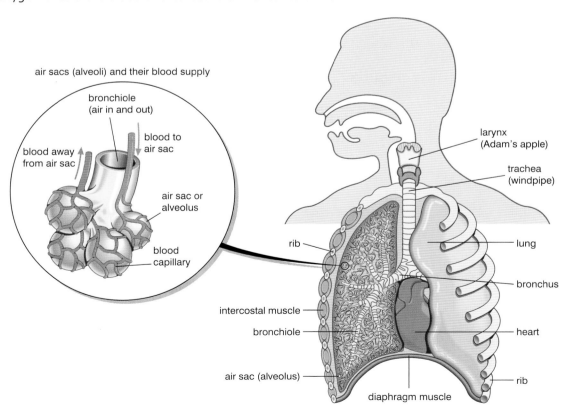

air sacs (alveoli) and their blood supply

bronchiole (air in and out)

blood to air sac

blood away from air sac

air sac or alveolus

blood capillary

larynx (Adam's apple)

trachea (windpipe)

rib

lung

bronchus

intercostal muscle

bronchiole

heart

air sac (alveolus)

rib

diaphragm muscle

☐ Inhalation and exhalation

- Breathing in is known as **inhalation** and breathing out **exhalation** (sometimes they are called inspiration and expiration).

- Both happen because of changes in the volume of the thorax (chest cavity). This causes pressure changes which in turn cause air to enter or leave the lungs.

- The changes in thorax volume are caused by the **diaphragm**, which is a domed sheet of muscle under the lungs, and the **intercostal muscles**, which connect the ribs. There are two sets: the internal intercostal muscles and the external intercostal muscles.

INHALATION

- We breathe in air in this way:

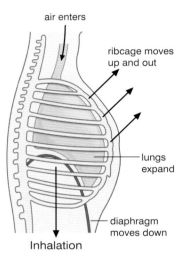

air enters

ribcage moves up and out

lungs expand

diaphragm moves down

Inhalation

  1 The diaphragm **contracts** and **flattens** in shape.

  2 The external intercostal muscles **contract**, making the ribs move upwards and outwards.

  3 These changes cause the **volume** of the thorax to **increase**.

  4 This causes the air **pressure** inside the thorax to **decrease**.

  5 This causes air to enter the lungs.

- Rings of **cartilage** in the trachea, bronchi and bronchioles keep the air passages open and prevent them from collapsing when the air pressure decreases.

EXHALATION

- Air is breathed out from the lungs as follows:

  1 The diaphragm **relaxes** and returns to its domed shape, pushed up by the liver and stomach. This means **it pushes up on the lungs**.

air leaves

ribcage moves down and in

lungs get smaller

diaphragm moves up

Exhalation

  2 The external intercostal muscles **relax**, allowing the ribs to drop back down. This also presses on the lungs. If you are breathing hard the internal intercostal muscles also contract, helping the ribs to move down.

  3 These changes cause the **volume** of the thorax to **decrease**.

  4 This causes the **air pressure** inside the thorax to **increase**.

  5 This causes air to leave the lungs.

⚡ A* EXTRA

▸ During inhalation air enters because the air pressure inside the lungs is lower than the air pressure outside the body.

▸ During exhalation air leaves the lungs because the air pressure inside is higher than the air pressure outside the body.

Composition of inhaled and exhaled air

- The air we breathe contains many gases. **Oxygen** is taken into the blood. **Carbon dioxide** and **water vapour** are added to the air we breathe out. The other gases in the air are breathed out almost unchanged, except for being warmer.

	In inhaled air	In exhaled air
Oxygen	21%	16%
Carbon dioxide	0.03%	4%
Nitrogen and other gases	79%	79%
Water	variable	high
Temperature	variable	high

Alveoli

- The alveoli are where oxygen and carbon dioxide diffuse into and out of the blood. For this reason the alveoli are described as the site of **gaseous exchange** or as the **respiratory surface**.

- The alveoli are adapted (have special features) to make them efficient at gaseous exchange:
  - **Thin, permeable walls** to allow a short pathway for diffusion.
  - **Moist lining** in which oxygen dissolves first before it diffuses through.
  - **Large surface area**. Lots of alveoli means a very large surface area.
  - **Good supply of oxygen** and **good blood supply**. This means that a concentration gradient is maintained ensuring that oxygen and carbon dioxide rapidly diffuse across.

QUESTION SPOTTER

You will often be asked to explain how alveoli are adapted for efficient gas exchange.

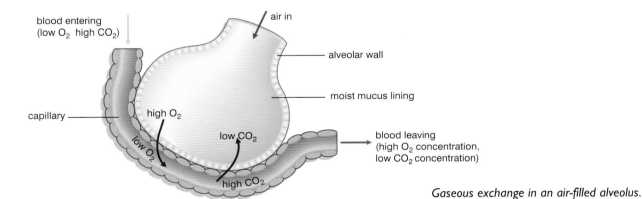

Gaseous exchange in an air-filled alveolus.

CHECK YOURSELF QUESTIONS

Q1 **a** How many cells does oxygen pass through on its way from the alveoli to the red blood cells?

  b Why is it important for oxygen to have a large concentration gradient between the inside of the alveoli and the blood?

Q2 When you breathe in, how do the positions of the diaphragm and ribcage change?

Q3 Why do we need rings of cartilage in the walls of the air passages?

Answers are on page 228.

Digestion

Why do we need to digest food?

■ If the food we eat is to be of any use it must enter the blood so that it can travel to every part of the body.

■ Many of the foods we eat are made up of **large insoluble molecules,** which would not easily enter the blood. This means they have to be **broken down into small soluble molecules,** which can easily enter and be carried dissolved in the blood. Breaking down the molecules is called **digestion**.

■ There are two stages of digestion:

1 **Physical digestion** occurs mainly in the mouth, where food is broken down into smaller pieces by the teeth and tongue.

2 **Chemical digestion** is the breakdown of large food molecules into smaller ones.

■ Some molecules, like glucose, vitamins, minerals and water are already small enough to pass through the gut wall and do not need to be digested.

Breaking down food for absorption.

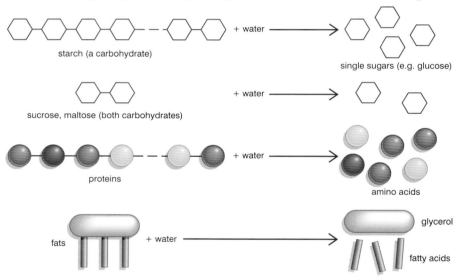

starch (a carbohydrate) + water ⟶ single sugars (e.g. glucose)

sucrose, maltose (both carbohydrates) + water ⟶

proteins + water ⟶ amino acids

fats + water ⟶ glycerol / fatty acids

Enzymes

■ Chemical digestion happens because of chemicals called **enzymes.** Enzymes are a type of catalyst found in living things. (You can find out more about catalysts in Unit 11.)

FEATURES OF ENZYMES

■ Enzymes are proteins.

■ They are produced by cells.

■ They change chemical substances into new products.

■ Enzymes are **specific,** which means that each enzyme only works on one substance.

- Enzymes work best at a particular temperature (around 35–40°C for digestive enzymes) called their **optimum temperature**. At temperatures that are too high the structure of an enzyme will be changed so that it will not work. This is irreversible and the enzyme is said to be **denatured**.

- They work best at a particular pH, called their **optimum pH**. Extremes of pH can also denature enzymes.

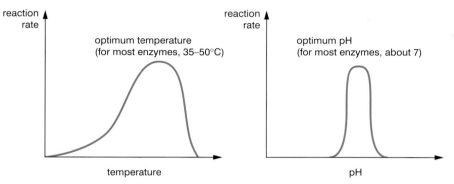

Enzymes work best at an optimum temperature and pH.

GROUPS OF DIGESTIVE ENZYMES

- Every cell contains many enzymes, which control the many chemical reactions that happen inside it. Digestive enzymes are only one kind. They are produced in the cells lining parts of the digestive system and are secreted to mix with the food.

- There are different groups of digestive enzymes, such as:
  - **proteases**, which break down proteins
  - **lipases**, which break down fats
  - **amylase**, which breaks down starch
  - **maltase**, **sucrase** and **lactase**, which break down the different sugars maltose, sucrose and lactose.

⌑ Substances that help digestion

- **Hydrochloric acid** is secreted in the stomach. This is important to **kill bacteria** in food. Also, the enzymes in the stomach work best at a low pH.

- **Sodium hydrogencarbonate** is secreted from the pancreas to **neutralise the acid** leaving the stomach so that the enzymes in the small intestine can work.

- **Bile** is produced in the liver, stored in the gall bladder, and passes along the bile duct into the duodenum. Bile **emulsifies fats**. It breaks down large fat droplets into smaller ones, which means that a larger surface area is exposed for the enzymes to work on.

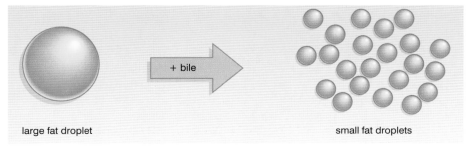

large fat droplet   small fat droplets

Bile lowers the surface tension of large droplets of fat so that they break up. This part of the digestive process is called emulsification.

⌷ The digestive system

- Eating food involves several different processes:
  - **ingestion** – taking food into the body
  - **digestion** of food into small molecules
  - **absorption** of digested food into the blood
  - **egestion** – removal of indigestible material (**faeces**) from the body. Note that egestion is not the same as excretion, which is the removal of waste substances that have been made in the body.

- All these different processes take place in different parts of the digestive system (the **alimentary canal**).

Part of digestive system	What happens there
Mouth	Teeth and tongue break down food into smaller pieces. Saliva from salivary glands moistens food so it is easily swallowed and contains amylase to begin breakdown of starch.
Oesophagus or gullet	Each lump of swallowed food, called a **bolus**, is moved along by waves of muscle contraction called **peristalsis**.
Stomach	Food enters through a ring of muscle known as a **sphincter**. Acid and protease are secreted to start protein digestion. Movements of the muscular wall churn up food into a liquid known as **chyme** (pronounced 'kime'). The bulk of the food is stored while a little of the partly digested food at a time passes through another sphincter into the duodenum.
Gall bladder	Stores bile. The bile is passed along the bile duct into the duodenum.
Pancreas	Secretes amylase, lipase and protease as well as sodium hydrogencarbonate into the duodenum.
Small intestine (made up of duodenum and ileum)	Secretions from the gall bladder and pancreas as well as sucrase, maltase, lactase, protease and lipase from the wall of the duodenum complete digestion. Digested food is absorbed into the blood through the **villi**.
Large intestine or colon	Water is absorbed from the remaining material.
Rectum	The remaining material (**faeces**), made up of indigestible food, dead cells from the lining of the alimentary canal and bacteria, is compacted and stored.
Anus	Faeces is egested through a sphincter.

The distance from mouth to anus is about nine metres.

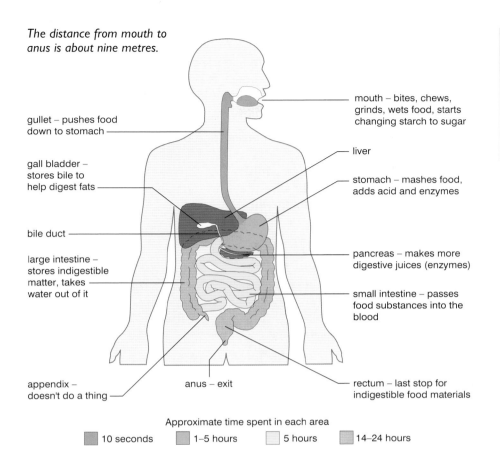

mouth – bites, chews, grinds, wets food, starts changing starch to sugar

gullet – pushes food down to stomach

liver

gall bladder – stores bile to help digest fats

stomach – mashes food, adds acid and enzymes

bile duct

pancreas – makes more digestive juices (enzymes)

large intestine – stores indigestible matter, takes water out of it

small intestine – passes food substances into the blood

appendix – doesn't do a thing

anus – exit

rectum – last stop for indigestible food materials

Approximate time spent in each area

10 seconds   1–5 hours   5 hours   14–24 hours

QUESTION SPOTTER

Make sure you know the name of each part of the digestive system as well as what happens there.

■ Food moves along the digestive system because of the contractions of the muscles in the walls of the alimentary canal. This is called **peristalsis**.

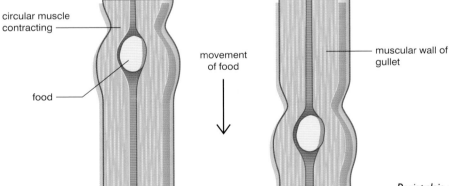

circular muscle contracting

food

movement of food

muscular wall of gullet

Peristalsis moves food along the digestive system.

⌂ Absorption of food

- After food has been digested it can enter the blood. This happens in the main part of the small intestine, known as the **ileum**. To help this process, the lining of the ileum is covered in millions of small finger-like projections called **villi** (singular: villus).

- The ileum is adapted for efficient absorption of food by having a large surface area. This is because:
  - it is **long** (6–7 metres in an adult)
  - the inside is covered with villi
  - the villi are covered in **microvilli**.

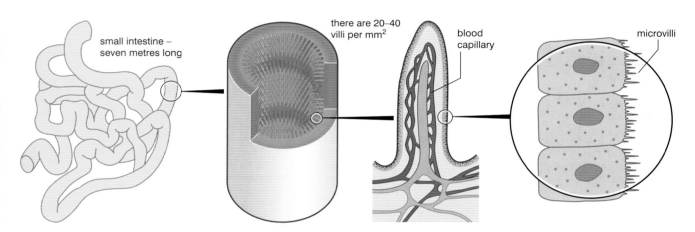

small intestine – seven metres long

there are 20–40 villi per mm^2

blood capillary

microvilli

The structure of the ileum.

- The villi themselves have features that also help absorption:
  - **thin, permeable walls**
  - **good blood supply**, which maintains a concentration gradient that aids diffusion
  - they contain **lymph vessels** (or lacteals), which absorb some of the fat. The lymph vessels eventually drain into the blood system.

? CHECK YOURSELF QUESTIONS

Q1 a Protein molecules are long chains of amino acid molecules joined together. Why do proteins need to be digested?

b What is the difference between physical and chemical digestion?

c What happens to enzymes at high temperatures?

d Why is the alkaline sodium hydrogencarbonate secreted into the duodenum?

Q2 a What is the difference between ingestion, egestion and excretion?

b Where do ingestion and egestion happen?

Q3 The villi are adapted to absorb food and the alveoli in the lungs are adapted to absorb oxygen. In what ways are they similar?

Answers are on page 228.

UNIT 3: BODY MAINTENANCE

The nervous system

⊡ What does the nervous system do?

■ The nervous system collects information about changes inside or outside the body, decides how the body should respond and controls that response.

⊡ Receptors

■ Information is collected by **receptor cells** that are usually grouped together in **sense organs**, also known as **receptors**.

■ Each type of receptor is sensitive to a different kind of change or **stimulus**.

Sense organ	Sense	Stimulus
Skin	Touch	Pressure, pain, hot/cold temperatures
Tongue	Taste	Chemicals in food and drink
Nose	Smell	Chemicals in the air
Eyes	Sight	Light
Ears	Hearing	Sound
	Balance	Movement/position of head

⊡ The eye

■ The eye is the receptor that detects light.

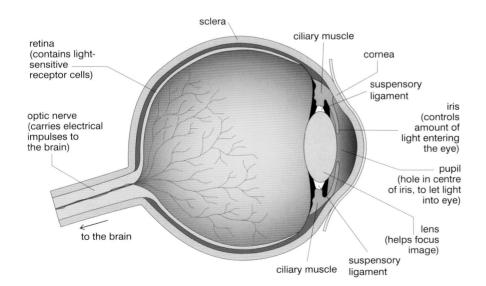

Part of eye	Job
Ciliary muscles	Contract or relax to alter the shape of the lens
Cornea	Transparent cover that does most of the bending of light
Iris	Alters the size of the pupil to control the amount of light entering the eye
Lens	Changes shape to focus light on to the retina
Humour	Clear jelly that fills the inside of the eye
Retina	Contains light-sensitive receptor cells, which change the light image into electrical impulses. There are two types of receptor cells: **rods**, which are sensitive in dim light but can only sense 'black and white', and **cones**, which are sensitive in bright light and can detect colour
Sclera	Tough outer layer
Suspensory ligaments	Hold the lens in position
Optic nerve	Carries electrical impulses to the brain

■ The **iris** (the ring shaped, coloured part of the eye) controls the amount of light entering the eye by controlling the size of the hole in the centre, the **pupil**. The iris contains **circular** and **radial** muscles. In bright light the circular muscles contract and the radial muscles relax, making the pupil smaller. This reduces the amount of light entering the eye, as too much could do damage. The reverse happens in dim light when the eye has to collect as much light as possible to see clearly.

circular muscle relaxed

circular muscle contracted

radial muscle contracted   pupil dilated

radial muscle relaxed   pupil constricted

■ The lens changes shape in order to focus light from objects which are distant or near. You can find out how glass lenses form images in Unit 17.

⌷ Nerves

■ The sense organs are connected to the rest of the nervous system, which is made up of the **brain**, **spinal cord** and **peripheral nerves**.

■ In the brain and spinal cord information is processed and decisions made. The brain and spinal cord together are called the **central nervous system** (CNS).

■ Signals are sent through the nervous system in the form of electro-chemical **impulses**.

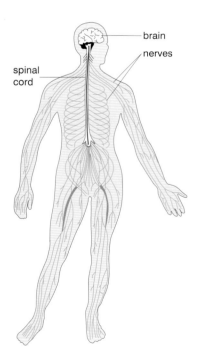

brain

nerves

spinal cord

The nervous system.

TYPES OF NERVE CELLS (OR NEURONES)

- **Sensory neurones** carry signals to the CNS.

- **Motor neurones** carry signals from the CNS, controlling how we respond.

- **Relay** (intermediate or connecting) **neurones** connect other neurones together.

Sensory neurone

Motor neurone

A relay neurone

NEURONES ARE SPECIALISED

- They can be **very long** to carry signals from one part of the body to another.

- They have many branched nerve endings or **dendrites** to collect and pass on signals.

- Many neurones are wrapped in a layer of fat and protein, the **myelin sheath**, which insulates cells from each other and allows the impulses to travel faster.

- Neurones are usually grouped together in bundles called **nerves**.

Cross-section of a nerve.

⃞ Reflexes

- The different parts of the nervous system may all be involved when we respond to a stimulus. The simplest type of response is a **reflex**. Reflexes are rapid, automatic responses which often act to protect us in some way – for example, blinking if something gets in your eye or sneezing if you breathe in dust.

- The pathway that signals travel along during a reflex is called a **reflex arc**:

stimulus → receptor → sensory neurone → CNS → motor neurone → effector → response

- Simple reflexes are usually **spinal reflexes**, which means that the signals are processed by the spinal cord, not the brain. The spine sends a signal back to the **effector**. Effectors are the parts of the body that respond – either muscles or glands. Examples of spinal reflexes include standing on a pin or touching a hot object.

stand on pin → nerve endings → sensory neurone → spinal cord → motor neurone → leg muscles → leg moves

- When the spine sends a signal to the effector, other signals are sent on to the brain so that it is aware of what is happening.

- There are also reflexes in which the signals are sent straight to the brain. These are called **cranial reflexes**. Examples include blinking when dirt lands in your eye, or salivating at the smell of food.

smell of food → nose → sensory neurone → brain → motor neurone → salivary glands → mouth waters

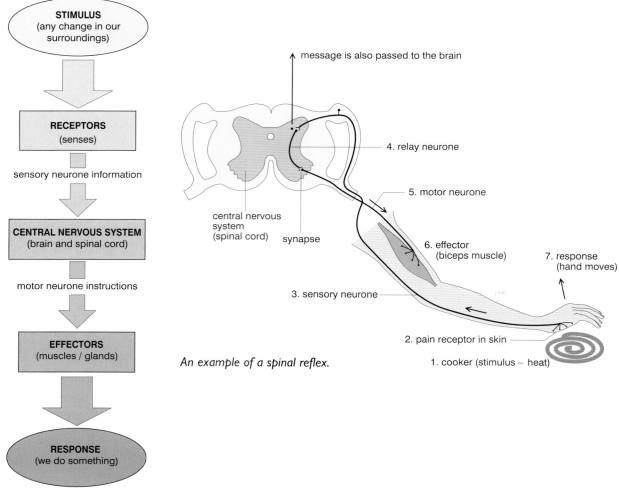

The flow of information from stimulus to response.

An example of a spinal reflex.

⧉ Synapses

- Between nerve endings there are very small gaps called **synapses,** where signals are passed from one neurone to another even though the cells do not touch.

- Signals can be passed across synapses because when an electrical impulse reaches a synapse, chemicals called **transmitter substances** are released from the membrane of one nerve ending and travel across to special **receptor sites** on the membrane of the next nerve ending, triggering off another nerve impulse.

- Sometimes signals are not passed across synapses, which stops us from responding to every single stimulus. You can find out more about synapses in the section about drugs on pages 35-36.

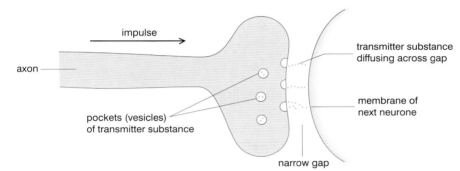

A synapse.

❓ CHECK YOURSELF QUESTIONS

Q1 **a** What is a stimulus?
    b What is the difference between a receptor and an effector?

Q2 **a** What are the two parts of the CNS?
    b What is the difference between a nerve and a neurone?
    c Describe three features that neurones have in common with other cells.
    d Describe two features that neurones have which make them different from other cells.

Q3 **a** Which of the following are reflexes?
    A Coughing when something 'goes down the wrong way'.
    B Changing channels on the TV when a programme ends.
    C Jumping up when you sit on something sharp.
    D Always buying the same brand of soft drink.
    b Why are reflexes important?

Answers are on page 229.

The endocrine system

⌷ Hormones

- **Hormones** are chemical messengers. They are made in **endocrine glands**.

- Endocrine glands do not have ducts (tubes) to carry away the hormones they make – the hormones are **secreted directly into the blood** to be carried around the body. (There are other types of glands, called exocrine glands, such as salivary or sweat glands, that *do* have ducts.)

- Most hormones affect several parts of the body, others only affect one part of the body, which is termed the **target organ**.

- The changes caused by hormones are usually slower and longer-lived than the changes brought about by the nervous system.

⌷ What hormones are made where?

ADRENAL GLANDS

- The adrenal glands produce **adrenaline**. This is released in times of excitement, anger, fright or stress and prepares the body for 'flight or fight' – the crucial moments when an animal must instantly decide whether to attack or run for its life.

- Effects of adrenaline:
  - increases heart rate
  - increases depth of breathing and breathing rate
  - increases sweating
  - makes hair stand on end (this makes a furry animal look larger but only gives humans goose bumps)
  - releases glucose from liver and muscles
  - makes pupils dilate
  - makes skin go pale as blood is redirected to muscles.

PITUITARY GLAND

- Among other hormones, the pituitary gland produces **growth hormone**.

- Growth hormone encourages mental and physical development in children.

- The pituitary gland also controls many other glands.

THYROID GLAND

- The thyroid gland produces **thyroxine**.

- Thyroxine encourages mental and physical development in children.

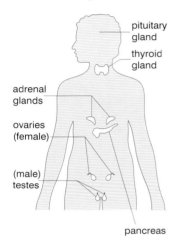

The endocrine system.

pituitary gland
thyroid gland
adrenal glands
ovaries (female)
(male) testes
pancreas

☀ QUESTION SPOTTER

- ▸ In exams you will not only be asked about the effects of hormones. Often you will also be required to explain these effects.
- ▸ An example would be: 'Why is it important that adrenaline increases heart rate in times of stress?'

PANCREAS

- The pancreas secretes **insulin** and **glucagon**. (It also secretes digestive enzymes through the pancreatic duct into the duodenum.)

- Insulin controls **glucose levels** in the blood. It is important that the blood glucose level remains as steady as possible. If it rises or falls too much you can become very ill.

- After a meal, the level of glucose in the blood tends to rise. This causes the pancreas to release **insulin**, which travels in the blood to the liver. Here it causes any excess glucose to be converted to another carbohydrate, **glycogen**, which is insoluble and is stored in the liver.

- Between meals, glucose in the blood is constantly being used up, so the level of glucose in the blood falls. When a low level of glucose is detected, the pancreas stops secreting insulin and secretes the hormone **glucagon** instead. Glucagon converts some of the stored glycogen back into glucose, which is released into the blood to raise the blood glucose level back to normal.

TESTES (MALES ONLY)

- **Testosterone** (male sex hormone) is secreted from the testes. Testosterone causes secondary sexual characteristics in boys:
  - growth spurt
  - hair grows on face and body
  - penis, testes and scrotum grow and develop
  - sperm is produced
  - voice breaks
  - body becomes broader and more muscular
  - sexual 'drive' develops.

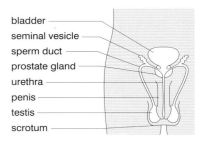

The male reproductive system.

OVARIES (FEMALES ONLY)

- The ovaries produce the female sex hormones **progesterone** and **oestrogen**. These hormones cause secondary sexual characteristics in girls:
  - growth spurt
  - breasts develop
  - vagina, oviducts and uterus develop
  - menstrual cycle (periods) start
  - hips widen
  - pubic hair and hair under the arms grows
  - sexual 'drive' develops.

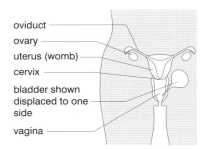

The female reproductive system.

- These hormones also control the changes that occur during the menstrual cycle:
  - oestrogen encourages the repair of the uterus lining after bleeding
  - progesterone maintains the lining
  - oestrogen and progesterone control ovulation (egg release).

The menstrual cycle.

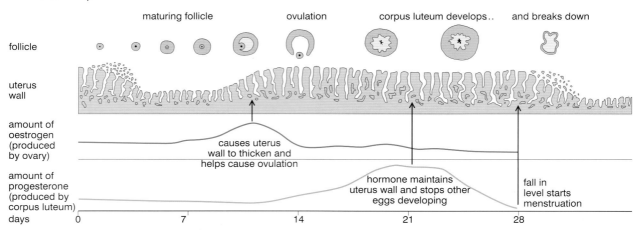

⛶ The menstrual cycle

■ About every 28 days an egg is released from one of a woman's ovaries. (The egg develops from one of the thousands of **follicles** present in the ovaries.) The egg travels down the oviduct to the uterus (womb) where, if it has been fertilised, it can implant and grow into a baby.

■ To prepare for this the lining of the uterus thickens – controlled by the release of progesterone from the **corpus luteum**, the remains of the follicle left behind in the ovary. If the egg has not been fertilised then the lining breaks down and is released (**menstruation**). Oestrogen from the ovary will encourage the uterus lining to grow again for the next released egg.

■ If the egg has been fertilised then progesterone continues to be released from the corpus luteum, which maintains the uterus lining during pregnancy and prevents further ovulation.

OTHER HORMONES INVOLVED IN THE MENSTRUAL CYCLE

■ **FSH (follicle-stimulating hormone)** is secreted by the pituitary gland. It causes eggs to mature in the ovaries and stimulates the ovaries to produce hormones such as oestrogen.

■ **LH (luteinising hormone)** is also secreted by the pituitary gland. It stimulates ovulation.

■ The release of FSH and LH is partially controlled by oestrogen, which inhibits FSH production and stimulates LH production.

⬚ Medical uses of hormones

- Hormones can be used to treat various medical conditions – for example in illnesses caused by the hormone not being made naturally in the correct quantities.

INSULIN

- There are different types of diabetes, but in **diabetes mellitus** the body is unable to make enough of the hormone insulin. Insulin controls the level of glucose in the blood. Someone with diabetes cannot store the excess glucose from their blood and it is excreted in urine instead. Other symptoms of diabetes include thirst, weakness, weight loss, coma.

- Some people can control their diabetes with their diet and activity. For example, they make sure they do not go a long time without a meal, eat snacks between meals and make sure that they eat some high-glucose food before any energetic activity.

- Another way of controlling diabetes is to inject insulin before a meal.

- Insulin can be extracted from animals' blood, but is now produced by genetically engineered bacteria.

CONTROLLING FERTILITY

- **Contraceptive pills** contain oestrogen and progesterone. They inhibit FSH production, so no eggs mature to be released.

- FSH is used as a **fertility drug** to stimulate eggs to mature.

GROWTH HORMONE

- Injections of growth hormone can be given during childhood to ensure that growth is normal.

⬚ Illegal uses of hormones

- Some drugs containing hormones, or chemicals similar to them, have been used by some athletes to enhance their performance. This is not only illegal but can have harmful side effects.

? CHECK YOURSELF QUESTIONS

Q1 Signals can be sent round the body by the nervous system and the endocrine system. How are the two systems different?

Q2 a How do the changes that adrenaline causes help the body react to a stressful situation (fight or flight)?
b After it has been released, adrenaline is broken down fairly quickly. Why is this important?

Q3 Explain the differences between glucose, glycogen and glucagon.

Answers are on page 230.

Homeostasis

What is homeostasis?

■ For our cells to stay alive and work properly they need the conditions in and around them, such as their temperature and the amount of water and other substances, to stay within acceptable limits. Keeping conditions inside these limits is called **homeostasis**.

Temperature control

■ The temperature inside your body is about 37°C, regardless of how hot or cold you may feel on the outside. This **core temperature** may naturally vary a little, but it is never very different unless you are ill.

■ Heat is constantly being released by respiration and other chemical reactions in the body, and is transferred to the surroundings outside the body. To maintain a constant body temperature these two processes have to balance. If the core temperature rises above or falls below 37°C various changes happen, mostly in the skin, to restore normal temperature.

Too cold?	Too hot?
Vasoconstriction: blood capillaries in the skin become narrower so they carry less blood close to the surface. Heat is kept inside the body.	**Vasodilation:** blood capillaries in the skin widen so they carry more blood close to the surface. Heat is transferred from the blood to the skin by **conduction**, then to the environment by **radiation**.
Sweating is reduced.	Sweating: sweat is released onto the skin surface and as it evaporates heat is taken away.
Hair erection: muscles make the hairs stand up, trapping a layer of air as insulation (air is a poor conductor of heat). This is more beneficial in animals but still occurs in humans (goose bumps).	Hairs lay flat so less air is trapped and more heat is transferred from the skin.
Shivering: muscle action releases extra heat from the increased respiration.	No shivering.
A layer of fat under the skin acts as insulation.	

Section through skin.

a cold day

air trapped between hairs – insulation layer

blood vessels close to the skin surface become narrower

blood vessels further from the surface widen

a hot day

less air between hairs – heat escapes from the body

blood vessels close to the skin surface widen

blood vessels further from the surface get narrower

■ The core temperature is monitored by the **hypothalamus** – a part of the brain that monitors the temperature of the blood passing through it.

Water balance

■ Our bodies are about two-thirds water. The average person loses and gains about three litres of water a day under normal conditions.

■ Water is constantly being **lost** from the body:
  • in the air we breathe out
  • in sweat (sweat also contains mineral salts)
  • in urine
  • in faeces.

■ Water is **gained** by the body:
  • in food and drink
  • from respiration and other chemical reactions.

The water balance for an average person.

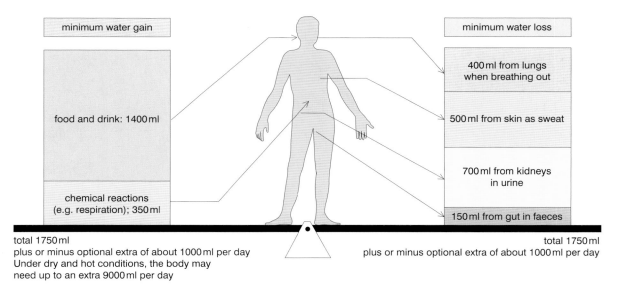

minimum water gain

food and drink: 1400 ml

chemical reactions (e.g. respiration); 350 ml

total 1750 ml
plus or minus optional extra of about 1000 ml per day
Under dry and hot conditions, the body may
need up to an extra 9000 ml per day

minimum water loss

400 ml from lungs when breathing out

500 ml from skin as sweat

700 ml from kidneys in urine

150 ml from gut in faeces

total 1750 ml
plus or minus optional extra of about 1000 ml per day

■ **The water lost cannot be much more or less than the water gained.**
So on a hot day, when you sweat more, you lose less water as urine, producing a smaller amount of more concentrated (darker) urine than normal.

THE ROLE OF THE KIDNEYS

- The amount of water that is lost as urine is controlled by the **kidneys**.

- The kidneys regulate the amounts of water and salt in the body by controlling the amounts in the blood.

- The kidneys remove waste products such as **urea** from the blood. Urea is formed in the liver from the breakdown of excess amino acids in the body. This is an example of **excretion**.

- As blood flows around the body it passes through the kidneys, which remove urea, excess water and salt from the blood:

  1 Blood enters the kidneys through the **renal arteries**, which divide to form many tiny capillaries.

  2 A lot of the blood plasma (water, urea and other substances) is forced under great pressure into tiny tubules called **nephrons**.

  3 Further along each nephron, useful contents (such as sugar) and some water are reabsorbed into the blood, leaving urea, excess water and excess salt. This mixture is called **urine**.

  4 The capillaries join up to form the **renal veins**, which carry blood away from the kidneys.

  5 The nephrons join up to form a **ureter**, which carries the urine to the bladder where it is stored until you go to the toilet when the urine leaves the body through the **urethra**.

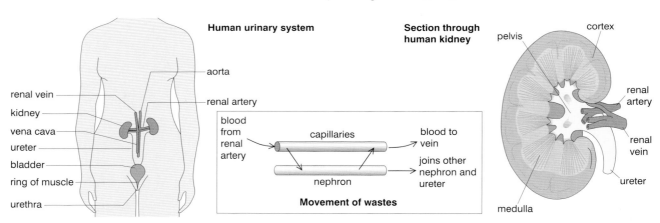

Human urinary system

Section through human kidney

renal vein
kidney
vena cava
ureter
bladder
ring of muscle
urethra

aorta
renal artery

blood from renal artery
capillaries
blood to vein
joins other nephron and ureter
nephron

Movement of wastes

cortex
pelvis
renal artery
renal vein
ureter
medulla

MONITORING WATER BALANCE

- Like temperature, the water content of the blood is monitored by the **hypothalamus**.

- If there is too little water in the blood – if you have been sweating a lot, for example – then the hypothalamus is stimulated and sends a hormone (called **ADH**) to the kidneys, making them reabsorb more water back into the blood so less is lost in urine.

- If your blood water level is high – if you have been drinking a lot, for example – the hypothalamus is much less stimulated so less hormone is released, less water is reabsorbed and more water is lost as urine.

Monitoring water level.

Negative feedback

- The body maintains a constant internal environment by monitoring changes and reacting to reduce these changes. This process is an example of **negative feedback**. It is 'negative' because the body attempts to **reduce** changes that occur.

EXAMPLES OF NEGATIVE FEEDBACK

- If the amount of glucose in your blood increases after a meal insulin is released to reduce the amount.

- If your body temperature falls then shivering and vasoconstriction will increase the temperature

- If you drink a lot, increasing the amount of water in your blood, the kidneys will remove more water in urine.

- When you exercise you breathe faster. Muscles respiring more than usual use up oxygen faster. Faster breathing increases the amount of oxygen in the blood. These two processes counter each other, producing a steady oxygen level. The faster breathing also removes the extra carbon dioxide that has been produced by the muscles respiring. In fact, it is mainly the carbon dioxide levels in the blood that the brain monitors to control the rate of breathing. This is because high levels of carbon dioxide in the blood are toxic and have to be reduced quickly.

> ### ⚡ A * EXTRA
>
> - Homeostasis and negative feedback do not mean exactly the same thing.
> - Homeostasis means keeping the conditions inside the body constant.
> - Negative feedback is the way this happens.

? CHECK YOURSELF QUESTIONS

Q1 A farmer who has been working outside all day on a hot summer's day produces a much smaller amount of urine than normal. It is also a much darker yellow colour than normal. Explain these points.

Q2 Why are the lungs organs of excretion?

Q3 How would the blood in the renal arteries be different from the blood in the renal veins?

Answers are on page 230.

Good health

Virus

protein coat

genes

Bacterium cell

cell wall

genes
(not in a nucleus)

cytoplasm

The two diagrams are not to scale. Viruses are much smaller than bacteria. They can reproduce only inside living cells.

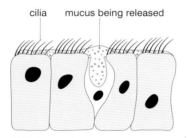

cilia   mucus being released

Cells lining the air passages in the trachea, bronchi and bronchioles.

⟦⟧ Preventing microbial attack

■ One main cause of disease is the presence of foreign organisms – **micro-organisms**, or **microbes,** in the body. Most of the time our bodies are able to prevent microbes, such as **viruses** or **bacteria**, from getting in or from spreading.

Barriers to infection	How they work
Skin	The skin provides a barrier that micro-organisms cannot penetrate unless through a wound or a natural opening.
Mucus and ciliated cells in lining of respiratory tract	The lining of the nasal passages, and the trachea, bronchi and bronchioles in the lungs are covered with a slimy mucus which traps air-borne micro-organisms as well as dirt. Tiny hair-like cilia use a waving motion to move the mucus upwards where it usually ends up going down the oesophagus.
Acid in the stomach	Stomach acid kills micro-organisms present in food or drink.
Blood clots	At the site of a wound, blood platelets break open, triggering off a series of chemical changes that result in the formation of a network of threads at the wound. This network traps red blood cells, forming a clot. The clot prevents blood escaping and provides a barrier to infection.

⟦⟧ The immune system

■ If micro-organisms do manage to enter the body they can cause harm by either damaging the cells around them or by releasing toxins (poisons) that make us ill. In either case they are attacked by **white blood cells**, which are part of our **immune system**.

■ There are two main types of white blood cells:
  • **Phagocytes**, because of their flexible shape, can engulf and then digest micro-organisms. This is called phagocytosis.
  • **Lymphocytes** produce chemicals called **antibodies**. Antibodies destroy the micro-organisms in various ways, for example by making them clump together so that they are more easily engulfed by phagocytes, by killing the micro-organisms themselves or by destroying the toxins they release (acting as **anti-toxins**).

Phagocytes

lobed nucleus

engulfing a bacterium

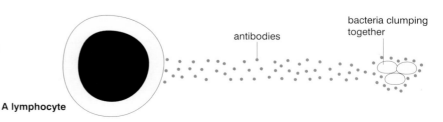

antibodies

bacteria clumping together

A lymphocyte

DEVELOPING IMMUNITY TO A DISEASE

- On the surface of all cells are chemicals called **antigens**. Each different type of micro-organism has its own **specific** antigens, which can only be attacked by the right type of antibody.

- When micro-organisms first invade the body, the white blood cells start to make the antibody to destroy these micro-organisms. This may take a while, and this is usually when you show the symptoms of the disease. When the white blood cells have made enough antibodies to attack the micro-organisms you (hopefully) recover from the disease.

- If you are ever invaded by the same type of micro-organism, your white blood cells 'remember' the antigen and can make the right type of antibody to quickly destroy the micro-organisms before the symptoms of the disease appear. You are then said to be **immune** to the disease.

- You can be artificially **immunised** against a disease by being injected with the antigen in the form of dead or harmless forms of the micro-organism or a harmless form of the toxin they release. The harmless foreign antigens stimulate your white blood cells to produce antibodies against them in the normal way but you won't be as ill as if you had the disease. Your white cells will 'remember' how to do this in the future and you will be protected if you ever catch the real disease-causing micro-organisms. Sometimes this immunity will last for the rest of your life but you may need 'booster' injections for some diseases.

ORGAN TRANSPLANTATION

- The reason that organ transplants are ideally taken from a close relative is that their organs are more likely to have antigens similar to the patient's own cells, and are therefore less likely to be attacked by the patient's immune system.

- When the immune system attacks a transplanted organ, the organ is said to be **rejected**. If the donor is not a close relative, **immunosuppressant drugs** have to be used to stop the transplant being rejected.

⌷ Drugs

- The various drugs, both illegal and otherwise, that people may take can also cause health problems. ('Drugs' in this case are defined as substances that affect the way our bodies behave. The effects may be useful but many can be dangerous.)

- **Stimulants** (e.g. caffeine, nicotine, ecstasy, cocaine, amphetamines) **increase nervous activity** – they can speed up your heart rate, keep you awake or help depression. Stimulants affect synapses so nervous impulses cross them more readily.

- **Depressants** (e.g. alcohol, painkillers, tranquillisers, solvents, heroin) **decrease nervous activity** – they can slow your heart rate or reaction times, deaden pain or relax you. They do this by restricting the passage of nervous impulses across synapses.

QUESTION SPOTTER

You will gain marks for correctly using terms like antibody and antigen.

A* EXTRA

Many drugs work by stimulating or inhibiting the synapses between nerve cells.

- **Hallucinogens** (e.g. LSD, marijuana) affect the way we **perceive things** so people see or hear things that are not there or perceive things more vividly.

- Some drugs can be **addictive** – if you stop taking the drug you will show various **withdrawal** symptoms, which may include cravings for the drug, nausea and sickness.

- Another danger with drugs is that you build up a **tolerance** to them. This means that your body gets used to them and you have to take larger amounts of the drug for it to have the same effect.

TOBACCO

- Contains **nicotine**, which is a stimulant, increases blood pressure and is addictive. Nicotine can also lead to the formation of blood clots, increasing the chances of heart disease.

- Tobacco smoke contains **tar**, which irritates the lining of the air passages in the lungs, making them inflamed and causing **bronchitis**. Tar can cause the lining cells to multiply, leading to **lung cancer**. Tar also damages the cilia lining the air passages and causes **extra mucus** to be made, which trickles down into the lungs as the cilia can no longer remove it. Bacteria can breed in the mucus so you are more likely to get chest infections and **smokers' cough** as you try to get rid of the mucus. The **alveoli** are also damaged, so it is more difficult to absorb oxygen into the blood. This condition is known as **emphysema**.

- Tobacco smoke contains **carbon monoxide**, which stops red blood cells from carrying oxygen by combining irreversibly with the haemoglobin in the cells. This could also seriously affect the development of the fetus in the womb of a pregnant smoker, leading to a baby with low birth weight.

ALCOHOL

- Long-term alcohol use can cause **liver damage** (because the liver has the job of breaking down the alcohol), **heart disease**, **brain damage** and other dangerous conditions.

- Alcohol is a **depressant**. Short-term effects include:
  - making you more relaxed – which is why in small amounts it can be pleasant
  - slower reactions and impaired judgement – which is why drinking and driving is so dangerous.

- Larger amounts of alcohol can cause lack of co-ordination, slurred speech, unconsciousness and even death.

SOLVENTS

- Solvents are **depressants** and slow down brain activity.

- The effects last for a much shorter time than alcohol but can include dizziness, loss of co-ordination and sometimes unconsciousness.

- Solvents can cause damage to the lungs, liver and brain.

QUESTION SPOTTER

If you are asked to describe the effects of alcohol, make sure you are clear whether the question is about its short-term or long-term effects.

THREAT OF HEART DISEASE

- Drinking large amounts of alcohol and smoking, combined with a diet containing a lot of fatty foods, little exercise and stress, can increase the chance of **coronary heart disease** – the main cause of death in Britain today.

- This disease affects the **coronary arteries**, which are the blood vessels that supply the heart muscle itself. Fatty substances such as **cholesterol** can build up on the inside of the vessels, narrowing them and restricting the blood flow. If a blood clot gets stuck in an artery the blood flow may be stopped altogether, so no oxygen or food can be supplied to part of the heart. If this stops the heart beating then the result is a **heart attack**.

Normal artery.

Artery affected by build up of cholesterol.

A* EXTRA

Don't confuse the coronary arteries with the large blood vessels carrying blood to and from the atria and ventricles. The coronary arteries are much smaller and take blood to the muscular walls of the heart.

CHECK YOURSELF QUESTIONS

Q1 a Most of the time there are very few white blood cells in the blood compared with the red blood cells. Explain why.

b When would you expect the numbers of white blood cells to increase?

Q2 If you have had measles once why are you unlikely to catch it again?

Q3 Why is it dangerous to drive after drinking alcohol?

Answers are on page 230.

REVISION SESSION I   ■ **Photosynthesis** ■

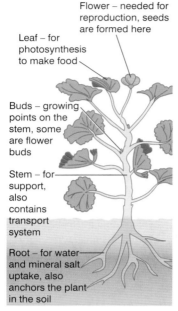

Flower – needed for reproduction, seeds are formed here

Leaf – for photosynthesis to make food

Buds – growing points on the stem, some are flower buds

Stem – for support, also contains transport system

Root – for water and mineral salt uptake, also anchors the plant in the soil

Anatomy of a plant.

⌷ What is photosynthesis?

■ Plants need and use the same types of foods as animals (carbohydrates, proteins and fats) but while animals have to eat other things to get their food, plants **make it themselves**. The way they do this is called **photosynthesis**. The other ways that plants are different from animals, such as having leaves and roots, or being green, are all linked with photosynthesis.

■ In photosynthesis, plants take **carbon dioxide** from the air and **water** from the soil, and use the energy from **sunlight** to convert them into food. The first food they make is **glucose** but that can later be changed into other food types.

■ **Oxygen** is also produced in photosynthesis and, although some is used inside the plant for respiration (releasing energy from food), most is not needed and is given out as a **waste product** (although it is obviously vital for other living things).

■ The sunlight is absorbed by the green pigment **chlorophyll**.

■ The process of photosynthesis can be summarised in a **word equation**:

$$\text{carbon dioxide} + \text{water} \quad \xrightarrow[\text{light}]{\text{chlorophyll}} \quad \text{glucose} + \text{oxygen}$$

■ It can also be written as a balanced **chemical equation**:

$$6CO_2 + 6H_2O \quad \xrightarrow[\text{light}]{\text{chlorophyll}} \quad C_6H_{12}O_6 + 6O_2$$

■ Much of the glucose is converted in to other substances such as **starch**. Starch molecules are made of lots of glucose molecules joined together. Starch is insoluble and so can be stored in the leaf without affecting water movement into and out of cells by **osmosis**.

■ Some glucose is converted to **sucrose** (a type of sugar consisting of two glucose molecules joined together), which is still soluble, but not as reactive as glucose, so it is easily carried around the plant in solution.

■ The energy needed to build up sugars into larger molecules comes from respiration.

☀ QUESTION SPOTTER

▸ You will almost certainly be set at least one question on photosynthesis in your exams.
▸ The key to answering many questions about photosynthesis is remembering the equation.

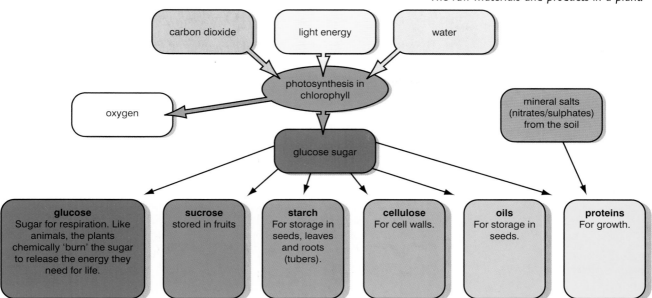

⌂ Where does photosynthesis occur?

■ Photosynthesis takes place mainly in the **leaves**, although it can occur in any cells that contain green chlorophyll. Leaves are adapted to make them very efficient at photosynthesis.

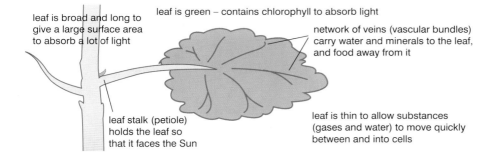

leaf is broad and long to give a large surface area to absorb a lot of light

leaf is green – contains chlorophyll to absorb light

network of veins (vascular bundles) carry water and minerals to the leaf, and food away from it

leaf stalk (petiole) holds the leaf so that it faces the Sun

leaf is thin to allow substances (gases and water) to move quickly between and into cells

■ Leaves are **broad**, so as much light as possible can be absorbed.

■ A leaf is **thin**, so it is easy for carbon dioxide to diffuse in to reach the cells in the centre of the leaf.

■ Leaves contain green **chlorophyll**, in the **chloroplasts**, which absorbs the light energy.

■ Leaves have **veins** to bring up water from the roots and carry food to other parts of the plant.

■ A leaf has a stalk, or **petiole**, that holds the leaf up so it can absorb as much light as possible.

INSIDE LEAVES

- The leaf has a transparent **epidermis** to allow light to penetrate.

- There are many **palisade cells**, tightly packed together in the top half of the leaf so as many as possible collect sunlight. Most photosynthesis takes place in these cells.

- **Chloroplasts** containing chlorophyll are concentrated in the top half of the leaf to absorb as much sunlight as possible.

- Air spaces in the **spongy mesophyll** layer allow the movement of gases (carbon dioxide and oxygen) through the leaf to and from cells.

- The leaf has a **large internal surface area to volume ratio** to allow the efficient absorption of carbon dioxide and removal of oxygen by the photosynthesising cells.

- Many pores or **stomata** (singular: stoma) allow the movement of gases into and out of the leaf.

Photosynthesis and respiration

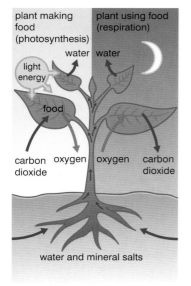

- Once plants have made food using sunlight, they will at some stage need to release the energy in the food. They do this in the same way that humans and other animals do – **respiration**.

- During the day, plants respire 'slower' than they photosynthesise so we only detect carbon dioxide entering and oxygen leaving the plant. During the night, photosynthesis stops and then we can detect oxygen entering and carbon dioxide leaving during respiration.

- At dawn and dusk, the rates of photosynthesis and respiration are the same and **no gases enter or leave** the plant because any oxygen produced by photosynthesis is immediately used up in respiration and any carbon dioxide produced is used up in photosynthesis. These occasions are known as **compensation points**.

⊡ Limiting factors

- If a plant gets more light, carbon dioxide, water or a higher temperature, then it might be able to photosynthesise at a faster rate. However, the rate of photosynthesis will eventually reach a maximum because there is not enough of one of the factors needed – one of them becomes a **limiting factor**.

- For example, if a farmer pumps extra carbon dioxide into a greenhouse the rate of photosynthesis might increase so the crop will grow faster. But if the light is not bright enough to allow the plants to use the carbon dioxide as quickly as it is supplied, the light intensity would be the limiting factor. The graphs show how the rate of photosynthesis is affected by limiting factors.

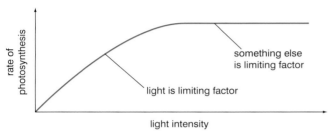

Increasing the levels of light and carbon dioxide, two of the factors necessary for photosynthesis, will increase the rate of photosynthesis until the rate is halted by some other limiting factor.

- If the limiting factor in the first graph was the amount of carbon dioxide and the plants were then given more carbon dioxide, the graph would look like this:

- **Temperature** is also a limiting factor. Temperature affects the enzymes that control the chemical reactions of photosynthesis. Compare the shape of the graph on the right with the graph showing the effect of temperature on enzyme activity on page 17.

❓ CHECK YOURSELF QUESTIONS

Q1 How does a plant get the raw materials it needs for photosynthesis?

Q2 Why isn't the food that is made in the leaves transported around the plant as starch?

Q3 Why are leaves usually broad and thin?

Answers are on page 231.

Transport in plants

⬚ How are materials carried round a plant?

- In humans and many other animals, substances are transported around the body in the blood through blood vessels. In plants, water and dissolved substances are also transported through a series of tubes or vessels. There are two types of transport vessel, called **xylem** and **phloem**.

- **Xylem vessels** are long tubes made of the hollow remains of cells that are now dead. They carry **water** and **dissolved minerals** up from the roots, through the stem, to the leaves. They also give **support** to the plant.

- **Phloem vessels** are living cells. They carry **dissolved food** materials, mainly sucrose, from the leaves to other parts of the plant such as growing roots or shoots, or storage areas such as fruit. This movement of food materials is called **translocation**.

- In roots the xylem and phloem vessels are usually grouped together separately, but in the stem and leaves they are found together as **vascular bundles** or 'veins'.

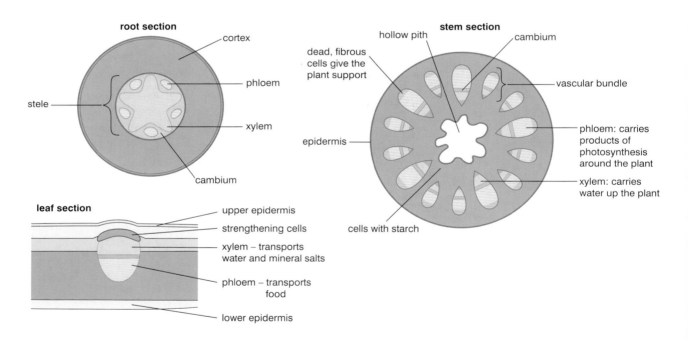

root section — cortex, phloem, xylem, cambium, stele

stem section — hollow pith, cambium, dead, fibrous cells give the plant support, vascular bundle, epidermis, phloem: carries products of photosynthesis around the plant, xylem: carries water up the plant, cells with starch

leaf section — upper epidermis, strengthening cells, xylem – transports water and mineral salts, phloem – transports food, lower epidermis

How do plants gain water?

- Roots are covered in tiny **root hair cells**, which increase the surface area for absorption. Water enters by **osmosis** because the solution inside the cells is more concentrated than the water in the soil.

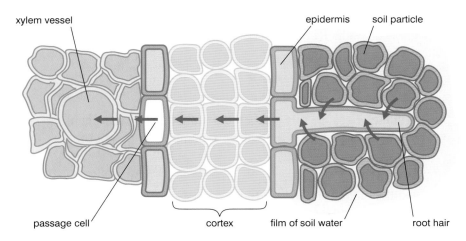

- Water continues to move between cells by osmosis until it reaches the xylem vessels, which carry it up to the leaves.

How do plants lose water?

- In the **leaves**, water moves out of the xylem and enters the leaf cells by osmosis (as they contain many dissolved substances). Water **evaporates** from the surface of the cells inside the leaf and then **diffuses** out through the open stomata. The evaporation of water causes more water to rise up the xylem from the roots rather like a drink flows up a straw when you suck at the top.

- Water loss from the leaves is known as **transpiration**. The flow of water through the plant from the roots to the leaves is known as the **transpiration stream**.

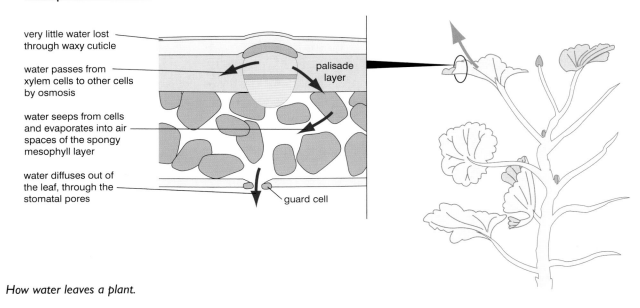

How water leaves a plant.

- It brings up **water and minerals** from the soil.

- As the water evaporates it **cools** the plant. (You can find out more about the cooling effect of evaporation in Unit 17.)

- Transpiration happens faster in conditions that encourage evaporation, when it is:
  - warm
  - windy
  - dry
  - very sunny (because this is when the stomata are most open)
  - and when the plant has a good water supply.

⌷ Water balance

- In a healthy plant the cells are full of water and the cytoplasm presses hard against the inelastic cell wall, making the cell rigid. The cell is **turgid** or has **turgor**.

- Most plants do not have wood to hold them up: they are only upright because of cell turgor. If cells lose water, the vacuole shrinks and the cytoplasm stops pressing against the cell wall. The cell loses its rigidity and becomes **flaccid**. The plant will start to droop, or **wilt**.

- If water loss continues the cytoplasm can shrink so much that it starts to come away from the cell wall. This process is known as **plasmolysis**.

> ⚡ **A* EXTRA**
>
> It is the effect of the pressure inside a turgid plant cell acting against the inelastic cell wall that makes it rigid.

turgid cell · flaccid cell · plasmolysed cell

inelastic cell wall stops cell from bursting

water · water · water · water · water · water

Water plays a key role in the structure of plant cells.

- Plants need open stomata for the gases involved in photosynthesis to move in and out – but they lose water through the stomata, and losing too much water can be a real problem. This is particularly important to plants living in places where water is not readily available, such as dry deserts or cold regions where the water in the soil is frozen.

- The leaf has a **waxy cuticle** – so water can not evaporate from epidermal cells.

- Stomata are located mostly on the **underside** of leaves – where it is cooler and evaporation is less.

- Some stomata are **sunk** below the surface of the leaf so they are less exposed.

- In some conditions the plant will **close** its stomata.

- Some plants have leaves covered with **hairs** – this creates a thin layer of still, moist air close to the leaf surface, which reduces evaporation.

- Plants in areas where water is very scarce reduce their leaves to **spines** – e.g. cactus spines or pine needles – so they have **less surface area**.

QUESTION SPOTTER

Examiners will often ask you to describe several of the ways water loss from leaves can be reduced.

GUARD CELLS

- Around each stoma there are two **guard cells**.

- In **daylight** these cells absorb water by osmosis, which makes them **swell**. The inner walls are thickened and can not stretch, unlike the outer ones. As the cells swell they curve and the gap between them opens up. During **darkness** the guard cells lose water by osmosis and the stomata **close**.

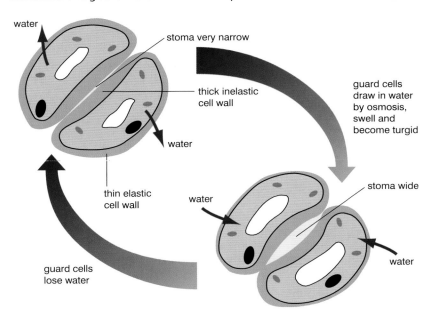

water

stoma very narrow

thick inelastic cell wall

water

thin elastic cell wall

guard cells lose water

water

guard cells draw in water by osmosis, swell and become turgid

stoma wide

water

The cell walls in guard cells are designed to open the stoma when the cell swells.

CHECK YOURSELF QUESTIONS

Q1 What are the differences between xylem and phloem?

Q2 Why does transpiration happen faster on a hot sunny day than on a cool dull day?

Q3 What is the difference between a turgid cell and a plasmolysed cell?

Answers are on page 231.

Minerals

⌂ Why do plants need minerals?

- To grow properly, plants need **minerals**, which they get from the **soil**. Some minerals are more important than others as they may be needed in larger amounts.

Mineral	Element	Use in plant	Problems caused by deficiency
Nitrates	Nitrogen	To make proteins, which are needed to make new cells	• poor growth • pale or yellow leaves
Phosphates	Phosphorus	Involved in respiration and photosynthesis	• poor growth of roots and stems • low fruit yield • small purple leaves
Potassium salts	Potassium	To control salt balance in cells. Helps enzymes involved in respiration and photosynthesis	• mottled leaves • low fruit yield • low disease resistance
Magnesium salts	Magnesium	The chlorophyll molecule contains magnesium	• yellow patches between leaf veins

⌂ Absorption

- Minerals may only be present in the soil in low concentrations and so may need to be absorbed by the root hairs against a concentration gradient. This means that they have to be absorbed by **active transport** (see Unit 1).

- They enter the roots in solution (dissolved in water) and are carried in the **transpiration stream** through the xylem up the plant.

- Although minerals are constantly being taken from the soil by plants they are restored when animal and plant materials decay. You will find out more about this and artificial fertilisers in Unit 5.

QUESTION SPOTTER

▸ You may be asked about nitrates in questions about the nitrogen cycle, or in questions about fertilisers, as well as in those about plants themselves.
▸ Expect some of the questions in your exams to link together ideas from more than one part of your course.

? CHECK YOURSELF QUESTIONS

Q1 a Plants make proteins from carbohydrates. What extra elements do they need to do this?
 b Why do plants need proteins?

Q2 Suggest why a lack of magnesium can cause yellow leaves.

Q3 Root hair cells contain many mitochondria. Suggest why.

Answers are on page 232.

REVISION SESSION 4 — Plant hormones

Controlling plant growth and development

- Many of the ways that plants grow and develop are controlled by chemicals called **plant hormones** or **plant growth regulators**.

- Like animal hormones they are made in one part of the organism and travel to other parts where they have their effects. They are different from animal hormones in that they are not made in glands and obviously do not travel through blood – they **diffuse** through the plant.

What plant hormones control

- Growth of roots, shoots and buds.

- flowering time.

- Formation and ripening of fruit.

- Germination.

- Leaf fall.

- Healing of wounds.

Commercial uses of hormones

- **Selective weedkillers** kill the weeds in a lawn without harming the grass. The hormones make the weeds grow very quickly, which usually results in death through a number of causes (e.g. a weighty structure the plant can't support, constricted veins).

- **Rooting powder**, which is applied to cuttings to make them grow roots.

- Keeping potatoes and cereals **dormant** so that they do not germinate during transport or storage.

- **Delaying the ripening** of soft fruit and vegetables so that they are not damaged during transport.

- Making crops such as apples **ripen at the same time** to make picking them less time-consuming.

QUESTION SPOTTER

Examiners will often ask you to explain why particular plant hormones are put to particular uses by humans.

Tropisms

- Tropisms are **directional growth** responses to stimuli.

- Examples include shoots growing towards the light and against the force of gravity or roots growing downwards away from the light but towards moisture and in the direction of the force of gravity. Growth in response to the direction of light is called **phototropism**. Growth in response to gravity is called **geotropism**.

- Tropisms are controlled by a hormone called **auxin**. Auxin is made in the tips of shoots and roots and diffuses away from the tip before it affects growth. One effect of auxin is to inhibit the growth of side shoots. This is why a gardener who wants a plant to stop growing taller and become more bushy will pinch off the shoot tip – removing a source of auxin.

A* EXTRA

Auxin causes curvature in shoots by causing elongation of existing cells, not by the production of more cells.

■ The growth of **shoots** towards light can be explained by the behaviour of auxin. Auxin moves **away** from the light side of a plant to the dark side. Here it encourages growth by increasing cell elongation. The dark side then grows more than the light side, and the shoot bends towards the light source.

■ In **roots**, gravity causes the auxin to collect on the **lower** side. Here it **stops** the cells elongating, which causes the root to bend downwards.

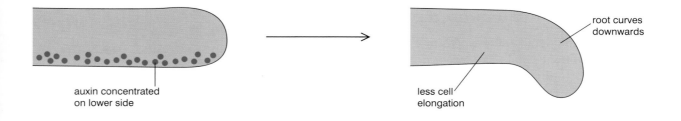

? CHECK YOURSELF QUESTIONS

Q1 How are plant hormones different from animal hormones?

Q2 Which are the following are controlled by plant hormones?
A flowering
B pollination
C germination
D leaf fall.

Q3 Once a plant shoot has changed direction so it is growing towards the light why does it stop bending?

Answers are on page 232.

UNIT 5: ECOLOGY AND THE ENVIRONMENT

The study of ecology

Some ecological terms

- **Ecology** is the study of how living things affect and are affected by other living things as well as by other factors in the environment.

- An **ecosystem** is a community and its environment – e.g. a pond.

- **Environment** is a term often used to refer only to the physical features of an area, but can include living creatures.

- A **community** means the different species in an area – e.g. the grassland community.

- A **species** is one type of organism, e.g. a robin. Only members of the same species can breed successfully with each other.

- **Population** means the numbers of a particular species in an area or ecosystem.

- An organism's **niche** is its way of life or part it plays in an ecosystem.

- An organism's **habitat** is where an organism lives.

Competition

- Animals and plants are always trying to survive and reproduce. However, there is always a 'struggle' for survival for various reasons.

- **Animals** struggle:
  - for food
  - for water
  - for protection against the weather
  - against being eaten by predators
  - against disease
  - against accidents.

- Survival of **plants** is affected by:
  - lack of water
  - lack of light
  - lack of minerals in the soil
  - weather
  - disease
  - being eaten.

- Animals and plants generally produce many young but their population sizes usually **do not vary significantly** from year to year because most of the young do not survive to adulthood. One reason for this is that they are having to **compete** for the resources they need, such as food, as there is not enough to go around.

- To help them survive, animals and plants are **adapted** to the environments in which they live. You will find out more about adaptations in Unit 6.

Predation

- One of the factors affecting a population of animals is the number of animals trying to eat them – their **predators**. The numbers of predators and **prey** are very closely connected.

- A famous example is that of snowshoe hares and lynxes in northern Canada. Both animals were hunted for their fur and the fur company kept records of how many animals were caught, so we can estimate the sizes of the populations over nearly a hundred years. This is such a vivid example because when a predator's prey reduces in number, the predators usually eat something else instead. In this case the lynx did not.

a good year for hares... ...followed by a good year for the lynx... ...followed by a poor year for the hares... ...followed by a poor year for the lynx...

number of animals (thousands)

140
120
100
80
60
40
20
0

1845 1855 1865 1875 1885 1895 1905 1915 1925 1935

year

lynx (eat hares)   snowshoe hare

Predators follow prey! Use this phrase to remember how the population graphs relate to each other.

Human population

- The human population is very rapidly increasing in size. The graph of human population growth is getting steeper and steeper. Not only is the population increasing but the rate of increase is also increasing. This is an **exponential** increase.

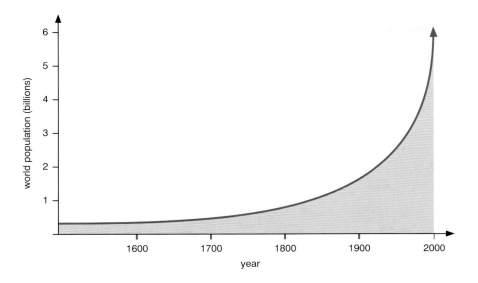

- Reasons for this increase include:
  - an increase in food production (through farming techniques)
  - advances in medicine such as immunisations and antibiotics
  - improved living conditions.

Associations

- **Parasitism** – **parasites** live in or on other organisms (their **hosts**) and harm the host. Examples are fleas living and feeding on a cat or tapeworms living inside a cow's gut.

- **Mutualism** – organisms of some species live together very closely, to the benefit of both. For example, **nitrogen-fixing bacteria** live in the root nodules of plants like peas, beans and clover. The bacteria gain sugars, vitamins and a sheltered habitat. The bacteria provide the plants with the nitrogen-containing compounds they need to make proteins (see the nitrogen cycle on page 57).

QUESTION SPOTTER

▸ You will often be asked to predict how the size of a population may change if other conditions change.
▸ Expect to be asked to explain your answer.

These root nodules contain nitrogen-fixing bacteria

CHECK YOURSELF QUESTIONS

Q1 In dense woodland there may not be many small plants growing on the ground. Suggest why.

Q2 In this country foxes eat rabbits. However, a graph of the two populations would not show the same oscillating (up and down) pattern as the lynxes and snowshoe hares on page 50. Why not?

Q3 In some summers there are much greater numbers of ladybirds than usual.
   a How would this affect the numbers of greenfly, their prey?
   b Why don't the high numbers of ladybirds persist year after year?

Answers are on page 232.

Relationships between organisms in an ecosystem

⬚ Food chains

- **Food chains** show how living things get their food. They also show how they get their **energy**. This is why they are sometimes written to include the Sun.

| Sun | grass | grasshoppers | voles | owls |

An example of a food chain.

- Food chains can be written going up or down a page, or even from right to left. All are correct, as long as the arrows always point **towards** the living thing that is taking in the food or energy.

STAGES OF A FOOD CHAIN

- **Producers** are the green plants (e.g. grass). They make their own food by **photosynthesis**, using energy from the Sun. (There is more about photosynthesis in Unit 4.)

- **Primary consumers** (e.g. grasshoppers) are animals that **eat plants** or parts of plants such as fruit. They are also called **herbivores**.

- **Secondary consumers** (e.g. voles) eat other animals. They may be called **carnivores** or predators.

- **Tertiary consumers** (such as owls) are animals that eat some secondary consumers. They are also called carnivores or predators.

- The animals hunted and eaten by predators are called prey.

- Animals that eat both plants and animals are called **omnivores**.

- The different stages of a food chain are sometimes called **trophic levels** (trophic means 'feeding'). So, for example, producers make up the first trophic level, primary consumers make up the second trophic level and so on.

- **Most food chains are not very long.** They usually end with a secondary consumer or a tertiary consumer but occasionally there is an animal that feeds on tertiary consumers. This would be called a **quaternary consumer**.

Food webs

- Food webs are different food chains joined together. It would be unusual to find a food chain that was not part of a larger food web. Here is part of a food web:

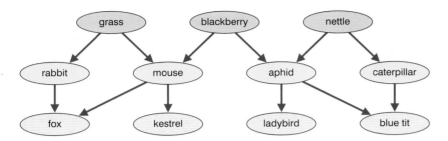

- Food webs show how different animals feed, and they can help us see what might happen if the food web is disturbed in some way.

- For example, what might happen if there was a disease that killed many, if not all, of the rabbits? From the food web above you can see that the foxes would have to eat more of the other animals – which might result in fewer mice. On the other hand, there would be more grass for the mice to eat, which might mean there are more mice.

- It is not possible to say for sure what would happen to all the organisms in a food web because there are so many living things involved.

Pyramids

- **Pyramids of numbers** show the **relative numbers** of each type of living thing in a food chain or web by trophic level. Sometimes pyramids of numbers can be 'inverted' – if, for example, the producers are much larger than the consumers.

A pyramid of numbers.   **An 'inverted' pyramid of numbers.**

- **Pyramids of biomass** show the mass of living material at each stage in the chain or web, so this shows what you would have if you could weigh all the producers together, then all the primary consumers and so on. Pyramids of biomass are almost **never** inverted.

- Pyramids either show organisms on a single food chain or trophic levels in a food web. If they show trophic levels, **each stage of the pyramid may be labelled** with all the living things at a particular trophic level, for example producers or primary consumers.

blue tits
caterpillars
oak tree

A pyramid of biomass.

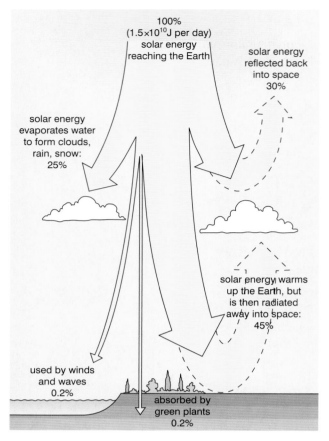

100%
(1.5×10¹⁰J per day)
solar energy
reaching the Earth

solar energy
reflected back
into space
30%

solar energy
evaporates water
to form clouds,
rain, snow:
25%

solar energy warms
up the Earth, but
is then radiated
away into space:
45%

used by winds
and waves
0.2%

absorbed by
green plants
0.2%

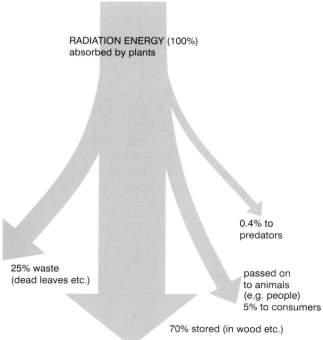

RADIATION ENERGY (100%)
absorbed by plants

0.4% to
predators

25% waste
(dead leaves etc.)

passed on
to animals
(e.g. people)
5% to consumers

70% stored (in wood etc.)

Energy flow in plants.

⊡ Energy flow

■ The arrows in food chains and webs show the **transfer of energy**. Not all the energy that enters an animal or plant is available to the next trophic level. Only energy that has resulted in an organism's growth will be available to the animal that eats it.

Example: cows feeding on grass in a field

Sun → grass → cow

■ Only a **small proportion** of the energy in the sunlight falling on a field is used by the grass in photosynthesis.
• Some may be **absorbed** or **reflected** by **clouds** or **dust** in the air.
• Some may be absorbed or reflected by **trees** or **other plants**.
• Some may **miss** the grass and hit the ground.
• Some will be **reflected** by the **grass** (grass reflects the green part of the spectrum and absorbs the red and blue wavelengths).
• Some will enter the grass but will **pass through** the leaves.

■ The remainder of the energy can be used in photosynthesis.

■ Some of the food made by the grass will be used for respiration to provide the grass's energy requirements, but some will be used for growth and will be available for a future consumer.

■ However, not all the energy in the grass will be available to the cows:
• Some grass may be eaten by **other animals** (the farmer would probably call these pests).
• The cows will **not eat all** of the grass (e.g. the roots remain).

■ Of the energy available in the grass the cows **ingest** (eat) they will use only a small proportion for growth. The diagram on page 55 shows what happens to the energy in an animal's food.

HOW ANIMALS LOSE ENERGY

- Energy is lost from animals in two main ways:

  1 **Egestion** – the removal from the body, in faeces, of material that may contain energy but has not been digested.

  2 **Respiration** – the release of energy from food is necessary for all the processes that go on in living things. Most of this energy is eventually lost as heat. (There is more about respiration in Unit 2.)

- Because **energy is lost** from the chain **at each stage** you almost always get a pyramid shape with a pyramid of biomass.

38 **units** used in respiration (given out as heat)

100 **units** of energy are eaten by the cow in a year

2 **units** used for growth

60 **units** wasted

grass produces **700 units** of energy a year

The energy flow in a young cow.

Farming

- A farmer raising plant or animal crops will get a greater yield by reducing energy losses from the food chain.

- For a **plant** crop this can be done by:
  - removing plants that are **competing** for light (e.g. weeds)
  - removing other organisms that might **damage** the plant crop (pests)
  - ensuring the plants have sufficient **water** and **minerals** to be able to photosynthesise and grow efficiently.

- The farmer could keep **animals indoors** so they do not have to use as much energy to stay warm or keep them **penned up** to reduce their movement and so lower the heat losses from respiration. This is sometimes known as **battery farming** and some people disagree with it on moral grounds.

QUESTION SPOTTER

You will often be required to describe some of the ways energy is lost from food chains.

CHECK YOURSELF QUESTIONS

Q1 Look at this food chain in a garden:

rose bushes → aphids → ladybirds

a Draw and label a pyramid of numbers for this food chain.

b Draw and label a pyramid of biomass for this food chain.

Q2 Which is more energy efficient, to grow crops that we eat ourselves or to use those crops to feed animals which we then eat?

Q3 Why are there usually not more than five stages in a food chain?

Answers are on page 233.

Natural recycling

▢ Supplies are limited

■ The minerals that plants need from the soil are mostly released from the decayed remains of animals and plants and their waste. This is one example of natural recycling. There is only a limited amount (on Earth) of the elements that living things need and use.

■ Four of the most important elements in living things are **carbon** (C), **hydrogen** (H), **oxygen** (O) and **nitrogen** (N). Important substances such as carbohydrates, fats and proteins are made up of carbon, hydrogen and oxygen. Proteins also contain nitrogen.

■ The only way that animals and plants can continue to take in and use substances containing these elements is if the substances are constantly cycled around the ecosystem for reuse.

▢ The carbon cycle

QUESTION SPOTTER

You may be given part of the carbon cycle or the nitrogen cycle and asked to add in the missing parts.

■ Plants take in carbon dioxide because they need the carbon (and oxygen) to use in photosynthesis to make carbohydrates and then other substances such as protein.

■ When animals eat plants they use some of the carbon-containing compounds to grow and some to release energy in respiration.

■ As a waste product of respiration animals breathe out carbon as carbon dioxide, which is then available for plants to use. (Don't forget that plants also respire producing carbon dioxide.)

■ Carbon dioxide is also released when animal and plant remains decay (**decomposition**) and when wood, peat or fossil fuels are burnt (**combustion**).

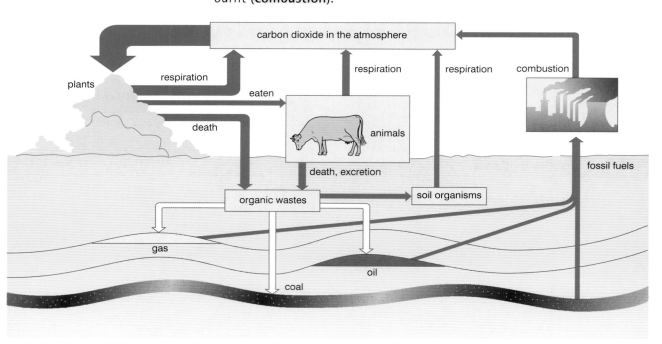

⌂ The nitrogen cycle

- Living things need nitrogen to make proteins – which are needed, for example, to make new cells for growth.

- The air is 79% nitrogen gas (N_2), but nitrogen gas is very unreactive and cannot be used by plants or animals. Instead plants use nitrogen in the form of **nitrates** (NO_3^- ions).

- The process of getting nitrogen into this useful form is called **nitrogen fixation**.

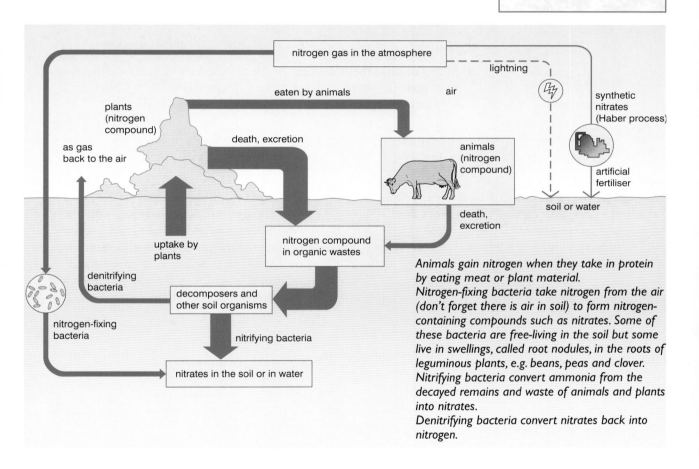

Animals gain nitrogen when they take in protein by eating meat or plant material.
Nitrogen-fixing bacteria take nitrogen from the air (don't forget there is air in soil) to form nitrogen-containing compounds such as nitrates. Some of these bacteria are free-living in the soil but some live in swellings, called root nodules, in the roots of leguminous plants, e.g. beans, peas and clover.
Nitrifying bacteria convert ammonia from the decayed remains and waste of animals and plants into nitrates.
Denitrifying bacteria convert nitrates back into nitrogen.

⌷ Decomposers

■ The decay of dead animal and plant remains is an important part of biological recycling. Decay happens because of the action of **bacteria** and **fungi**. These are known as **decomposers**.

■ Conditions that allow decomposers to thrive are conditions that will help decay:
  • **warm** (but not too hot to kill the micro-organisms)
  • **moist**
  • the presence of **oxygen**.

■ Other organisms, known as **detritivores** (such as worms or woodlice), feed on and break down dead remains (known as **detritus**). This exposes a greater surface area for the decomposers to act upon.

■ Materials that can decompose are known as **biodegradable**.

■ Micro-organisms that cause decay are used by humans – for example:
  • in **sewage works** to break down human waste
  • in **compost heaps** to break down waste plant material.

? CHECK YOURSELF QUESTIONS

Q1 **a** In the carbon cycle, which main process removes carbon dioxide from the atmosphere?

b How is carbon dioxide put back into the atmosphere?

Q2 Nitrogen-fixing bacteria cannot live in waterlogged soil but denitrifying bacteria can, which is why this kind of soil is low in nitrates. Some plants that live in these conditions are carnivorous, trapping and digesting insects. Suggest why you often find carnivorous plants in bogs.

Q3 What is the difference between nitrifying and denitrifying bacteria?

Answers are on page 233.

Human influences on the environment

Why is the effect of humans on the environment increasing?

- An **increasing population** means that more **resources** are needed and used (e.g. land, raw materials for industry, sources of energy and food).

- **Technological advances** and an overall increase in the standard of living also mean that more resources are used.

- Following on from this there is an increase in waste production – **pollution**.

- These problems are caused particularly by the developed countries of the world.

Consequences of misuse of the environment

- The use of some resources like minerals and fossil fuels cannot continue forever – there is only a limited amount of them (they are **finite**). Once they have been used they cannot be replaced. In the future we will have to recycle these materials or find replacements that are renewable.

- Pollution caused by putting waste into the environment is causing changes that may be irreversible.

WAYS OF TACKLING THESE PROBLEMS

- **Reducing the amount** of raw materials we use (e.g. by using less packaging on products).

- **Recycling** more materials, so reducing the need for, and energy cost of, extracting more raw materials.

- Being more **energy efficient** (e.g. by reducing heat losses from buildings or turning off lights when not needed).

- Using **renewable energy sources** that will not run out and which cause little pollution (e.g. solar, wind or wave power).

- Using **sustainable** or renewable **raw materials** that can be produced again (such as wood).

Farming and use of agrochemicals

- **Insecticides** are chemicals which kill insects that damage the crops. They can cause unwanted effects by killing animals that are not pests.

- Some insecticides can enter the food chain. The animals that ingest them cannot break them down or excrete them, so they remain in the animals' bodies. Such substances are described as being **persistent**. This means that predators can contain much higher levels of the substance than the animals below them in a food chain.

- Use of the insecticide DDT is the reason why many birds of prey in Britain, like sparrowhawks and peregrine falcons, suffered in the 1950s and 1960s. DDT is now banned in many countries. Most modern insecticides are not persistent and break down naturally in the environment after a short while.

DDT affected many food chains. In this one, the figures give the relative concentration of DDT at each stage.

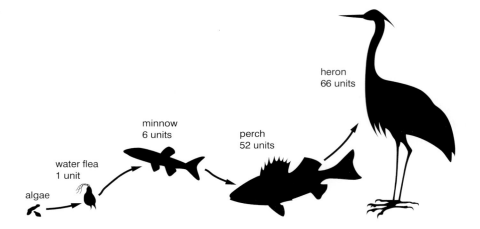

heron
66 units

minnow
6 units

perch
52 units

water flea
1 unit

algae

- **Biological control,** introducing another organism that will kill the pests, is an alternative to using chemical insecticides. This does not cause pollution and pests cannot become resistant to it (as they can to chemical insecticides). However, biological control can have unwanted effects – for instance the introduced predators might also attack harmless or even useful animals.

- **Fungicides** are chemicals that kill the fungi responsible for many plant diseases. Insecticides and fungicides together are often known as **pesticides**.

- **Herbicides,** or weedkillers, are chemicals which kill plants that would otherwise grow among the crop and compete with them for light, water and minerals. These other plants might also be the home of pests. However, such plants could be used by other animals. Also, by increasing the crop, any pests that normally feed on it will have plenty of food, may rapidly increase in numbers and could become a bigger problem.

- **Fertilisers** are added to improve the growth of crops. **Organic** (natural) fertilisers include compost or manure. **Inorganic** (artificial) fertilisers are mined or manufactured to contain the necessary minerals. Artificial fertilisers come in powdered or liquid form so they are easy to spread, but they can cause pollution.

EUTROPHICATION

- When it rains, the soluble fertiliser dissolves in the water and is carried away into lakes and rivers – it is **leached** from the soil.

- The fertiliser causes excessive growth of plants in rivers and lakes – especially **algae**. The plant overgrowth makes the water murky and blocks much of the light, and plants under the surface die and decay. The bacteria that cause the decay use up the oxygen in the water, so fish and other water animals die.

- This whole process is called **eutrophication**.

- Eutrophication can be reduced by using **less fertiliser**. This may actually help the farmer because there is a point beyond which adding more fertiliser will not help, and may even hinder, crop growth.

This river is blocked with algae because of excess nitrates washed in from nearby fields.

1 rainwater dissolves nitrates

2 nitrates leach into rivers

3 algae grows and blooms

4 light cut off from river-bed plants

5 bacteria that aid plant decay use up river's oxygen

6 fish deprived of oxygen die

The process of eutrophication.

OTHER WAYS OF MAINTAINING SOIL FERTILITY

- Using **organic fertilisers**, which release minerals into the soil at a slower rate. This also helps to improve soil structure, making it easier to plough for example.

- Using **crop rotation**, which includes growing crops that contain nitrogen-fixing bacteria in their root nodules. This restores soil fertility when the crops or their roots are ploughed back into the soil.

☐ The greenhouse effect

- Carbon dioxide, methane and CFCs are known as **greenhouse gases**. The levels of these gases in the atmosphere are increasing due to the burning of fossil fuels, pollution from farm animals and the use of CFCs in aerosols and refrigerators.

- Short-wave radiation from the Sun warms the ground and the warm Earth gives off heat as long-wave radiation. Much of this radiation is stopped from escaping from the Earth by the greenhouse gases. This is known as the **greenhouse effect**.

- The greenhouse effect is responsible for keeping the Earth warmer than it otherwise would be. The greenhouse effect is normal – and important for life on Earth. However, it is thought that increasing levels of greenhouse gases are stopping even more heat escaping and the Earth is slowly warming up. This is known as **global warming.** If global warming continues the Earth's climate may change and sea levels rise as polar ice melts.

- The temperature of the Earth *is* gradually increasing, but we do not know for certain if the greenhouse effect is responsible. It may be that the observed rise in recent global temperatures is part of a natural cycle – there have been Ice Ages and intermediate warm periods before. Many people are concerned that it is not part of a cycle and say we should act now to reduce emissions of these greenhouse gases.

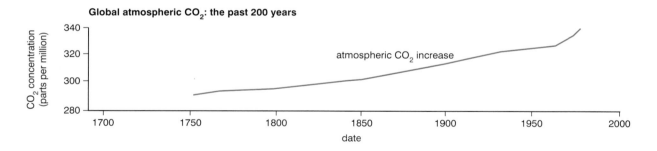

Global atmospheric CO_2: the past 200 years

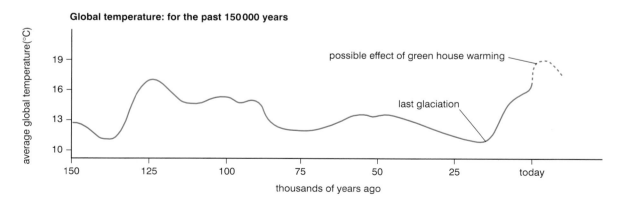

Global temperature: for the past 150 000 years

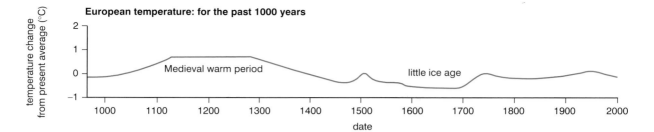

European temperature: for the past 1000 years

☐ Acid rain

- Burning fossil fuels gives off many gases, including **sulphur dioxide** and various **nitrogen oxides**.

- Sulphur dioxide combines with water to form sulphuric acid. Nitrogen oxide combines with water to form nitric acid. These substances can make the rain acidic (called **acid rain**).

- Acid rain **harms plants** that take in the acidic water and the **animals** that live in the affected rivers and lakes. Acid rain also washes ions such as calcium and magnesium out of the soil, **depleting the minerals available to plants**. It also washes **aluminium**, which is poisonous to fish, out of the soil and into rivers and lakes.

- Reducing emission of the gases causing acid rain is expensive, and part of the problem is that the acid rain usually falls a long way from the places where the gases were given off.

- Fitting **catalytic converters** stops the emission of these gases from cars.

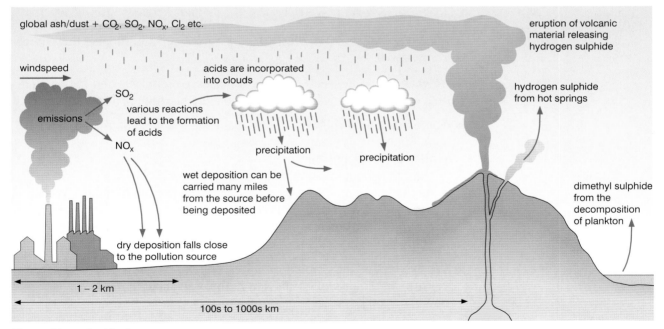

The problem of acid rain.

Depletion of the ozone layer

- High in the atmosphere there is a layer of a gas called **ozone**, a form of oxygen in which the molecules contain three oxygen atoms (O_3). Ozone in the atmosphere is continually being broken down and reformed:

ozone formation	ozone breakdown
$O_2 \xrightarrow{\text{UV light}} O + O$	$O_3 \rightarrow O_2 + O$
$O_2 + O \rightarrow O_3$	$O_3 + O \rightarrow 2O_2$

- The ozone layer reduces the amount of **ultraviolet radiation** (UV) that reaches the Earth's surface. This is important because UV radiation can cause skin cancer.

- Normally the rates at which the ozone forms and breaks down are about the same. **CFCs**, which are gases used as aerosol propellants and in refrigerator cooling systems, **speed up** the rate of ozone breakdown without affecting how quickly it reforms. This means that there is **less ozone** in the atmosphere and that **more UV radiation** will be reaching the Earth's surface. This could cause an increase in skin cancer in people who are exposed to a lot of sunlight.

- We can reduce the damage to the ozone layer by finding alternatives to CFCs, but many of these seem to contribute to other problems, such as the greenhouse effect.

- Even if all CFC emissions stopped today it will still take around a hundred years for all the CFCs presently in the atmosphere to break down.

Household waste

- People produce a lot of waste, including sewage and rubbish they simply throw away.

- **Sewage** has to be treated to remove disease organisms and the nutrients that cause eutrophication, before it can be discharged into the sea.

- Some **household rubbish** is burnt, causing acid gas pollution and acid rain. Rubbish tips create their own problems:
  - they are ugly and can smell
  - they can encourage rats and other pests
  - methane gas produced by rotting material may build up in tips that are covered with soil – this gas is explosive
  - covered-over tips can not be used for building on because the ground settles.

- We can reduce the amount of material in our dustbins by **recycling** or **reusing** materials and not buying **highly packaged** materials.

⌶ Habitat destruction

- Many natural habitats are being **destroyed** to create land for farming or building on. The rainforests are being cut down for their wood and to create farming or grazing land. Many species of animals and plants are only found in wetland areas, which are being drained to 'reclaim' the land.

- Destruction of habitats **reduces species diversity**.

- Removing plants exposes the soil to rain, which **washes the soil away**, blocking rivers and causing flooding.

- Habitat destruction can also **alter the climate** – less water is transpired into the atmosphere.

⌶ Endangered species

- Many species of animals and plants are in danger of **extinction** because of habitat destruction and hunting.

- Endangered species can be protected by:
  - making some areas protected
  - legal protection (e.g. laws against hunting)
  - educating people so that they are aware of species that are endangered and know how to protect them.

⌶ Sustainable development

- One way of reducing the impact of human activity on the environment is to **replace** materials or crops we use.

- For example, quotas on fishing mean that fish stocks do not drop so far that the fish disappear altogether.

- Another example is to replant woodland after trees have been cut down.

QUESTION SPOTTER

Questions about environmental damage may use examples that you have not studied in detail. You will be given enough information to be able to answer them.

❓ CHECK YOURSELF QUESTIONS

Q1 Why are some pesticides described as 'persistent'?

Q2 What is the difference between the greenhouse effect and global warming?

Q3 Acid rain can be reduced by passing waste gases through lime to remove sulphur dioxide. Why don't all factories automatically do this?

Answers are on page 233.

Sampling techniques

QUESTION SPOTTER

Not all exam boards will ask questions on this section. Check with your teacher.

Ecological surveys

■ You may have already carried out an **ecological survey** of an area such as your school grounds. This involves finding out what organisms live there, where they live, and the sizes of their populations. To do this you can use different equipment and techniques.

Pooter

■ The end of the short tube is placed over the animal and you suck on the other tube, collecting the animal in the bottle. This is suitable for collecting small **insects** or **spiders**, which would otherwise quickly move away.

A simple pooter

Pitfall trap

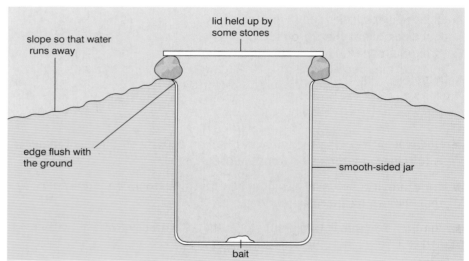

lid held up by some stones

slope so that water runs away

edge flush with the ground

smooth-sided jar

bait

The standard way of using a pitfall trap.

■ The trap can be left overnight. It is useful for collecting insects such as **beetles** that are more active at night and are too heavy to climb out. A lid or drainage holes will prevent water collecting and drowning the animals.

Tullgren funnel

lamp

funnel

collecting pot

The apparatus used to make a Tullgren funnel.

■ Soil contains many **small animals**. One way of extracting these from the soil is to put a soil sample inside the funnel. The heat from the lamp makes the animals go deeper until they fall through the sieve inside the funnel and can be collected in a pot underneath. The collecting pot can be filled with ethanol if you wish to preserve the animals.

Sweep net

- A sweep net can be waved or brushed over grass or other vegetation to collect any insects there.

Beating tray

- The tray is held under a bush or branch, which is then shaken to dislodge any small animals – which can then be caught using a pooter.

Quadrat

- A quadrat can be used to carry out a **plant survey**, for example to compare the plant life in two different areas. You would randomly place the quadrat a number of times in each area, each time identifying and counting the plants within the quadrat. Then you would pool the results to find the average for the two areas.

- If the area of the region being investigated and the area of the quadrat are both known, then an estimate can be made of the total numbers of each species. Using quadrats in this way is called **sampling**, because only a sample of the region is inspected. Inspecting every plant throughout the region would take too long.

- Sampling using a quadrat works best if:
  - the quadrat is placed **randomly**
  - a reasonable **number of samples** is taken, so any 'odd' results will be 'evened out' when averages are taken
  - the plants being investigated are reasonably **evenly spread** throughout the area.

- You could also place a quadrat at regular intervals **along a line** to see how the habitat changes. This is called a **transect**.

- Quadrats can also be used to investigate the numbers or distribution of **animals** in a habitat – as long as they are evenly distributed and not constantly moving around the area.

CHECK YOURSELF QUESTIONS

Q1 What equipment would be best to use to collect:
  a tiny insects living in the soil
  b large ground beetles that come out at night
  c small insects living in a thick bush
  d ants.

Q2 A pupil wanted to estimate the number of dandelions in a field. She used a large quadrat that was 1 m^2 and the field was 200 m^2. She used the quadrat 10 times and counted a total of 25 dandelions. Estimate the number of dandelions in the field.

Q3 Why is it important that quadrats are placed randomly?

Answers are on page 234.

UNIT 6: GENETICS AND EVOLUTION

Variation

▢ Types of variation

- No two people are the same. Similarly, no two oak trees will be exactly the same in every way – they will be different heights, have different trunk widths and different numbers of leaves.

- There are two types of variation:

  1 **Discontinuous variation** – a characteristic can have one of a certain number of specific alternatives. Examples would be gender, where you are either male or female, or blood groups where you are either A, B, AB or O. This is sometimes referred to as discrete variation.

  2 **Continuous variation** – a characteristic can have any value in a range. Examples would be body weight or length of hair.

▢ Causes of variation

- **Environmental causes.** Your diet, the climate you live in, accidents, your surroundings, the way you have been brought up or your lifestyle all influence your characteristics.

- **Genetic causes** – the characteristic is controlled by your genes. Genes are inherited from your parents. Examples of characteristics in humans purely influenced by genes are eye colour and gender.

- Many characteristics are influenced by environment **and** genes. For instance people in your family might tend to be tall, but unless you eat correctly when you are growing you will not become tall even though genetically you have the tendency to be tall. Other examples are more controversial, such as human intelligence, where it is unclear whether the environment or genes is more influential.

▢ Genes

- Genes are **instructions** that direct the processes going on inside cells. They affect the way cells grow and work and so can affect features of your body such as the shape of your face or the colour of your eyes. All the information needed to make a fertilised egg grow into an adult is contained in its genes.

- Inside virtually every cell in the body is a **nucleus**, which contains long threads called **chromosomes**. These threads are usually spread throughout the nucleus, but when the cell splits they gather into bundles that can be seen through a microscope. The chromosomes are made of a chemical called deoxyribonucleic acid (**DNA**).

- DNA is a very long molecule that contains a series of chemicals called **bases**. There are four different types of base in DNA: thymine (T), adenine (A), guanine (G) and cytosine (C). The order in which the bases occur is a **genetic code**. The code spells out instructions that control how the cell

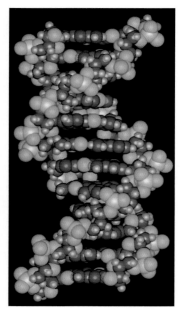

The 'double-helix' structure of DNA was discovered by James Watson and Francis Crick working in Cambridge in 1953. Rosalind Franklin, working in London, contributed important work on DNA's structure.

works. Each length of DNA that spells out a different instruction is known as a **gene**. Each chromosome contains thousands of genes.

- All the genes in a particular living thing are known as its **genome**.

- Genes tell cells how to make different **proteins**. Many proteins are enzymes that control the chemical processes inside cells.

- Most of our features that are controlled genetically are affected by several genes.

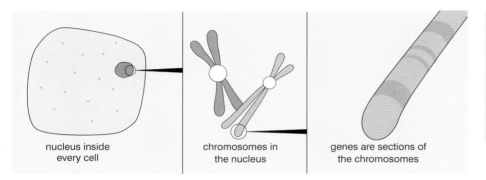

nucleus inside every cell

chromosomes in the nucleus

genes are sections of the chromosomes

Mutations

- Sometimes genes can be altered so that their message becomes meaningless or a different instruction. This is known as a **mutation**. Mutations can be caused by:
  - radiation
  - certain chemicals, called **mutagens**
  - spontaneous changes.

- Mutations that occur in **sex cells** can be passed on to offspring, who may develop abnormally or may die at an early stage of development.

- If mutations occur in **body cells** they may multiply uncontrollably. This is **cancer**.

DNA is found in the nucleus of cells.

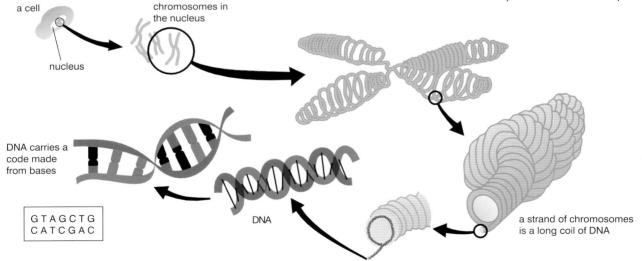

a cell

nucleus

chromosomes in the nucleus

DNA carries a code made from bases

GTAGCTG
CATCGAC

DNA

a strand of chromosomes is a long coil of DNA

A spider plant forms new plants at the end of stalks ('runners'). These new plants eventually grow independently of the parent plant. This is an example of asexual reproduction.

⌷ Cell division

- Cells grow by splitting in two. This is called **cell division**, and is part of normal body growth. It is also the way that single-celled organisms reproduce and is the only type of cell division involved during **asexual reproduction** (reproduction that does not involve sex cells).

- Before a cell splits, its chromosomes **duplicate** themselves. The new cells formed, sometimes called the **daughter cells**, contain chromosomes identical with the original cell. This type of cell division, in which the new cells are genetically identical to the original, is known as **mitosis**. Cells or organisms that are genetically identical to each other are known as **clones**.

Stage 1. The chromosomes get fatter and become visible.

Stage 4. The colour chromosomes part and move to opposite halves of the cell.

Stage 2. Each chromosome makes an exact copy of itself

Stage 5. The cell splits in two.

The process of mitosis.

Stage 3. The chromosomes line up in the middle of the cell

- There is another type of reproduction in which the new individuals have been formed by two special cells, called **sex cells** or **gametes**, usually one from each parent. This type of reproduction is called **sexual reproduction**.

- A different type of cell division called **meiosis** ensures that the gametes only have half the number of chromosomes that body cells have. In humans the gametes are sperm cells and egg cells. In flowering plants the gametes are the pollen cells and the female 'egg' cells or ovules.

- The gametes contain half the normal number of chromosomes so that when they join together (at **fertilisation**) the normal number is restored. For example, human cells normally contain 23 pairs of chromosomes: 46 in total. Human egg and sperm cells contain only 23 chromosomes, so when they join together the new cell formed has the normal 46. (The number of chromosomes depends on an organism's species.)

- The offspring produced by sexual reproduction are genetically **different** from their parents.

The 23 pairs of chromosomes in a human cell, including the X and tiny Y.

Stage 1. A normal cell in the sex organs. It has the usual number of chromosomes, which fatten and become visible.

Stage 2. Each chromosome makes a copy of itself

Stage 3. Remember that each chromosome has its own 'partner'. They carry similar 'blueprints' – one from the original father and one from the mother. These partner chromosomes get together and line up across the middle of the cell.

Stage 4. The chromosome pairs swap genes, split up and move to opposite halves of the cell.

Stage 6. In each new cell, the chromosomes part and move to opposite halves of their cells.

Stage 5. The cell splits into two new cells. These special cells have half the usual number of chromosomes.

Stage 7. The two new cells split once more to make four new cells. Each has half the usual number of chromosomes.

The process of meiosis.

■ Every gamete formed has one of each pair of chromosomes. However, which one of each chromosome pair ends up in a particular gamete is purely random. An individual human can produce gametes with billions of different combinations of chromosomes.

■ Add this to the fact that when chromosome pairs are lying next to each other they swap lengths of DNA (this is called **crossing over**), altering the combination of genes on a chromosome. It is not surprising that, even with the same parents, we can look very different from our brothers and sisters.

CHECK YOURSELF QUESTIONS

Q1 Which of the following are examples of (a) continuous and (b) discontinuous variation?
   A Hair colour
   B Blood group
   C Foot size
   D Gender
   E Hair length.

Q2 Bob and Dave are identical twins. Dave emigrates to Australia, where he works outside on building sites. Bob stays in England and works in an office. Suggest how they might look (a) similar and (b) different. Explain your answers.

Q3 Put the following in order of size, starting with the smallest: cell nucleus, chromosome, gene, cell, chemical base.

Answers are on page 234.

■ Inheritance ■

⌷ How features are passed on

■ Some features, such as the colour of your eyes, are passed on, or **inherited**, from your parents, but other features may not be passed on. Sometimes features appear to miss a generation – for instance you and your grandmother might both have ginger hair, but neither of your parents do.

DOMINANT AND RECESSIVE ALLELES

■ Leopards occasionally have a cub that has completely black fur instead of the usual spotted pattern. It is known as a black panther but is still the same species as the ordinary leopard.

■ Just as in humans, leopard chromosomes occur in **pairs**. One pair carries a gene for fur colour. There are two copies of the gene in a normal body cell (one on each chromosome). Both copies of the gene may be identical but sometimes they are different, one being for a spotted coat and the other for a black coat. Different versions of a gene are called **alleles**.

■ Leopard cubs receive half their genes from each parent. Eggs and sperm cells only contain half the normal number of chromosomes as normal body cells. This means that egg and sperm cells contain only one of each pair of alleles. When an egg and sperm join together at fertilisation the new cell formed, the **zygote**, which will develop into the new individual, now has two alleles of each gene.

■ **Different combinations** of alleles will produce different fur colour:

> spotted coat allele + spotted coat allele = spotted coat
>
> spotted coat allele + black coat allele = spotted coat
>
> black coat allele + black coat allele = black coat

■ The black coat only appears when **both** of the alleles for the black coat are present. As long as there is at least one allele for a spotted coat, the coat will be spotted because the allele for a spotted coat overrides the allele for a black coat. It is the **dominant allele**. Alleles like the one for the black coat are described as **recessive**.

■ Having two identical alleles is described as being **homozygous**. Animals that have two different alleles are **heterozygous**.

MONOHYBRID CROSSES

■ An individual's combination of genes is their **genotype**. An individual's combination of physical features is called their **phenotype**. Your genotype influences your phenotype.

■ We can show the influence of the genotype in a **genetic diagram**. In a genetic diagram we use a **capital letter** for the **dominant** allele and a **lower case** letter for the **recessive** allele.

- Using the example of the leopards, the letter S stands for the dominant allele for a spotted coat and letter s will stand for the recessive allele for the black coat. Two spotted parents who have a black cub must each be carrying an S and an s. The genetic diagram below shows the different offspring that may be born.

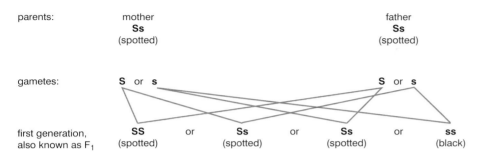

parents: mother   father
            Ss   **Ss**
            (spotted)   (spotted)

gametes: **S** or **s**   **S** or **s**

first generation,   **SS**   or   **Ss**   or   **Ss**   or   **ss**
also known as F₁   (spotted)   (spotted)   (spotted)   (black)

- Because we are looking at only one characteristic (fur colour), this is an example of a **monohybrid cross**. 'Mono' means one, and a 'hybrid' is produced when two different types breed, or cross.

- Another type of genetic diagram is known as a **Punnett square**. The example above can be shown in a Punnett square:

		male gametes	
		S	**s**
female gametes	**S**	**SS** (spotted)	**Ss** (spotted)
	s	**Ss** (spotted)	**ss** (black)

- When two heterozygous parents are crossed, the offspring that have the feature controlled by the dominant allele and those showing the feature controlled by the recessive allele appear in a **3:1 ratio**. This is because of the random way that gametes combine. The 3:1 ratio refers to the **probabilities** of particular combinations of alleles – there is a 1 in 4 chance of a leopard cub being black, for example.

- With a large number of offspring you would expect something near the 3:1 ratio of spotted to black cubs. However, because it does refer only to probabilities you would not be too surprised if in a litter of four two of the cubs were black or none were black.

- How genes are inherited was first worked out in the nineteenth century by an Austrian monk, **Gregor Mendel**, who did lots of breeding experiments using pea plants.

QUESTION SPOTTER

- In your exam you could be asked to use genetic diagrams to show the results of a cross.
- Unless you are asked otherwise, make sure you clearly show all the possible gametes (sex cells) and offspring, and how they have been produced.

⌷ Inherited diseases

■ Some diseases or disorders can be inherited. Examples include:
- **cystic fibrosis** – in which the lungs become clogged up with mucus
- **haemophilia** – in which blood does not clot as normal
- **diabetes** – in which insulin is not made in the pancreas (see Unit 3)
- **sickle–cell anaemia** – in which the red blood cells are misshapen and do not carry oxygen properly
- **Huntington's disease** – a disorder of the nervous system.

■ Most inherited diseases are caused by **faulty genes**. For example, one form of diabetes is caused by a fault in the gene carrying the instructions telling the pancreas cells how to make insulin.

■ Most of these faulty alleles are **recessive**, which means that you have to have two copies of the faulty allele to show the disorder. Many people will be **carriers**, having one normal allele as well as the faulty version. The diagram below shows how two carrier parents could have a child with a disorder.

		male gametes	
		D	**d**
female gametes	**D**	**DD** (makes insulin)	**Dd** (makes insulin)
	d	**Dd** (makes insulin)	**dd** (has diabetes)

⌷ Sex determination

■ Whether a baby is a boy or a girl is decided by one pair of chromosomes called the **sex chromosomes**. There are two sex chromosomes, the **X chromosome** and the **Y chromosome**. Boys have one of each and girls have two X chromosomes.

■ **Egg** cells always contain **one X chromosome** but **sperm** cells have an equal chance of containing **either** an X chromosome **or** a Y chromosome. This means that a baby has an equal chance of being either a boy or a girl. This is shown in the diagram below.

		male gametes	
		X	**Y**
female gametes	**X**	**XX** (girl)	**XY** (boy)
	X	**XX** (girl)	**XY** (boy)

■ Some genetic disorders such as red–green colour blindness are more common in men than women. The recessive allele causing the disorder is found on the X chromosome, on a part for which there is no equivalent on the Y chromosome as it is smaller (see photograph on page 70). This means that males only need to have one copy of the recessive allele to show the disorder while females would need two copies.

CHECK YOURSELF QUESTIONS

Q1 In humans, the gene that allows you to roll your tongue is a dominant allele. Use a genetic diagram to show how two 'roller' parents could have a child who is a 'non-roller'.

Q2 In leopards the allele for being spotted, S, is dominant to the allele for being black, s. How could you tell whether a spotted leopard was Ss or SS, given that you have black leopards that you know are ss?

Q3 John and Mary have a little girl who has cystic fibrosis. Cystic fibrosis is caused by a recessive allele. What is the probability of their next child also having cystic fibrosis? Neither John nor Mary have the condition.

Answers are on page 234.

■ Applications ■

▢ Selective breeding

- ■ Selective breeding (also known as **artificial selection**) has been used by farmers for hundreds of years to change and improve the features of the animals or plants they grow. Examples would be breeding:
  - apples that are bigger and more tasty
  - sheep that produce more or better quality wool
  - cows that produce more milk or meat
  - wheat that can be planted earlier so giving an extra crop
  - plants that are more resistant to disease.

- ■ In every case the principle is the same. You select two individuals with the features closest to those you want and breed them together. From the next generation you again select the best offspring and use these for breeding. Repeat this over many generations.

- ■ For example, if you wanted to produce dogs that had short tails, you would breed the male and female with the shortest tails from the dogs you had available. From their offspring you would select those with the shortest tails to use for breeding. After repeating this over many generations you would find that you almost always produced short-tailed dogs – they would be **breeding true**.

- ■ Simply selecting for different features such as size or shape has produced all the breeds of dogs we have today, which are all descended from wolves that were domesticated thousands of years ago.

⚡ A* EXTRA

- ▸ Selective breeding usually causes a reduction in variation.
- ▸ It may also lead to an accumulation of harmful recessive characteristics. This is the danger of inbreeding.

The power of selection. Selective breeding has produced an enormous variety of dog breeds from wild wolf stock (right).

Cloning

- If you have an animal or plant with features that you want, its offspring might not show those features. A simple way of producing new **plants** that are genetically identical to the original is by taking **cuttings**. A cutting is a shoot or branch that is removed from the original and planted in soil to grow on its own. Some plants do this easily, others may need rooting hormones (see Unit 4) to encourage them to grow roots.

A small cutting from a geranium that has been encouraged to grow fresh roots.

- A more modern version of taking cuttings is **tissue culture**. This is used to grow large numbers of plants quickly as only a **tiny part** of the original is needed to grow a new plant. Special procedures have to be followed:

  1 Cut many small pieces from the chosen plant. These are called **explants**.

  2 **Sterilise** the pieces by washing them in mild bleach to kill any microbes.

  3 In sterile conditions transfer the explants on to a jelly-like growth medium that contains nutrients as well as plant hormones to encourage growth.

  4 The explants should develop roots and shoots and leaves.

  5 When the plants are large enough they can be transferred to other growth media and eventually to a normal growth medium like compost.

These tiny sundew plants have all grown from tiny cuttings of a single plant.

- Cloning can also now be used with **animals**. For example, cells from a developing **embryo** (such as from a cow) can be split apart before they become specialised and then transplanted, as identical embryos, into **host mothers**.

- Another way of cloning animals involves making ordinary **body cells** grow into new animals. Dolly the sheep was the first mammal clone grown from the cell of a fully grown organism – in Dolly's case a cell from the udder of a sheep.

Genetic engineering

- Selective breeding works by trying to bring together desirable combinations of genes. **Genetic engineering** allows this to be done quickly and directly. It involves taking genes from **one organism** and **inserting** them into cells of **another**. For example, genes have been inserted into crop plants to make them more resistant to attack by pests.

- The gene that carries the instructions for making the human hormone insulin has been inserted into bacteria, which now produce insulin. This is where much of the insulin to treat diabetes comes from. The gene was originally from a human cell so the insulin is identical to that made normally in the human pancreas.

STEPS INVOLVED IN GENETIC ENGINEERING

1 **Find** the part of the DNA that contains the gene you want.

2 **Remove the gene** using special enzymes that cut the DNA either side of the gene.

3 **Insert the gene** into the cells of the organism you want to change.

- Step 3 may be done directly but it often involves using **other organisms**, such as bacteria or viruses, to act as **vectors**. This means the gene is first inserted in the vectors, which transfer the gene to the host when they infect it.

- Inserting the gene into bacteria means that many copies can be made of the gene because bacteria reproduce asexually, producing new cells that are genetically identical to the original.

DANGERS OF GENETIC ENGINEERING

- Although genetic engineering promises many benefits for the future, such as curing genetic diseases or changing crops to make them disease resistant, there are possible dangers.

- For example, the **wrong genes** could accidentally be transferred or viral infection could transfer inserted genes to other unintended organisms. Imagine the problems if, instead of crops becoming resistant to disease, weeds became immediately resistant to herbicides or if harmful bacteria became immediately resistant to medicines like antibiotics.

CHECK YOURSELF QUESTIONS

Q1 A farmer wants to produce sheep with finer wool. How could this be done by selective breeding?

Q2 What are the advantages and disadvantages of producing new roses by tissue culture (cloning)?

Q3 Both genetic engineering and selective breeding are ways of producing new combinations of genes in an organism. What are the advantages of genetic engineering?

Answers are on page 235.

■ Evolution ■

⊡ Evidence for evolution

- Animal and plant species can change over long periods of time. This change is called **evolution**.

- We cannot **prove** that evolution has happened as we can't go back in time and watch. However, there is a lot of evidence that evolution has happened.

THE FOSSIL RECORD

- **Fossils** show that very different animals and plants existed in the past. In some cases we can see steady **progressive changes** over time. In other cases there is no evidence of a particular organism's ancestors or descendants.

- The likelihood of a fossil forming in the first place is very rare. Fossils may form in various ways:
  - from **hard body parts** that do not decay easily
  - from body parts that have not decayed because of the **conditions** the body was left in
  - when part of the animal or plant decays and is **replaced** by other materials
  - as **traces** – e.g. footprints or burrows.

- Even if fossils did form they might not be discovered or could be destroyed by erosion. If evolution happened relatively quickly there would be less chance of finding fossils of the intermediate stages. Even when fossils are found they usually only provide a record of the hard tissues like bone.

AFFINITIES

- **Affinities** are similarities that exist between different species. For example, humans, dolphins and rats have much the same number and basic arrangement of bones in their skeletons. The easiest explanation is that they are similar because they are related, in other words they have evolved from a common ancestor.

⊡ Accepting the idea of evolution

- It was only after 1859, when **Charles Darwin** published his famous book *On the Origin of Species*, that ideas about evolution were widely discussed. (The scientist **Alfred Wallace** also came up with the same ideas as Darwin, but he did not publish them first.)

- Many people were angered by Darwin's ideas as they believed they went against the Christian Church's teachings that God had created the world and all the living things in it. Many newspaper cartoons and articles ridiculed Darwin's ideas. Some of these were based on the mistaken idea that Darwin had said that humans had evolved from apes like those present today such as chimpanzees.

- The idea of evolution is not that the animals and plants we see around us evolved from each other, but that some have similar features because they evolved from some **common ancestor**. The diagram below illustrates how humans and apes may have evolved from a common ancestor. Humans and chimpanzees share more similarities than the other types of apes, which means that they probably share a more recent ancestor than do the others.

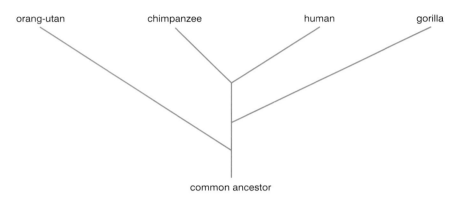

orang-utan   chimpanzee   human   gorilla

common ancestor

- Today there are still people who do not believe in the idea of evolution.

Natural selection

- Darwin suggested how evolution could have happened. He called his theory **natural selection**. He based his ideas on his observations of the wildlife he found on several lengthy sea voyages. He also used his knowledge of selective breeding.

- Natural selection is the same basic idea as selective breeding, except it is 'nature' rather than the breeder that determines which animals or plants are able to reproduce and pass on their features.

THE IDEAS OF NATURAL SELECTION

1 Animals and plants produce more offspring than will ever survive. This means that if some individuals are slightly better **adapted** they will have a better chance of surviving than the others. For example, a zebra that could run faster than the others would be less likely to be caught by lions, or a cactus with slightly sharper spines would be less likely to be eaten. This idea is sometimes known as the **'survival of the fittest'**.

A* EXTRA

- Most mutations are harmful or neutral in their effects.
- Only a minority of mutations are beneficial and able to be spread by natural selection.

The cactus is well adapted to dry desert conditions.
- *Long roots reach water far below ground.*
- *Swollen stem stores water.*
- *Leaves are small spines, which deter animals and reduce water loss by having a small surface area.*
- *Rounded shape reduces surface area and therefore water loss.*

2 The animals and plants that are more likely to survive are more likely to **reproduce**. If the features that helped them survive are genetically controlled they may be passed onto their offspring. Offspring who inherit those good features are in turn more likely to survive and reproduce than offspring that do not inherit the best features.

The polar bear is well adapted to its environment.

- *Eyes on front of head for good judgement of size and distance.*
- *Sharp teeth for killing prey and tearing through flesh.*
- *White fur is good camouflage to hide from prey.*
- *Thick fur to trap heat to keep warm.*
- *Lots of fat to act as a food store and to keep warm.*
- *Strong legs for walking and swimming long distances.*
- *Sharp claws to grip ice.*
- *Hair on the soles of the feet provides a grip on icy surfaces.*

3 As this process continues over many generations, organisms with the **best** features will make up a **larger proportion** of the population and those with features that are **not as helpful** will gradually **disappear**. For example, if the fastest zebras in every generation survive, then over many generations zebras will get faster and faster.

■ Natural selection explains why animals and plants are adapted to their surroundings. If the environment changes, the organisms that do not evolve and adapt may become **extinct**.

QUESTION SPOTTER

▶ In questions about natural selection you will often be asked to describe the steps in the process.
▶ Although the examples you are given will vary, the steps themselves will be the same.

CHECK YOURSELF QUESTIONS

Q1 a Why do we have a clearer idea of how vertebrate animals like mammals, birds and reptiles evolved than of how invertebrates like worms and slugs evolved?

b Why are there many gaps in the fossil record even for animals with skeletons?

Q2 The long necks of giraffes are an adaptation allowing them to feed on the high branches of trees where many other animals cannot reach. Use the theory of natural selection to explain how giraffes could have evolved long necks from shorter-necked ancestors.

Answers are on page 235.

UNIT 7: CHEMICAL FORMULAE AND EQUATIONS

How are chemical formulae calculated?

⊏⊐ Chemical symbols and formulae

- All substances are made up from simple building blocks called **elements**. Each element has a unique **chemical symbol**, containing one or two letters. Elements discovered a long time ago often have symbols that don't seem to match their name. For example, sodium has the chemical symbol Na. This is derived from the Latin name for sodium – 'nadium'.

- When elements chemically combine they form **compounds**. A compound can be represented by a **chemical formula**.

⊏⊐ Simple compounds

- Many compounds contain just two elements. For example, when magnesium burns in oxygen a white ash of magnesium oxide is formed. To work out the chemical formula of magnesium oxide:

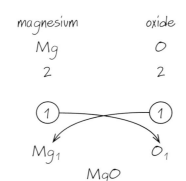

1 Write down the name of the compound.

2 Write down the chemical symbols for the elements in the compound.

3 Use the periodic table to find the 'combining power' of each element. Write the combining power of each element under its symbol.

4 If the numbers can be cancelled down do so.

5 Swap over the combining powers. Write them after the symbol, slightly below the line (as a 'subscript').

6 If any of the numbers are 1 you do not need to write them.

- Magnesium oxide has the chemical formula you would have probably guessed. What about calcium chloride?

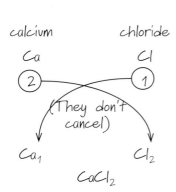

1 Write down the name of the compound.

2 Write down the chemical symbols for the elements in the compound.

3 Use the periodic table to find the 'combining power' of each element. Write the combining power of each element under its symbol.

4 If the numbers can be cancelled down do so.

5 Swap over the combining powers. Write them after the symbol, slightly below the line (as a subscript).

6 If any of the numbers are one there is no need to write them.

- The chemical formula of a compound is not always immediately obvious, but if you follow these rules you will have no problems.

'Combining powers' of elements

■ There is a simple relationship between an element's **group number** in the periodic table and its combining power. Groups are the vertical columns in the periodic table.

Group number	1	2	3	4	5	6	7	8(or 0)
Combining power	1	2	3	4	3	2	1	0

RULES FOR DETERMINING COMBINING POWER

■ Groups 1–4: combining power = group number.

■ Groups 5–8: combining power = 8 – (group number).

■ If an element is not in one of the main groups, its combining power will be included in the name of the compound containing it. For example, copper is a transition metal and is in the middle block of the periodic table. In copper(II) oxide, copper has a combining power of 2.

■ Sometimes an element does not have the combining power you would predict from its position in the periodic table. The combining power of these elements is also included in the name of the compound containing it. For example, phosphorus is in group 5, so you would expect it to have a combining power of 3, but in phosphorus(V) oxide its combining power is 5.

■ **The only exception is hydrogen.** Hydrogen is often not included in a group, nor is its combining power given in the name of compounds containing hydrogen. It has a combining power of 1.

■ The combining power is linked to the **number of electrons** in the atom of the element.

Compounds containing more than two elements

■ Some elements exist bonded together in what is called a **radical**. For example, in copper(II) sulphate, the sulphate part of the compound is a radical.

■ There are a number of common radicals, each having its own combining power. You cannot work out these combining powers easily from the periodic table – you have to learn them. The shaded ones in the table are the ones you are most likely to encounter at GCSE.

combining power = 1		combining power = 2		combining power = 3	
hydroxide	OH	carbonate	CO_3	phosphate	PO_4
hydrogen carbonate	HCO_3	sulphate	SO_4		
nitrate	NO_3				
ammonium	NH_4				

■ The same rules apply to radicals as to elements. For example:

copper(II) sulphate	potassium nitrate
Cu SO$_4$	K NO$_3$
2 2	1 1
CuSO$_4$	KNO$_3$

■ If the formula contains **more than one radical** unit the radical must be put in brackets. For example:

calcium hydroxide	ammonium carbonate
Ca OH	NH$_4$ CO$_3$
2 1	1 2
Ca(OH)$_2$	(NH$_4$)$_2$CO$_3$

■ The brackets are used just as they are used in maths – the number outside the bracket multiplies everything inside it. Be careful how you use the brackets – for example, do not be tempted to write calcium hydroxide as CaOH$_2$ rather than Ca(OH)$_2$. This is incorrect.

CaOH$_2$ contains one Ca, one O, two H   ✗

Ca(OH)$_2$ contains one Ca, two O, two H   ✓

CHECK YOURSELF QUESTIONS

Q1 Work out the chemical formulae of the following compounds:
   a sodium chloride
   b magnesium fluoride
   c aluminium nitride
   d lithium oxide
   e carbon oxide (carbon dioxide).

Q2 Work out the chemical formulae of the following compounds:
   a iron(III) oxide
   b phosphorus(V) chloride
   c chromium(III) bromide
   d sulphur(VI) oxide (sulphur trioxide)
   e sulphur(IV) oxide (sulphur dioxide).

Q3 Work out the chemical formulae of the following compounds:
   a potassium carbonate
   b ammonium chloride
   c sulphuric acid (hydrogen sulphate)
   d magnesium hydroxide
   e ammonium sulphate.

Answers are on page 236.

REVISION SESSION 2 ▭ Chemical equations ▭

⊡ Writing chemical equations

■ In a **chemical equation** the starting chemicals are called the **reactants** and the finishing chemicals are called the **products**.

■ Follow these simple rules to write the chemical equation.

　1　Write down the **word equation**.

　2　Write down the **symbols** (for elements) and **formulae** (for compounds).

　3　**Balance the equation** (to make sure there are the same number of each type of atom on each side of the equation).

■ Many elements are **diatomic**. They exist as molecules containing two atoms.

Element	Form in which it exists
hydrogen	H_2
oxygen	O_2
nitrogen	N_2
chlorine	Cl_2
bromine	Br_2
iodine	I_2

The reaction between hydrogen and oxygen produces a lot of energy as well as water – enough to launch a rocket.

WORKED EXAMPLES

1　When a lighted splint is put into a test tube of hydrogen the hydrogen burns with a 'pop'. In fact the hydrogen reacts with oxygen in the air (the reactants) to form water (the product). Write the chemical equation for this reaction.

Word equation:	hydrogen + oxygen → water
Symbols and formulae:	$H_2 + O_2 → H_2O$
Balance the equation:	$2H_2 + O_2 → 2H_2O$

For every two molecules of hydrogen that react, one molecule of oxygen is needed and two molecules of water are formed.

$$2H_2 \quad + \quad O_2 \quad → \quad 2H_2O$$
two molecules　　　　one molecule　　　　two molecules

2　What is the equation when natural gas (methane) burns in air to form carbon dioxide and water?

Word equation:	methane + oxygen → carbon dioxide + water
Symbols and formulae:	$CH_4 + O_2 → CO_2 + H_2O$
Balance the equation:	$CH_4 + 2O_2 → CO_2 + 2H_2O$

Methane is burning in the oxygen in the air to form carbon dioxide and water.

⟦⟧ Balancing equations

- Balancing equations can be quite tricky. Basically it is done by trial and error. However, the golden rule is that **balancing numbers can only be put in front of the formulae.**

- For example, to balance the equation for the reaction between methane and oxygen:

	Reactants	Products
Start with the unbalanced equation.	$CH_4 + O_2$	$CO_2 + H_2O$
Count the number of atoms on each side of the equation.	1C ✓, 4H, 2O	1C ✓, 2H, 3O
There is a need to increase the number of H atoms on the products side of the equation. Put a '2' in front of the H_2O.	$CH_4 + O_2$	$CO_2 + 2H_2O$
Count the number of atoms on each side of the equation again.	1C ✓, 4H ✓, 2O	1C ✓, 4H ✓, 4O
There is a need to increase the number of O atoms on the reactant side of the equation. Put a '2' in front of the O_2.	$CH_4 + 2O_2$	$CO_2 + 2H_2O$
Count the atoms on each side of the equation again.	1C ✓, 4H ✓, 4O ✓	1C ✓, 4H ✓, 4O ✓

No atoms have been created or destroyed in the reaction. The equation is balanced!

The number of each type of atom is the same on the left and right sides of the equation.

$$CH_4 \quad + \quad 2O_2 \quad \rightarrow \quad CO_2 \quad + \quad 2H_2O$$

- In balancing equations involving **radicals** you can use the same procedure. For example, if lead(II) nitrate solution is mixed with potassium iodide solution, lead(II) iodide and potassium nitrate are produced.

1 Words:
   lead(II) nitrate + potassium iodide → lead(II) iodide + potassium nitrate

2 Symbols:
   $Pb(NO_3)_2$ + KI → PbI_2 + KNO_3

3 Balance the nitrates:
   $Pb(NO_3)_2$ + KI → PbI_2 + $2KNO_3$

   Balance the iodides:
   $Pb(NO_3)_2$ + $2KI$ → PbI_2 + $2KNO_3$

This reaction occurs simply on mixing the solutions of lead(II) nitrate and potassium iodide. Lead iodide is an insoluble yellow compound.

⌷ Ionic equations

- **Ionic equations** show reactions involving **ions** (charged atoms or molecules). The size of the charge on an ion is the same as the combining power – whether it is positive or negative depends on which part of the periodic table the element is placed in. (If you have not come across ions before you will need to look at Unit 8. You will get further practice using ionic equations in Unit 12.)

- In many ionic reactions some of the ions play no part in the reaction. These ions are called **spectator ions**. A simplified ionic equation can therefore be written, using only the important ions. In these equations **state symbols** are often used.

- The equation must **balance** in terms of chemical symbols and charges.

WORKED EXAMPLES

1 In the reaction given to produce lead(II) iodide, the potassium and nitrate ions are spectators – the important ions are the lead(II) ions and the iodide ions.

The simplified ionic equation is:

$$Pb^{2+}(aq) + 2I^-(aq) \rightarrow PbI_2(s)$$

Balance the equation:

	Reactants	Products
	$Pb^{2+}(aq) + 2I^-(aq)$	$PbI_2(s)$
symbols	1Pb ✓, 2I ✓	1Pb ✓, 2I ✓
charges	2^+ and $2^- = 0$ ✓	0 ✓

The equation shows that any solution containing lead(II) ions will react with any solution containing iodide ions to form lead(II) iodide.

2 Any solution containing copper(II) ions and any solution containing hydroxide ions can be used to make copper(II) hydroxide, which appears as a solid:

$$Cu^{2+}(aq) + 2OH^-(aq) \rightarrow Cu(OH)_2(s)$$

	Reactants	Products
	$Cu^{2+}(aq) + 2OH^-(aq)$	$Cu(OH)_2(s)$
symbols	1Cu ✓, 2O ✓, 2H ✓	1Cu ✓, 2O ✓, 2H ✓
charges	2^+ and $2^- = 0$ ✓	0 ✓

State	State symbol
solid	s
liquid	l
gas	g
solution	aq

States and their symbols

QUESTION SPOTTER

▸ You are most likely to be asked to write equations including the four common state symbols.
▸ Questions may ask you to explain what a particular state symbol represents.

A* EXTRA

▸ An ionic equation only shows the ions that change in some way during the reaction – the spectator ions are not shown.
▸ The reaction between copper(II) sulphate solution and sodium hydroxide solution will have the same ionic equation as the reaction between copper(II) nitrate solution and potassium hydroxide solution.

⊡ Half equations

■ In electrolysis, the reactions at the electrodes can be shown as **half equations**.

■ For example, when copper is deposited at the **cathode** the half equation can be written as:

$$Cu^{2+}(aq) + 2e^- \rightarrow Cu(s)$$

The symbol e^- stands for an **electron**. At the cathode positive ions gain electrons and become neutral. The equation must **balance** in terms of symbols and charges.

■ A typical reaction at the **anode** during electrolysis would be:

$$2Cl^-(aq) \rightarrow Cl_2(g) + 2e^-$$

In this reaction two chloride ions combine to form one molecule of chlorine, releasing two electrons.

■ Further examples of half equations are given in Unit 10.

CHECK YOURSELF QUESTIONS

Q1 Write symbol equations from the following word equations:
 a carbon + oxygen → carbon dioxide
 b iron + oxygen → iron(III) oxide
 c iron(III) oxide + carbon → iron + carbon dioxide
 d calcium carbonate + hydrochloric acid → calcium chloride + carbon dioxide + water.

Q2 Write ionic equations for the following reactions:
 a calcium ions and carbonate ions form calcium carbonate
 b iron(II) ions and hydroxide ions form iron(II) hydroxide
 c silver(I) ions and bromide ions form silver(I) bromide.

Q3 Write half equations for the following reactions:
 a the formation of aluminium atoms from aluminium ions
 b the formation of sodium ions from sodium atoms
 c the formation of oxygen from oxide ions
 d the formation of bromine from bromide ions.

Answers are on page 237.

UNIT 8: STRUCTURE AND BONDING

How are atoms put together?

▢ Sub-atomic articles

■ The smallest amount of an element that still behaves like that element is an **atom**. Each element has its own unique type of atom. Atoms are made up of smaller 'sub-atomic' particles. There are three main sub-atomic particles: **protons**, **neutrons** and **electrons**.

■ These particles are very small and have very little mass. However, it is possible to compare their masses using a **relative** scale. Their charges can also be compared in a similar way. The proton and neutron have the **same** mass, and the proton and electron have **opposite** charges.

Sub-atomic particle	Relative mass	Relative charge
proton	1	+1
neutron	1	0
electron	$\frac{1}{2000}$	−1

■ Protons and neutrons are found in the centre of the atom, in a cluster called the **nucleus**. The electrons form a series of 'shells' around the nucleus.

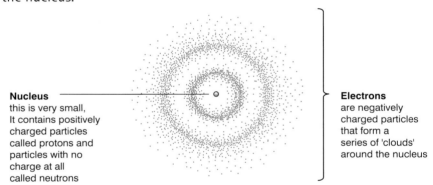

Nucleus
this is very small,
It contains positively
charged particles
called protons and
particles with no
charge at all
called neutrons

Electrons
are negatively
charged particles
that form a
series of 'clouds'
around the nucleus

▢ What are atomic number and mass number?

■ In order to describe the numbers of protons, neutrons and electrons in an atom, scientists use two numbers. These are called the **atomic number** and the **mass number**.

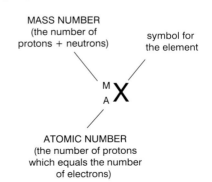

MASS NUMBER
(the number of
protons + neutrons)

symbol for
the element

$^{M}_{A}X$

ATOMIC NUMBER
(the number of protons
which equals the number
of electrons)

- The atomic number is used to order the elements in the periodic table. The atomic structures of the first ten elements are shown in the table.

Element	Atomic number	Mass number	Number of protons	Number of neutrons	Number of electrons
Hydrogen	1	1	1	0	1
Helium	2	4	2	2	2
Lithium	3	7	3	4	3
Beryllium	4	9	4	5	4
Boron	5	10	5	5	5
Carbon	6	12	6	6	6
Nitrogen	7	14	7	7	7
Oxygen	8	16	8	8	8
Fluorine	9	19	9	10	9
Neon	10	20	10	10	10

- **Hydrogen** is the only atom that has **no neutrons**.

Isotopes

- Atoms of the same element with the **same number** of protons and electrons but **different** numbers of neutrons are called **isotopes**.

- Isotopes have the same chemical properties but slightly different physical properties. For example, there are three isotopes of hydrogen:

Isotope	Symbol	Number of neutrons
normal hydrogen	$_1^1H$	0
deuterium	$_1^2H$	1
tritium	$_1^3H$	2

How are electrons arranged in the atom?

- The electrons are arranged in **shells** around the nucleus. The shells do not all contain the same number of electrons – the shell nearest to the nucleus can only take two electrons whereas the next one further from the nucleus can take eight.

- Oxygen has an atomic number of 8, so has 8 electrons. Of these 2 will be in the first shell and 6 will be in the second shell. This arrangement is written 2, 6. A phosphorus atom with an atomic number of 15 has 15 electrons, arranged 2, 8, 5.

Electron shell	Maximum number of electrons
1	2
2	8
3	8

- The electron arrangements are very important as they determine the way that the atom reacts chemically.

A* EXTRA

Isotopes are atoms with the same atomic number but different mass numbers.
- Some isotopes are radioactive and so can be used as 'tracers'.
- Most naturally occurring isotopes are not radioactive.

QUESTION SPOTTER

- You will often be given atomic and mass numbers and asked to complete a table showing the number of protons, neutrons and electrons.
- Questions asking you to show how the electrons are arranged in shells are quite common.

⬚ Atom diagrams

■ The atomic structure of an atom can be shown simply in a diagram.

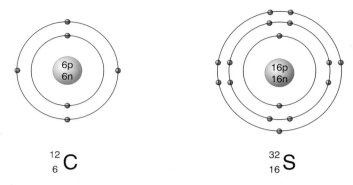

$$^{12}_{6}C \qquad \qquad ^{32}_{16}S$$

Atom diagrams for carbon and sulphur showing the number of protons, neutrons and the electron arrangements.

CHECK YOURSELF QUESTIONS

Q1 Explain the meanings of:
a atomic number
b mass number.

Q2 Copy out and then complete the table.

Atom	Number of protons	Number of neutrons	Number of electrons	Electron arrangement
$^{28}_{14}Si$				
$^{26}_{12}Mg$				
$^{32}_{16}S$				
$^{40}_{18}Ar$				

Q3 The table below shows information about the structure of six particles (A–F).

a In each of the questions (i) to (v) choose one of the six particles A–F above. Each letter may be used once, more than once or not at all. Choose a particle that:
   i has a mass number of 12
   ii has the highest mass number
   iii has no overall charge
   iv has an overall positive charge
   v is the same element as particle E.

b Draw an atom diagram for particle F.

Particle	Protons (positive charge)	Neutrons (neutral)	Electrons (negative charge)
A	8	8	10
B	12	12	10
C	6	6	6
D	8	10	10
E	6	8	6
F	11	12	11

Answers are on page 237.

Chemical bonding

⌂ How do atoms combine?

- Atoms bond together with other atoms in a chemical reaction to make a **compound**. For example, sodium will react with chlorine to make sodium chloride; hydrogen will react with oxygen to make water.

- This reactivity is due to the electron arrangements in atoms. If atoms have **incomplete electron shells** they will usually react with other atoms. Only atoms with complete electron shells tend to be unreactive. Atoms in group 8 (sometimes referred to as group 0) of the periodic table, the **noble gases**, fall into this category.

- When atoms combine they try to achieve **full outer electron shells**. They do this either by gaining electrons to fill the gaps in the outer shell or by losing electrons from the outer shell to leave an inner complete shell.

- There are two different ways in which atoms can bond together: **ionic** bonding and **covalent** bonding.

⌂ What happens in ionic bonding?

- Ionic bonding involves **electron transfer** between metals and non-metals. Both metals and non-metals try to achieve complete outer electron shells.

- **Metals lose electrons** from their outer shells and form **positive** ions. This is an example of **oxidation**.

- **Non-metals gain electrons** into their outer shells and form **negative** ions. This is an example of **reduction**.

- The ions are held together by strong electrical (electrostatic) forces.

- The bonding process can be represented in **dot-and-cross diagrams**. Look at the reaction between sodium and chlorine as an example.

When atoms form ions they try to complete their outer electron shell. For metals to do this it is easier to lose electrons than to gain them. For non-metals it is easier to gain electrons than to lose them. The number of electrons that need to be lost or gained is equal to the group number in the periodic table.

Sodium is a metal. It has an atomic number of 11 and so has 11 electrons, arranged 2, 8, 1. Its atom diagram looks like this:

Chlorine is a non-metal. It has an atomic number of 17 and so has 17 electrons, arranged 2, 8, 7. Its atom diagram looks like this:

Sodium has one electron in its outer shell. It can achieve a full outer shell by losing this electron. The sodium atom transfers its outermost electron to the chlorine atom.

Chlorine has seven electrons in its outer shell. It can achieve a full outer shell by gaining an extra electron. The chlorine atom accepts an electron from the sodium.

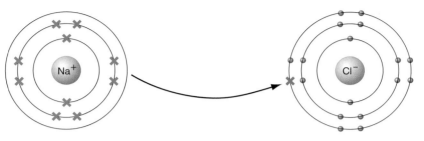

The sodium is no longer an atom; it is now an ion. It does not have equal numbers of protons and electrons, it is no longer neutral. It has one more proton than it has electrons, so it is a positive ion with a charge of 1+. The ion is written as Na^+.

The chlorine is no longer an atom; it is now an ion. It does not have equal numbers of protons and electrons, it is no longer neutral. It has one more electron than protons, so it is a negative ion with a charge of 1–. The ion is written as Cl^-.

METALS CAN TRANSFER MORE THAN ONE ELECTRON TO A NON-METAL

■ Magnesium combines with oxygen to form **magnesium oxide**. The magnesium (electron arrangement 2, 8, 2) transfers two electrons to the oxygen (electron arrangement 2, 6). Magnesium therefore forms a Mg^{2+} ion and oxygen forms an O^{2-} ion.

Dot and cross diagram for magnesium oxide, MgO

■ Aluminium has an electron arrangement 2, 8, 3. When it combines with fluorine with an electron arrangement 2, 7 three fluorine atoms are needed for each aluminium atom. The formula of **aluminium fluoride** is therefore AlF_3.

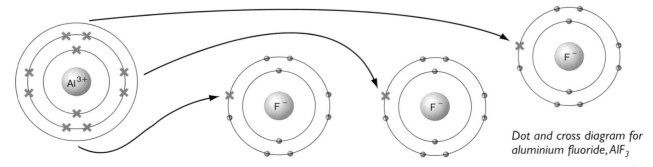

Dot and cross diagram for aluminium fluoride, AlF_3

What ions can an element form?

■ The ion formed by an element can be worked out from the **position of the element in the periodic table**. The elements in group 4 and group 8 (or 0) generally do not form ions.

Group number	I	2	3	4	5	6	7	8 (or 0)
Ion charge	I+	2+	3+	X	3–	2–	I–	X

What is covalent bonding?

■ Covalent bonding involves electron sharing. It occurs between atoms of non-metals. It results in the formation of a **molecule**. The non-metal atoms try to achieve complete outer electron shells.

■ A **single covalent bond** is formed when two atoms each contribute one electron to a shared pair of electrons. For example, hydrogen gas exists as an H_2 molecule. Each hydrogen atom wants to fill its electron shell. They can do this by sharing electrons.

The dot-and-cross diagram and displayed formula of H_2.

represented as

H — H

■ A single covalent bond can be represented by a single line. The formula of the molecule can be written as a **displayed formula**, H–H. The hydrogen and oxygen atoms in water are also held together by single covalent bonds.

Water contains single covalent bonds.

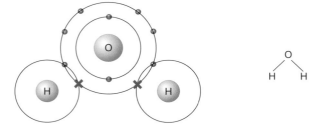

QUESTION SPOTTER

▸ Questions on covalent bonding often ask you to draw a diagram to show how the atoms combine.
▸ Always draw the shared electrons in the region where the electron shells overlap.

Carbon dioxide contains double bonds.

■ Some molecules contain **double covalent bonds**. In carbon dioxide, the carbon atom has an electron arrangement of 2, 4 and needs an additional four electrons to complete its outer electron shell. It needs to share its four electrons with four electrons from oxygen atoms (electron arrangement 2, 6). Two oxygen atoms are needed, each sharing two electrons with the carbon atom.

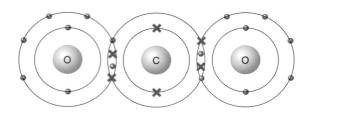

O═C═O

- Compounds containing covalent bonds have very different properties to compounds that contain ionic bonds. These differences are considered in the next section.

⌷ How many covalent bonds can an element form?

- The number of covalent bonds a non-metal atom can form is linked to its position in the periodic table. Metals (groups 1, 2, 3) do not form covalent bonds. The noble gases in group 8 are unreactive and usually don't form covalent bonds.

Group in the periodic table	1	2	3	4	5	6	7	8 (or 0)
Covalent bonds formed	X	X	X	4	3	2	1	X

? CHECK YOURSELF QUESTIONS

Q1 For each of the following reactions say whether the compound formed is ionic or covalent:
a hydrogen and chlorine
b carbon and hydrogen
c sodium and oxygen
d chlorine and oxygen
e calcium and bromine.

Q2 Write down the ions formed by the following elements:
a potassium
b aluminium
c sulphur
d fluorine.

Q3 Draw dot-and-cross diagrams to show the bonding in the following compounds:
a methane, CH_4
b oxygen, O_2
c nitrogen, N_2
d potassium sulphide
e lithium oxide.

Answers are on page 238.

▬ Structures and properties ▬

⟦⟧ What structures do ionic compounds form?

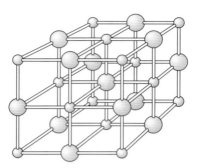

○ chloride ion   ○ sodium ion

In solid sodium chloride, the ions are held firmly in place – they are not free to move. Ionic compounds have giant ionic lattice structures like this.

- Ionic compounds form **giant lattice structures**. For example, when sodium chloride is formed by ionic bonding the ions do not exist in pairs. Each sodium ion is surrounded by six chloride ions and each chloride ion is surrounded by six sodium ions.

- The electrostatic attractions between the ions are very strong. The properties of sodium chloride can be explained using this model of its structure.

Property	Explanation in terms of structure
Hard crystals	Strong forces between the ions
High melting point (801°C)	Strong forces between the ions
Dissolves in water	The water is also able to form strong electrostatic attractions with the ions – the ions are 'plucked' off the lattice structure
Does not conduct electricity when solid	Strong forces between the ions prevent them from moving
Does conduct electricity when molten or dissolved in water	The strong forces between the ions have been broken down and so the ions are able to move

---

⚡ A* EXTRA

▸ Ionic compounds are electrolytes. They conduct electricity when molten or when dissolved in water (i.e. when the ions are free to move).
▸ Insoluble compounds such as calcium carbonate will only conduct electricity when they are molten.

⟦⟧ Covalent compounds

- Covalent bonds are also strong bonds. They are **intramolecular** bonds – formed *within* each molecule. There are also **intermolecular** bonds – much weaker forces *between* the individual molecules.

- The properties of covalent compounds can be explained using a simple model involving these two types of bond or forces.

Properties	Explanation in terms of structure	
Hydrogen is a gas with a very low melting point (−259°C)	The intermolecular forces between the molecules are weak	H—H ⟍ covalent bond
Hydrogen does not conduct electricity	There are no ions or free electrons present. The covalent bond (intramolecular bond) is a strong bond and the electrons cannot be easily removed from it	≡ intermolecular force H—H

- Some covalently bonded compounds do not exist as simple molecular structures in the way that hydrogen does. Diamond, for example, exists as a **giant structure** with each carbon atom covalently bonded to four others. The bonding is extremely strong – diamond has a melting point of about 3730°C. Another form of carbon is graphite. Graphite has a different giant structure as seen in the diagram. Different forms of the same element are called **allotropes**.

(a)

—— strong bond

(b)

------ weak bond

In diamond (a) each carbon atom forms four strong covalent bonds. In graphite (b) each carbon atom forms only three strong covalent bonds and one weak intermolecular bond. This explains why graphite is flaky and can be used as a lubricant. The layers of hexagons can slide over each other. The electrical conductivity of graphite can be explained by the fact that each carbon atom has one electron which is not strongly bonded. These electrons can move through the structure.

QUESTION SPOTTER

▸ A typical question will give a table of data (including melting points and boiling points) for different substances and ask you to identify the ones that have a simple molecular structure or a giant structure.
▸ Use the melting points to decide whether they are giant (high melting point) or simple molecular structures (low melting point).

■ Structures can usually be identified as being giant or molecular from their melting points.

Structure	Atom	Molecule	Ion
Giant	Diamond, graphite, metals High melting points	Sand (silicon oxide molecules) High melting point	All ionic compounds, e.g. sodium chloride High melting points
Simple molecular	Nobel gases, e.g. helium Low melting points	Carbon dioxide, water Low melting points	None

CHECK YOURSELF QUESTIONS

Q1 Explain why an ionic substance such as potassium chloride:
 a has a high melting point
 b behaves as an electrolyte.

Q2 Use the structure of graphite to explain
 a how carbon fibres can add strength to tennis racquets
 b how graphite conducts electricity.

Q3 Explain why methane (CH_4), which has strong covalent bonds between the carbon atom and the hydrogen atoms, has a very low melting point.

Answers are on page 239.

REVISION SESSION I

Obtaining fossil fuels

What are fossil fuels?

- Crude oil, natural gas and coal are **fossil fuels**.

- Crude oil was formed millions of years ago from the remains of animals that were pressed together under layers of rock. It is usually found deep underground, trapped between layers of rock that it can't seep through (**impermeable** rock). Natural gas is often trapped in pockets above the crude oil.

- The supply of fossil fuels is limited – they are called 'finite' or **non-renewable** fuels. They are an extremely valuable resource which must be used efficiently.

- Fossil fuels contain many useful chemicals, and we need to separate these chemicals so that they are not wasted. For example, coal is often converted into coke by removing some of the chemicals in the coal. When the coke is burnt as a fuel these chemicals are not wasted.

Separating the fractions

- The chemicals in crude oil are separated into useful **fractions** by a process known as **fractional distillation**.

> **QUESTION SPOTTER**
>
> You could be asked to label the part of the fractionating column where the temperature is the highest and the parts where liquids like petrol and heavy oil are formed.

The fractionating column converts the crude oil into many useful fractions.

	number of carbon atoms in each fraction
gases (butane, propane for gas 'bottles')	1-4
gasoline (petrol)	5-8
naphtha (to make chemicals)	9-12
kerosene (paraffin, fuel)	10-14
gas oil (diesel oil)	14-20
lubricants and waxes	over 20
fuel oil (for ships etc.) bitumen (tar)	

gases bubble up

liquid falls down

preheated crude oil 340 °C

65 °C
170 °C
250 °C
340 °C
500 °C

bubble cap

kept hot (over 500° C)

vapour

- The crude oil is heated in a furnace and passed into the bottom of a **fractionating column**. The vapour mixture given off rises up the column and the different fractions condense out at different parts of the column. The fractions that come off near the top of the column are light-coloured runny liquids. Those removed near the bottom of the column are dark and treacle-like. Thick liquids that are not runny, such as these bottom-most fractions, are described as 'viscous'.

How does fractional distillation work?

- The components present in crude oil separate because they have different boiling points. Why they have different boiling points can be understood using a simple particle model. Crude oil is a mixture of **hydrocarbon** molecules, which contain only carbon and hydrogen. The molecules are chemically bonded in similar ways with strong covalent bonds (see Unit 8), but contain different numbers of carbon atoms.

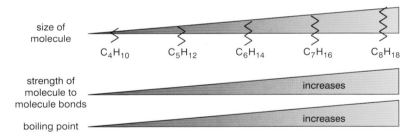

You will notice that octane has one more carbon atom and two more hydrogen atoms than heptane. Their formulae differ by CH_2.

- The weak bonds between the molecules have to be broken if the hydrocarbon is to boil. The longer a hydrocarbon molecule is then the stronger the bonds between the molecules. The stronger these bonds, the higher the boiling point as more energy is needed to overcome the larger forces.

> **⚡ A* EXTRA**
>
> As a general rule, the greater the surface area for contact, the stronger the force between the molecules.

size of molecule

C_4H_{10} C_5H_{12} C_6H_{14} C_7H_{16} C_8H_{18}

strength of molecule to molecule bonds — increases

boiling point — increases

- The smaller molecule hydrocarbons more readily form a vapour – they are more **volatile**. For example, petrol (with molecules containing between 5 and 10 carbon atoms) smells much more than engine oil (with molecules containing between 14 and 20 carbon atoms) because it is more volatile.

- Another difference between the fractions is how easily they burn and how smoky their flames are.

⌧ Cracking the oil fractions

- The amounts of the different fractions produced by fractional distillation do not match the amounts that are needed or usable. The lower boiling point fractions (e.g. petrol and gas) are in greater demand than the heavier ones (e.g. naphtha and paraffin). The table shows the composition of a sample of crude oil from the Middle East after fractional distillation, and the demand for each fraction.

Fraction (in order of increasing boiling point)	Percentage produced by fractional distillation	Percentage needed (demand)
liquefied petroleum gases (LPG)	3	4
petrol	13	22
naphtha	9	5
paraffin	12	7
diesel	14	24
heavy oils and bitumen	49	38

- The larger molecules can be broken down into smaller ones by **cracking**. Cracking requires a **high temperature** and a **catalyst**.

The decane molecule ($C_{10}H_{22}$) is converted into the smaller molecules butane (C_4H_{10}) and propene (C_3H_6).

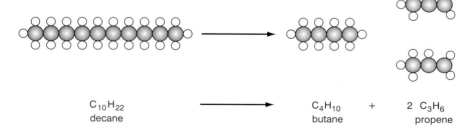

$$C_{10}H_{22} \longrightarrow C_4H_{10} + 2\ C_3H_6$$
decane   butane   propene

- The butane and propene formed in this example of cracking have different types of structures. These structures will be looked at in more detail in the next section.

A* EXTRA

- Prop*ene* belongs to a family of hydrocarbons called alk*enes*.
- Alkenes are much more reactive (and hence useful) than hydrocarbons like dec*ane* (alk*anes*).

CHECK YOURSELF QUESTIONS

Q1 **a** How was crude oil formed?
     b Why is crude oil a non-renewable fuel?

Q2 The diagram shows part of a column used to separate the components present in crude oil.

   a Name the process used to separate crude oil into fractions.
   b What happens to the boiling point of the mixture as it goes up the column?
   c The mixture of vapours arrives at level X. What now happens to the various parts of the mixture?

The table shows some of the properties of the crude oil components:

component	liquid temperature (°C)	how runny?	colour	how it burns
A	up to 70	very	colourless	easily, blue flame
B	70 to 150	fairly	pale yellow	fairly easily, a smoky flame
C	150 to 230	not very	dark yellow	difficult to light, a very smoky flame

   d Another component was collected between 230°C and 300°C. What would it be like?
   e Component A is used as a fuel in a car engine. Suggest why component C would not be suitable as a fuel in a car engine.

Q3 The cracking of decane molecules is shown by the equation $C_{10}H_{22} \rightarrow Y + C_2H_4$
   a Decane is a hydrocarbon. What is a hydrocarbon?
   b What conditions are needed for cracking?
   c Write down the molecular formula for hydrocarbon Y.

Answers are on page 240.

How are hydrocarbons used?

Combustion

- Most of the common fuels used today are hydrocarbons – substances that contain **only** carbon and hydrogen atoms.

- When a hydrocarbon is burnt in a plentiful supply of air it reacts with the oxygen in the air (it is **oxidised**) to form carbon dioxide and water. This reaction is an example of **combustion**.

| hydrocarbon | + | oxygen | → | carbon dioxide | + | water |

For example, when methane (natural gas) is burnt:

$$CH_4(g) + 2O_2(g) \rightarrow CO_2(g) + 2H_2O(l)$$

The complete combustion of methane in a plentiful supply of air.

- The air contains only about 20% oxygen by volume. When a hydrocarbon fuel is burnt there is not always enough oxygen for complete combustion. Instead **incomplete combustion** occurs, forming **carbon** or **carbon monoxide**:

| methane | + | oxygen | → | carbon monoxide | + | water |
| $2CH_4(g)$ | + | $3O_2(g)$ | → | $2CO(g)$ | + | $4H_2O(l)$ |

| methane | + | oxygen | → | carbon | + | water |
| $CH_4(g)$ | + | $O_2(g)$ | → | $C(s)$ | + | $2H_2O(l)$ |

- Incomplete combustion is **costly** because the full energy content of the fuel is not being released and the formation of carbon or soot reduces the efficiency of the 'burner' being used. It can be **dangerous** as carbon monoxide is extremely poisonous. Carbon monoxide molecules attach to the haemoglobin of the blood, preventing oxygen from doing so. Brain cells deprived of their supply of oxygen will quickly die.

- The tell-tale sign that a fuel is burning incompletely is that the flame is **yellow**. When complete combustion occurs the flame will be **blue**.

What problems does burning fossil fuels cause?

- **Sulphur** is an impurity in many fuels. When the fuel is burnt the sulphur is oxidised to sulphur dioxide:

| sulphur | + | oxygen | → | sulphur dioxide |
| $S(s)$ | + | $O_2(g)$ | → | $SO_2(g)$ |

- In the atmosphere, in the presence of oxygen and water, **sulphuric acid** is formed:

sulphur dioxide	+	oxygen	+	water	$\rightarrow$	sulphuric acid
$2SO_2(g)$	+	$O_2(g)$	+	$2H_2O(l)$	$\rightarrow$	$2H_2SO_4(aq)$

This falls as **acid rain**.

- Buildings, particularly those made of limestone and marble, are damaged by acid rain. Metal constructions are also attacked by the sulphuric acid. Acid rain can also damage trees and kill fish.

- Power stations are now being fitted with 'Flue Gas Desulphurisation Plants' (FGD) to reduce the release of sulphur dioxide into the atmosphere.

- Acid rain is also caused by solutions of the oxides of **nitrogen**, which are produced in the exhaust fumes of cars and aeroplanes. Catalytic converters are fitted to car exhaust systems to convert the oxides of nitrogen into harmless nitrogen gas.

- **Carbon dioxide** in the atmosphere traps energy from the Sun as heat instead of reflecting it straight back into space – this is the **greenhouse effect**. If there is too much carbon dioxide in the Earth's atmosphere the overall temperature of the planet will increase (**global warming**), causing the polar ice caps to melt and the sea level to rise. The level of carbon dioxide in the atmosphere is rising because we are increasing our use of fossil fuels and cutting down vast areas of forest. The effect of these changes can be seen by understanding the **carbon cycle** (see also Unit 5).

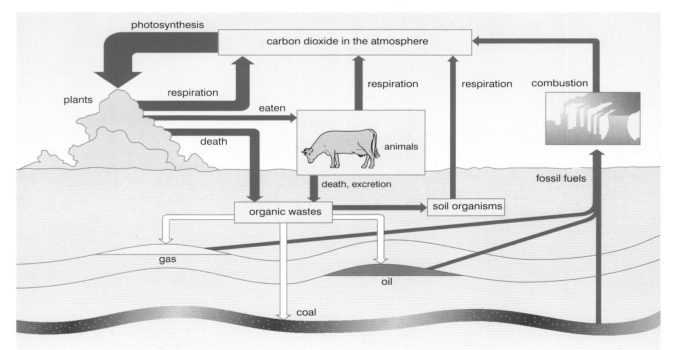

The importance of plants in the carbon cycle is that they remove carbon dioxide from the atmosphere by photosynthesis. Carbon dioxide is also removed from the atmosphere as it dissolves in the oceans.

- Many people feel that the best way to minimise the greenhouse effect is to reduce emissions of carbon dioxide but others feel that the problem may be caused by other **greenhouse gases**. Some scientists are not even sure that there is such a thing as global warming, and say that the recent rises in average temperature are just one of many climatic changes that have occurred on Earth over the last 1000 years. See Unit 5 for more on this.

Alkanes and alkenes

- There are two common families of hydrocarbons, the **alkanes** and the **alkenes**. Members of a family have similar chemical properties, and physical properties that change gradually from one member to the next.

A* EXTRA

All alkanes have the general formula C_nH_{2n+2}, all alkenes have the general formula C_nH_{2n}, where n represents the number of carbon atoms in the molecule.

		Molecular formula	Displayed formula	Boiling point (°C)	State at room temperature and pressure
Alkanes	methane	CH_4		−162	gas
	ethane	C_2H_6		−89	gas
	propane	C_3H_8		−42	gas
	butane	C_4H_{10}		0	gas
	pentane	C_5H_{12}		36	liquid
Alkene	ethene	C_2H_4		−104	gas
	propene	C_3H_6		−48	gas
	butene	C_4H_8		−6	gas
	pentene	C_5H_{10}		30	liquid

- Many alkanes are obtained from **crude oil** by **fractional distillation**. The first members of the family are used extensively as fuels. Apart from burning, however, they are remarkably unreactive. Alkanes are made up of atoms joined by single covalent bonds, so they are known as **saturated** hydrocarbons.

- The alkenes are often formed in the cracking process. They contain a carbon–carbon double bond. Hydrocarbons with at least one double bond are known as **unsaturated** hydrocarbons. Alkenes burn well and are reactive in other ways as well. Their reactivity is due to the carbon–carbon double bond.

- Alkenes can be distinguished from alkanes by adding **bromine water** to the hydrocarbon. Alkanes do not react with bromine water, but an alkene will decolourise it. The type of reaction is known as an **addition** reaction:

ethene	+	bromine	→	1,2-dibromoethane
(colourless gas)		(brown liquid)		(colourless liquid)

many small molecules

catalyst and heat

one large molecule

Ethene molecules link together to produce a long polymer chain of poly(ethene).

⬜ Polymers

- Alkenes can be used to make **polymers**, very large molecules made up of many identical smaller molecules called **monomers**. Alkenes are able to react with themselves. They join together into long chains like adding beads to a necklace. When the monomers add together like this the material produced is called an **addition polymer**. Poly(ethene) or polythene is made this way.

- By changing the atoms or groups of atoms attached to the carbon–carbon double bond a whole range of different polymers can be made:

name of monomer	displayed formula of monomer	name of polymer	displayed formula of polymer	uses of polymer
ethene		poly(ethene)		buckets, bowls, plastic bags
chloroethene (vinyl chloride)		poly(chloroethene) (polyvinylchloride)		plastic sheets, artificial leather
phenylethene (styrene)		poly(phenylethene) (polystyrene)		yoghurt cartons, packaging
tetrafluoroethene		poly(tetrafluroethene) or PTFE		non-stick coating in frying pans

QUESTION SPOTTER

Questions will either give you the displayed formula of the monomer and ask you to write the displayed formula of a polymer or ask you to write the displayed formula of the monomer by working back from the formula of the polymer.

- **Plastics** are very difficult to dispose of. Most of them are not **biodegradable** – they cannot be decomposed by bacteria in the soil. Currently most waste plastic material is buried in landfill sites or is burnt, but burning plastics produces toxic fumes and landfill sites are filling up.

- Some types of plastic can be melted down and used again. These are **thermoplastics**. Other types of plastic decompose when they are heated. These are **thermosetting** plastics. Recycling is difficult because the different types of plastic must be separated.

In thermoplastics the intermolecular bonds are weak and break on heating. The plastic can be melted and re-moulded. In thermosetting plastics the intermolecular bonds are strong inter-linking covalent bonds. The whole structure breaks down when these bonds are broken by heating.

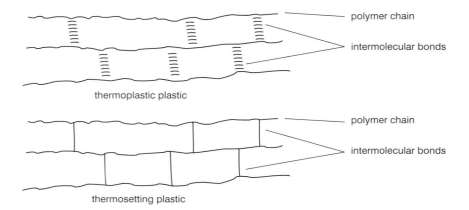

thermoplastic plastic

thermosetting plastic

CHECK YOURSELF QUESTIONS

Q1 **a** Petrol is a hydrocarbon. Write a word equation for the reaction when petrol burns in a plentiful supply of air.

   b When petrol is burnt in a car engine carbon monoxide may be formed. What condition causes the formation of carbon monoxide?

   c Explain what effect carbon monoxide has on the body.

Q2 **a** Draw displayed formulae for
   (i) hexane;
   (ii) hexene.

   b Describe a test that could be used to distinguish between hexane and hexene.

Q3 **a** Draw the displayed formula for propene.

   b Write an equation using displayed formulae to show how propene can be polymerised.

   c What is the name of the polymer formed in **b**?

   d Explain why propane cannot form polymers as propene does.

Answers are on page 240.

REVISION SESSION 3

Energy transfers

☐ Measuring energy transfers

■ In most reactions energy is transferred to the surroundings and the temperature goes up. These reactions are **exothermic**. In a minority of cases energy is absorbed from the surroundings as a reaction takes place and the temperature goes down. These reactions are **endothermic**.

temperature goes up
EXOTHERMIC

temperature goes down
ENDOTHERMIC

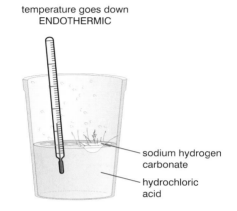

magnesium ribbon

hydrochloric acid

sodium hydrogen carbonate

hydrochloric acid

Energy transfers in a wide range of chemical reactions can be measured using a polystyrene cup as a calorimeter. If a lid is put on the cup, very little energy is transferred to the air and quite accurate results can be obtained.

■ All reactions involving the combustion of fuels are exothermic. The energy transferred when a fuel burns can be measured using a **calorimetric technique**, as shown in the figure on the right.

■ The rise in temperature of the water is a measure of the energy transferred to the water. This technique will not give a very accurate answer because much of the energy will be transferred to the surrounding air. Nevertheless, the technique can be used to compare the energy the same amounts of different fuels release.

■ It is often worth calculating the exact amount of energy transferred using the equation:

400g of water

metal can

draught excluder

paraffin burner

Measuring the energy produced on burning a liquid fuel.

| energy transferred to the water | = | mass of water | × | specific heat capacity of water | × | rise in temperature of water |

The specific heat capacity of water is 4.2 J/g/°C (or 4200 J/kg/°C). As the density of water is 1 g/cm^3, the mass of water in grams is the same as the volume of water in cm^3.

WORKED EXAMPLE

2.0 g of paraffin were burned in a spirit burner under a metal can containing 400cm^3 of water. The temperature of the water rose from 20°C to 70°C. Calculate the energy produced by the paraffin.

Equation:	Energy	=	mass of water × 4.2 × temperature rise
Substitute values:	E	=	400 × 4.2 × 50
Calculate:	E	=	84000 J per 2 g of paraffin
		=	42000 J per g of paraffin

QUESTION SPOTTER

In a question asking you to calculate the energy change in a reaction you might not be given the equation E = *mst*. So you will need to remember it.

■ When a fuel is burnt the reaction can be considered to take place in two stages. In the first stage the **covalent bonds** between the atoms in the fuel molecules and the oxygen molecules are **broken**. In the second stage the atoms combine and **new covalent bonds are formed**. For example, in the combustion of propane:

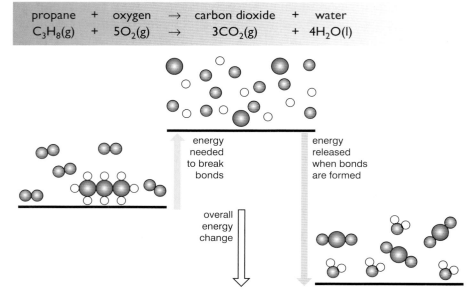

propane	+	oxygen	→	carbon dioxide	+	water
$C_3H_8(g)$	+	$5O_2(g)$	→	$3CO_2(g)$	+	$4H_2O(l)$

energy needed to break bonds

energy released when bonds are formed

overall energy change

The two stages of the chemical reaction between propane and oxygen. Existing bonds are broken and new bonds are formed.

C_3H_8 + $5O_2$

Energy

$3CO_2$ + $4H_2O$

Stage 1: Energy is needed (absorbed from the surroundings) to break the bonds. This process is endothermic.

Stage 2: Energy is released (transferred to the surroundings) as the bonds form. This process is exothermic.

■ The overall reaction is exothermic because more energy is released when bonds are formed than is needed initially to break the bonds. A simplified **energy level diagram** showing the exothermic nature of the reaction is shown on the left.

■ The larger the alkane molecule the more energy is released on combustion. This is because, although more bonds have to be broken in the first stage of the reaction, more bonds are formed in the second stage.

■ The increase in energy from one alkane to the next is almost constant, due to the extra CH_2 unit in the molecule. In the table the energy released on combustion has been worked out per mole of alkane. In this way the comparison can be made when the same number of molecules of each alkane is burnt. (More information on moles is given in Unit 13.)

Alkane		Energy of combustion (kJ/ mole)
methane	CH_4	882
ethane	C_2H_6	1542
propane	C_3H_8	2202
butane	C_4H_{10}	2877
pentane	C_5H_{12}	3487
hexane	C_6H_{14}	4141

CHECK YOURSELF QUESTIONS

Q1 A 0.2 g strip of magnesium ribbon is added to 40 cm³ of hydrochloric acid in a polystyrene beaker. The temperature rises by 32°C. (The specific heat capacity of the hydrochloric acid can be assumed to be the same as that of water, i.e. 4.2 J/g/°C.) Calculate **a** the energy released in the reaction and **b** the energy released per gram of magnesium.

Q2 Calcium oxide reacts with water as shown in the equation:

$$CaO(s) + H_2O(l) \rightarrow Ca(OH)_2(s)$$

An energy level diagram for this reaction is shown below.

a What does the energy level diagram tell us about the type of energy change that takes place in this reaction?

b What does the energy level diagram indicate about the amounts of energy required to break bonds and form new bonds in this reaction?

Q3 Chlorine (Cl_2) and hydrogen (H_2) react together to make hydrogen chloride (HCl). The equation can be written as:

$$H-H + Cl-Cl \rightarrow H-Cl + H-Cl$$

When this reaction occurs energy is transferred to the surroundings. Explain this in terms of the energy transfer processes taking place when bonds are broken and when bonds are made.

Answers are on page 241.

UNIT 10: ROCKS AND METALS

REVISION SESSION 1 ▰▰▰ *Geological change* ▰▰▰

⟦⟧ Layers of the Earth

- Evidence obtained by monitoring the shock waves produced by earthquakes suggests that the Earth is made up of three layers: a thin rocky **crust**, the **mantle** and the **core**.

The layered structure of the Earth.

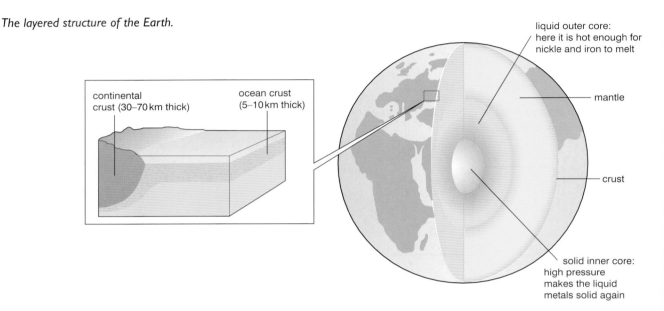

continental crust (30–70 km thick)

ocean crust (5–10 km thick)

liquid outer core: here it is hot enough for nickle and iron to melt

mantle

crust

solid inner core: high pressure makes the liquid metals solid again

- Due to large amounts of energy released by the decay of radioactive material in the core, the outer core and the mantle are in a liquid state.

- So the outer crust is really 'floating' on the liquid material of the mantle, which is called **magma**.

- Energy from the hot core is transferred out through the magma by the process of convection. This results in the formation of huge **convection currents** in the magma.

⟦⟧ Plate tectonics

- Until the beginning of the 20th century scientists thought that the Earth's crust had remained unchanged for millions of years. Then in 1912 the theory of **plate tectonics** was proposed.

- The crust is made up of large **tectonic plates** with boundaries between the different plates. Millions of years ago the continents were joined together. Some plates carry continents (**continental plates**), others carry oceans (**oceanic plates**). The convection currents in the mantle cause these plates to move by a few centimetres each year.

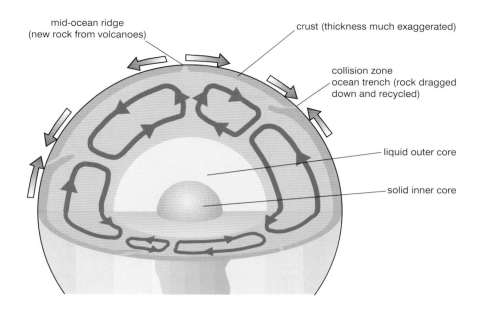

mid-ocean ridge
(new rock from volcanoes)

crust (thickness much exaggerated)

collision zone
ocean trench (rock dragged
down and recycled)

liquid outer core

solid inner core

The huge convection currents in the mantle cause the plates to move across the surface of the Earth.

■ When the tectonic plates grind together, **earthquakes** occur. When they move apart, a weakness or gap forms in the crust and magma forces its way up through this gap, forming a **volcano** – or, if the gap is in the ocean, a **mid–ocean ridge**. If continental plates collide **mountain ranges** can be formed – the Himalayas are thought to have been formed in this way. If the collision is between an oceanic plate and a continental plate, the denser oceanic plate is pushed down into the mantle, forming an **ocean trench**. This process is known as **subduction**.

A* EXTRA

Subduction is the process where rock at the plate edges is forced into the mantle and melts. The denser plate is forced into the mantle and the less dense plate 'floats' on top of it.

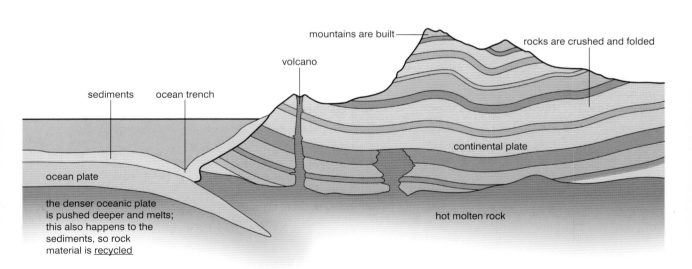

mountains are built

rocks are crushed and folded

volcano

sediments

ocean trench

continental plate

ocean plate

the denser oceanic plate is pushed deeper and melts; this also happens to the sediments, so rock material is <u>recycled</u>

hot molten rock

■ By identifying areas of volcanic action, the occurrence of ocean trenches, and areas prone to earthquakes, scientists have been able to identify the separate plates and their boundaries.

What happens when plates collide. This shows the process of subduction – 'drawing under'. This is happening along the west coast of America.

⊏⊐ The rock cycle

- Rocks are constantly being broken down and new rocks are constantly forming in the **rock cycle**.

- Molten rocks in the magma cool and form **igneous rocks**.

- **Weathering** and **erosion** produce small sediments of rock, which are transported (**transportation**) by water into streams and rivers. Here they are ground into even smaller particles, which are compressed by the particles above them, eventually forming **sedimentary rock**. This process can take millions of years.

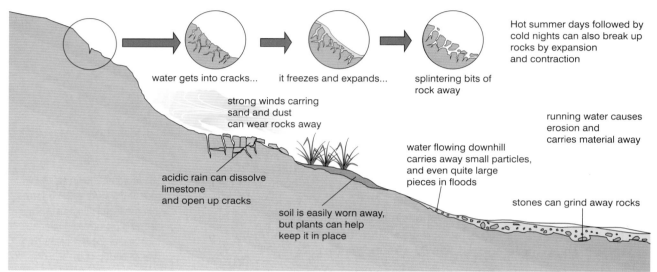

water gets into cracks...

it freezes and expands...

splintering bits of rock away

Hot summer days followed by cold nights can also break up rocks by expansion and contraction

strong winds carring sand and dust can wear rocks away

running water causes erosion and carries material away

acidic rain can dissolve limestone and open up cracks

water flowing downhill carries away small particles, and even quite large pieces in floods

soil is easily worn away, but plants can help keep it in place

stones can grind away rocks

Weathering, erosion and transportation – all important processes in the formation of sedimentary rocks.

- When sedimentary rocks are subjected to high temperature and pressure **metamorphic rocks** are formed. If the sedimentary or metamorphic rocks are forced into the magma in the process of subduction, igneous rocks are formed and the rock cycle is completed.

Type of rock	Method of formation	Appearance	Examples
Igneous	Cooling of hot, liquid rock (lava from a volcano or underground magma).	Hard, containing crystals of different minerals. Crystal size depends on how quickly the molten rock crystallised. Large crystals are produced on slow cooling; small crystals are formed when the cooling is quick.	Granite, basalt
Sedimentary	Layers of mud, sand or the shells and bones of living creatures are compressed under high pressure.	The rocks exist in layers with newer layers forming on top of older layers. Fossils are commonly found.	Limestone, sandstone.
Metamorphic	Formed from igneous and sedimentary rocks under conditions of high temperature and pressure.	Grains and crystals are often distorted and fossils are rarely present.	Marble (made from limestone), slate.

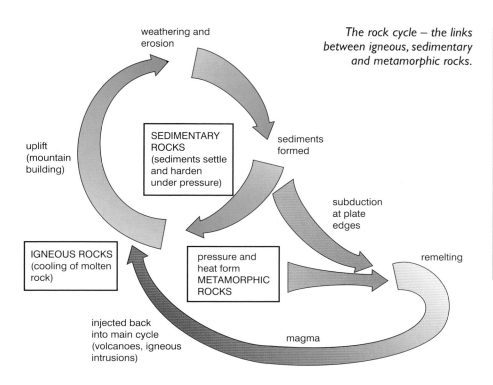

weathering and erosion

The rock cycle – the links between igneous, sedimentary and metamorphic rocks.

uplift (mountain building)

SEDIMENTARY ROCKS (sediments settle and harden under pressure)

sediments formed

subduction at plate edges

IGNEOUS ROCKS (cooling of molten rock)

pressure and heat form METAMORPHIC ROCKS

remelting

injected back into main cycle (volcanoes, igneous intrusions)

magma

QUESTION SPOTTER

▸ Questions are likely to focus on the formation of the different types of rock and may require extended answers.
▸ When writing about the formation of sedimentary rocks you should mention the separate processes of weathering, erosion, transportation and sedimentation.

■ Evidence obtained from the structure of rocks (the **rock record**) has provided information on the age of the Earth and about the changes that have taken place over billions of years. When sedimentary rocks are formed the lower layers are older than the upper layers. The thickness of the layers and the **fossils** they contain have provided a lot of information about the evolution of plants and animals.

CHECK YOURSELF QUESTIONS

Q1 In the diagram A, B and C represent plates of the Earth's crust moving in the direction of the arrows.

a Write down one natural occurrence that could happen at the boundary between plates.
b Explain how igneous rock is formed at the plate boundary X.
c Metamorphic rock forms at Y. What two conditions are needed for the formation of metamorphic rock?

Q2 The crust of the Earth is divided into several tectonic plates.
a What causes the tectonic plates to move?
b Describe what happens to tectonic plates when they collide.

Q3 Sedimentary rock can be made from igneous rock. Three processes are involved. These are weathering, erosion and transportation. Explain how these three processes lead to the formation of sedimentary rock.

Answers are on page 241.

Extraction of metals

How are metals extracted?

- Metals are found in the form of ores containing minerals mixed with waste rock. In almost all cases the mineral is a compound of the metal, not the pure metal. One exception is gold, which can be found in a pure state.

- Extracting a metal from its ore usually involves two steps:

  1 the mineral is physically separated from unwanted rock

  2 the mineral is chemically broken down to obtain the metal.

Reactivity of metals

- The chemical method chosen to break down a mineral depends on the reactivity of the metal. The **more reactive** a metal is the **harder** it is to break down its compounds. The more reactive metals are obtained from their minerals by a process known as **electrolysis**.

- The less reactive metals can be obtained by heating their oxides with carbon. This method will only work for metals below carbon in the reactivity series. It involves the **reduction** of a metal oxide to the metal.

QUESTION SPOTTER

The most frequently asked questions test understanding of the relationship between the method chosen for extracting a metal from its ore and the reactivity of that metal.

Metal	Extraction method
potassium sodium calcium magnesium aluminium	The most reactive metals are obtained using electrolysis.
(carbon)	
zinc iron tin lead copper	These metals are below carbon in the reactivity series and so can be obtained by heating their oxides with carbon.
silver gold	The least reactive metals are found as pure elements.

Using carbon to extract copper

- Copper is extracted by heating the mineral **malachite** (copper(II) carbonate) with carbon. The reaction takes place in two stages:

Stage 1 – The malachite decomposes:

copper(II) carbonate $\rightarrow$ copper(II) oxide + carbon dioxide
$$CuCO_3(s) \rightarrow CuO(s) + CO_2(g)$$

Stage 2 – The copper(II) oxide is reduced by the carbon:

copper(II) oxide + carbon $\rightarrow$ copper + carbon dioxide
$$2CuO(s) + C(s) \rightarrow 2Cu(s) + CO_2(g)$$

- The copper produced by this process is purified by electrolysis (see page 117).

☐ The blast furnace

■ Iron is produced on a very large scale by reduction using carbon. The reaction is undertaken in a huge furnace called a **blast furnace**.

■ Three important raw materials are put in the top of the furnace: **iron ore** (iron(III) oxide) – the source of iron – **coke** (the source of carbon needed for the reduction) and **limestone**, needed to remove the impurities as a 'slag'.

A blast furnace is used to reduce iron(III) oxide to iron.

1 Iron ore, limestone and coke are fed into the top of the blast furnace

2 Hot air is blasted up the furnace from the bottom

3 Oxygen from the air reacts with coke to form carbon dioxide:
   $C(s) + O_2(g) \longrightarrow CO_2(g)$

4 Carbon dioxide reacts with more coke to form carbon monoxide:
   $CO_2(g) + C(s) \longrightarrow 2CO(g)$

5 Carbon monoxide is a reducing agent. Iron (III) oxide is reduced to iron:
   ┌── reduction = loss of oxygen ──┐
   $Fe_2O_3(s) + 3CO(g) \longrightarrow 2Fe(l) + 3CO_2(g)$

6 Dense molten iron runs to the bottom of the furnace and is run off. There are many impurities in iron ore. The limestone helps to remove these as shown in 7 and 8.

7 Limestone is broken down by heat to calcium oxide:
   $CaCO_3(s) \longrightarrow CaO(s) + CO_2(g)$

8 Calcium oxide reacts with impurities like sand (silicon dioxide) to form a liquid called 'slag':
   $CaO(s) + SiO_2(s) \longrightarrow CaSiO_3(l)$
           impurity   slag
   The liquid slag falls to the bottom of the furnace and is tapped off.

■ The overall reaction is:

iron oxide	+	carbon	→	iron	+	carbon dioxide
$2Fe_2O_3(s)$	+	$3C$	→	$4Fe$	+	$3CO_2$

■ The reduction happens in three stages.

Stage 1 – The coke (carbon) reacts with oxygen 'blasted' into the furnace:

carbon	+	oxygen	→	carbon dioxide
$C(s)$	+	$O_2(g)$	→	$CO_2(g)$

Stage 2 – The carbon dioxide is reduced by unreacted coke to form carbon monoxide:

carbon dioxide	+	carbon	→	carbon monoxide
$CO_2(g)$	+	$C(s)$	→	$2CO(g)$

Stage 3 – The iron(III) oxide is reduced by the carbon monoxide to iron:

iron(III) oxide	+	carbon monoxide	→	iron	+	carbon dioxide
$Fe_2O_3(s)$	+	$3CO(g)$	→	$2Fe(s)$	+	$3CO_2(g)$

⚡ A* EXTRA

In a blast furnace the iron oxide is reduced to iron by carbon monoxide, formed when the carbon reacts with the air blasted into the furnace. In this reaction the carbon monoxide is oxidised to carbon dioxide.

Extraction of other metals

- Lead and zinc are also extracted in large quantities by heating their oxides with carbon.

- Metals that are above carbon in the reactivity series cannot be obtained by heating their oxides with carbon. They are reduced by **electrolysis**. Electrolysis is the breakdown of a chemical compound by an electric current.

Conditions for electrolysis

- The substance being electrolysed (the **electrolyte**) must contain ions and these ions must be free to move. In other words the substance must either be molten or dissolved in water.

- A d.c. voltage must be used. The **electrode** connected to the **positive** terminal of the power supply is known as the **anode**. The electrode connected to the **negative** terminal of the power supply is known as the **cathode**. The electrical circuit can be drawn as follows:

QUESTION
SPOTTER

▷ Common questions ask you to define terms such as electrode, electrolyte and electrolysis.
▷ You could also be asked to label a diagram to show these, together with the anode and cathode.

A typical electrical circuit used in electrolysis.

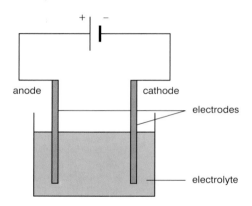

How does the electrolyte change?

- The negative ions are attracted to the anode and release electrons. (Loss of electrons is oxidation.) For example:

chloride ions → chlorine molecules + electrons
$$2Cl^-(aq) \rightarrow Cl_2(g) + 2e^-$$

- The positive ions are attracted to the cathode and gain electrons. (Gaining electrons is reduction.) For example:

copper ions + electrons → copper atoms
$$Cu^{2+}(aq) + 2e^- \rightarrow Cu(s)$$

- The electrons move through the external circuit from the anode to the cathode.

Extracting aluminium

- Aluminium is extracted from the ore **bauxite** (aluminium oxide) by electrolysis. The aluminium oxide is insoluble so it is **melted** to allow the ions to move when an electric current is passed through it. The anodes are made from carbon and the cathode is the carbon-lined steel case.

carbon anodes

pure aluminium oxide is added continually

carbon lining of the cell is the cathode

the electrolyte is molten cryolite and aluminium oxide

molten aluminium tapped off

molten aluminium

The extraction of aluminium is expensive. A mineral called cryolite is added to the aluminum oxide to lower the melting point and save energy costs.

- At the cathode **aluminium** is formed:

aluminium ions	+	electrons	→	aluminium
$Al^{3+}(l)$	+	$3e^-$	→	$Al(l)$

- At the anode **oxygen** is formed:

oxide ions	→	oxygen molecules	+	electrons
$2O^{2-}(l)$	→	$O_2(g)$	+	$4e^-$

- The oxygen reacts with the carbon anodes to form carbon dioxide. The rods constantly need to be replaced because of this.

Using electrolysis to purify copper

- Copper is extracted from its ore by reduction with carbon but the copper produced is not pure enough for some of its uses, such as making electrical wiring. It can be purified using electrolysis.

- The impure copper is made the anode in a cell with copper(II) sulphate as an electrolyte. The cathode is made from a thin piece of pure copper.

- At the anode the copper atoms dissolve, forming copper ions:

copper atoms	→	copper ions	+	electrons
$Cu(s)$	→	$Cu^{2+}(aq)$	+	$2e^-$

- At the cathode the copper ions are deposited to form copper atoms:

copper ions	+	electrons	→	copper atoms
$Cu^{2+}(aq)$	+	$2e^-$	→	$Cu(s)$

Copper is purified by electrolysis.

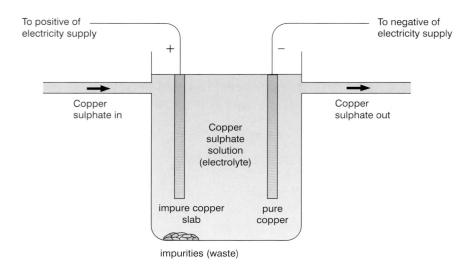

To positive of electricity supply

To negative of electricity supply

Copper sulphate in

Copper sulphate out

Copper sulphate solution (electrolyte)

impure copper slab

pure copper

impurities (waste)

CHECK YOURSELF QUESTIONS

Q1 Iron is made from iron ore (iron oxide) in a blast furnace by heating with carbon.
  a Write a word equation for the overall reaction.
  b Is the iron oxide oxidised or reduced in this reaction? Explain your answer.
  c Why is limestone also added to the blast furnace?

Q2 Explain the following terms:
  a electrolysis
  b electrolyte
  c electrode
  d anode
  e cathode.

Q3 Aluminium is extracted from aluminium oxide (Al_2O_3) by electrolysis. Aluminium oxide contains Al^{3+} and O^{2-} ions. The aluminium oxide is heated until it is in a molten state.
  a Why is the electrolysis carried out on molten rather than solid aluminium oxide?
  b Which electrode does the aluminium form at?
  c Explain how aluminium atoms are formed from aluminium ions. Write an ionic equation for this change.
  d The carbon electrodes need to be replaced regularly. Explain why.

Answers are on page 242.

REVISION SESSION 1

Chemical change

☐ What happens in chemical reactions?

- A chemical change, or **chemical reaction**, is quite different from the physical changes that occur, for example, when sugar dissolves in water.

FEATURES OF A CHEMICAL REACTION

- One or more **new substances** are produced.

- In many cases an **observable change** is apparent, for example the colour changes or a gas is produced.

- An **apparent change in mass** occurs. This change is often quite small and difficult to detect unless accurate balances are used. (Mass is conserved in a chemical reaction – the apparent change in mass usually occurs because one of the reactants or products is a gas.)

- An **energy change** is almost always involved. In most cases energy is released and the surroundings become warmer. In some cases energy is absorbed from the surroundings and so the surroundings become colder. Note: Some physical changes, such as evaporation, also produce energy changes.

☐ Collision theory

- For a chemical reaction to occur, the reacting particles (atoms, molecules or ions) must **collide**. The energy involved in the collision must be enough to break the chemical bonds in the reacting particles – or the particles will just bounce off one another.

- A collision that has enough energy to result in a chemical reaction is an **effective collision**.

QUESTION SPOTTER

Questions on the collision theory are very common. You will often be asked why not every collision leads to a reaction.

unsuccessful   successful

Particles must collide with sufficient energy to make an effective collision.

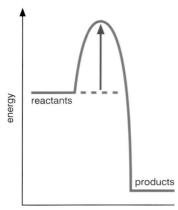

energy

reactants

products

course of reaction

If the activation energy of a reaction is low, more of the collisions will be effective and the reaction will proceed quickly. If the activation energy is high a smaller proportion of collisions will be effective and the reaction will be slow.

■ Some chemical reactions occur extremely quickly (for example, the explosive reaction between petrol and oxygen in a car engine) and some more slowly (for example, iron rusts over days or weeks). This is because they have different **activation energies**. Activation energy is the minimum amount of energy required in a collision for a reaction to occur. As a general rule, the bigger the activation energy the slower the reaction will be at a particular temperature.

⌑ Speed, rate and time

■ A quick reaction takes place in a short time. It has a high **rate of reaction**. As the time taken for a reaction to be completed increases, the rate of the reaction decreases. In other words:

$$\text{rate} \propto \frac{1}{\text{time}}$$

Speed	Rate	Time
quick or fast	high	short
slow	low	long

⌑ Monitoring the rate of a reaction

■ When marble (calcium carbonate) reacts with hydrochloric acid the following reaction starts straight away:

calcium carbonate	+	hydrochloric acid	→	calcium chloride	+	carbon dioxide	+	water
$CaCO_3(s)$	+	$2HCl(aq)$	→	$CaCl_2(aq)$	+	$CO_2(g)$	+	$H_2O(l)$

■ The reaction can be monitored as it proceeds either by measuring the **volume of gas** being formed or by measuring the **change in mass** of the reaction flask.

The volume of gas can be measured every 10 seconds.

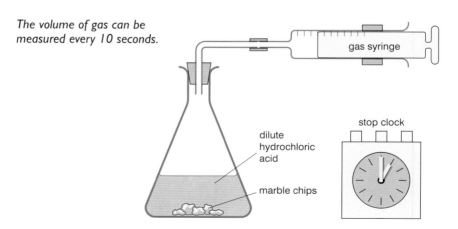

gas syringe

dilute hydrochloric acid

marble chips

stop clock

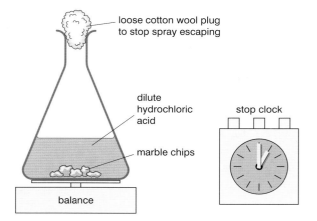

loose cotton wool plug
to stop spray escaping

dilute
hydrochloric
acid

stop clock

marble chips

balance

The change in mass can be measured every 10 seconds. The carbon dioxide produced in the reaction escapes into the air. The cotton wool plug is there to stop acid spray from escaping.

■ Graphs of the results from both experiments have almost identical shapes.

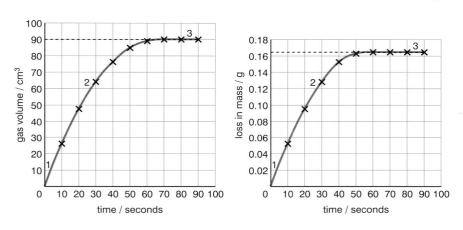

The rate of the reaction decreases as the reaction proceeds.

■ The **rate of the reaction** at any point can be calculated from the **gradient** of the curve. The shapes of the graphs can be divided into three regions:

1 The curve is the steepest (has the greatest gradient) and the reaction has its highest rate at this point. The maximum number of reacting particles are present and the number of effective collisions per second is at its greatest.

2 The curve is not as steep (has a lower gradient) at this point and the rate of the reaction is lower. Fewer reacting particles are present and so the number of effective collisions per second will be less.

3 The curve is horizontal (gradient is zero) and the reaction is complete. At least one of the reactants has been completely used up and so no further collisions can occur between the two reactants.

QUESTION SPOTTER

You will often be given a graph showing the change in rate during a reaction. You will be asked questions about *how* the rate changes and *why* it changes during the reaction.

Q1 For a chemical reaction to occur the reacting particles must collide. Why don't all collisions between the particles of the reactants lead to a chemical reaction?

Q2 The diagrams below show the activation energies of two different reactions A and B. Which reaction is likely to have the greater rate of reaction at a particular temperature?

Q3 Look at the table of results obtained when dilute hydrochloric acid is added to marble chips.

Time/seconds	0	10	20	30	40	50	60	70	80	90
Volume of gas/cm^3	0	20	36	49	58	65	69	70	70	70

a What is the name of the gas produced in this reaction?
b Use the results to calculate the volume of gas produced:
  i in the first 10 seconds
  ii between 10 and 20 seconds
  iii between 20 and 30 seconds
  iv between 80 and 90 seconds.
c Explain how your answers to part (b) show that the rate of reaction decreases as the reaction proceeds.
d Use collision theory to explain why the rate of reaction decreases as the reaction proceeds.
e In this experiment the rate of the reaction was followed by measuring the volume of gas produced every 10 seconds. What alternative measurement could have been used?

Answers are on page 243.

REVISION SESSION 2 ▰▰ Controlling the rate of reaction

▢ What can change the rate of a reaction?

■ There are six key factors that can change the rate of a reaction:
  • **concentration** (of a solution)
  • **temperature**
  • **surface area** (of a solid)
  • **pressure** (of a gas)
  • **light**
  • a **catalyst**.

■ A simple **collision theory** can be used to explain how these factors affect the rate of a reaction. Two important parts of the theory are:

1 The reacting particles must collide with each other.

2 There must be sufficient energy in the collision to overcome the activation energy.

▢ Concentration

■ **Increasing the concentration** of a reactant will **increase the rate** of a reaction. If a piece of magnesium ribbon is added to a solution of hydrochloric acid the following reaction occurs:

| magnesium | + | hydrochloric acid | → | magnesium chloride | + | hydrogen |
| Mg(s) | + | 2HCl(aq) | → | $MgCl_2(aq)$ | + | $H_2(g)$ |

■ As the magnesium and acid come into contact, the acid **effervesces** – hydrogen is given off. The graph below shows the volume of gas collected every 10 seconds when two different concentrations of hydrochloric acid are used.

☀ QUESTION SPOTTER

▸ You are often asked to explain the differences in shapes of the graphs in experiments like these.
▸ You may also be asked to add further lines to a graph to represent what you would expect when conditions changed. (e.g. if the temperature was increased).

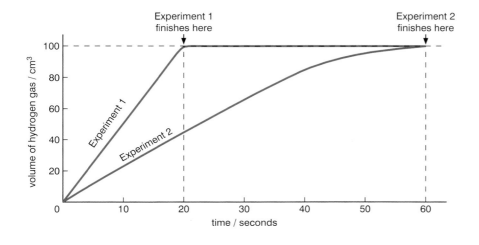

The same length of magnesium was used in each experiment. In experiment 1 the concentration of the acid was 2.0 M, in experiment 2 it was 0.5 M.

■ In experiment 1 the curve is steeper (has a greater gradient) than in experiment 2. In experiment 1 the reaction is complete after 20 seconds whereas in experiment 2 it takes 60 seconds. The rate of the reaction is higher with 2.0 M hydrochloric acid than with 0.5 M hydrochloric acid. In the 2.0 M hydrochloric acid solution the hydrogen ions are more likely to collide with the surface of the magnesium ribbon than in the 0.5 M hydrochloric acid.

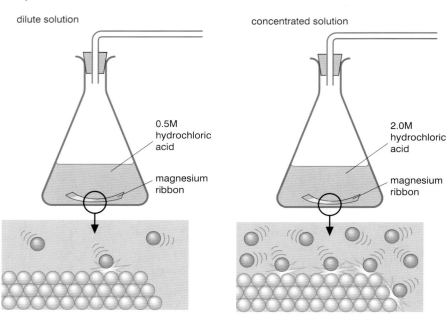

dilute solution

concentrated solution

0.5M hydrochloric acid

magnesium ribbon

2.0M hydrochloric acid

magnesium ribbon

⌂ Temperature

■ **Increasing the temperature** will **increase the rate** of reaction. Warming a chemical transfers kinetic energy to the chemical's particles. More kinetic energy means that the particles move faster. As they are moving faster there will be more collisions each second. The increased energy of the collisions also means that the proportion of collisions that are effective will increase.

■ Increasing the temperature of a reaction such as that between calcium carbonate and hydrochloric acid will not increase the final amount of carbon dioxide produced. The **same amount** of gas will be produced in a **shorter time**.

20° C

30° C

The rates of the two reactions are different but the final loss in mass is the same.

30°C

20°C

mass of carbon dioxide lost (g)

time (minutes)

⟦⟧ Surface area

- **Increasing the surface area** of a solid reactant will **increase the rate** of a reaction. The reaction can only take place if the reacting particles collide. This means that the reaction takes place at the surface of the solid. The particles within the solid cannot react until those on the surface have reacted and moved away.

- Powdered calcium carbonate has a much larger surface area than the same mass of marble chips. A lump of coal will burn slowly in the air whereas coal dust can react explosively.

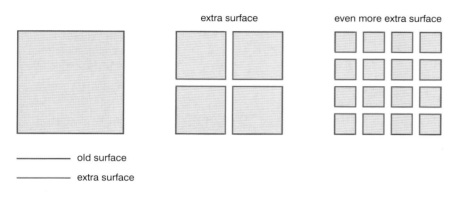

extra surface   even more extra surface

——————— old surface

——————— extra surface

On a large lump of marble hydrochloric acid can only react with the outside surfaces. Breaking the lump into smaller pieces creates extra surfaces for the reaction.

☀ **QUESTION SPOTTER**

Questions often focus on the effects of concentration, temperature, surface area and catalysts on the rate of a reaction. You will usually be asked to *describe* and *explain* how the rate changes.

⟦⟧ Pressure

- **Increasing the pressure** on the reaction between gases will **increase the rate** of the reaction. Increasing the pressure reduces the volume of the gas, moving the particles closer together. If the particles are closer together there will be more collisions and therefore more effective collisions.

The same number of particles are closer together in a smaller volume. There will be more effective collisions each second.

low pressure

high pressure

⟦⟧ Light

- **Increasing the intensity of light** will **increase the rate** of some reactions. This fact is important in photography. The photographic film is coated with chemicals that react when in contact with the light.

- Some laboratory chemicals, for example silver nitrate and hydrogen peroxide, are stored in brown glass bottles to reduce the effect of the light.

⟦⟧ Catalysts

- A **catalyst** is a substance that alters the rate of a chemical reaction without being used up itself. The mass of the catalyst remains unchanged throughout the reaction.

- Hydrogen peroxide decomposes slowly at room temperature into water and oxygen. This reaction is catalysed by manganese(IV) oxide.

⚡ **A* EXTRA**

Catalysts do not always increase the rate of a reaction. Most catalysts are positive catalysts (they increase the rate of a reaction) but inhibitors slow down reactions. Inhibitors are like negative catalysts – they act by increasing the activation energy of the reaction.

hydrogen peroxide $\xrightarrow{\text{manganese (IV) oxide}}$ water + oxygen

$2H_2O_2 \xrightarrow{\text{MnO}_2} 2H_2O + O_2$

The manganese(IV) oxide has a dramatic effect on the rate of decomposition of hydrogen peroxide. The catalyst doesn't produce any extra oxygen but gives the same amount at a higher rate.
1 = no catalyst
2 = one spatula measure
3 = two spatula measures

■ Most catalysts work by providing an alternative 'route' for the reaction that has a lower activation energy 'barrier'. This increases the number of effective collisions each second.

■ Some catalysts slow down reactions. These are called negative catalysts or **inhibitors**. Inhibitors are added to petrol to prevent 'pre-ignition' of the petrol vapour in the engine.

The catalyst provides a lower energy route from reactants to products.

CHECK YOURSELF QUESTIONS

Q1 Why does increasing the temperature increase the rate of a reaction?

Q2 The graph shows the results obtained in three different experiments. In each experiment marble chips were added to 50 cm³ of 1 M hydrochloric acid (an excess) at room temperature. The same mass of marble was used each time but different sized chips were used in each experiment.

a i In which experiment was the reaction the fastest?
  ii Give a reason for your answer.
b i Which experiment used the largest marble chips?
  ii Give a reason for your answer.
c i How long did it take for the reaction in experiment 2 to finish?
  ii Why did the reaction finish?
d Why was the same mass of carbon dioxide lost in each experiment?

e Experiment 3 was repeated at 50°C rather than room temperature. How would the results be different from those shown for experiment 3?

Q3 a What is a catalyst?
  b How does the catalyst affect the rate of a reaction?

Answers are on page 244.

REVISION SESSION 3 ■■■ Making use of enzymes ■■■

⊡ What are enzymes?

- An **enzyme** is a biological catalyst. Enzymes are protein molecules that control many of the chemical reactions that occur in living cells.

- Enzymes are used in a wide range of manufacturing processes – some of the more important ones are shown in the table.

Process	Enzyme involved	Description
Brewing	Enzymes present in yeast	A mixture of sugar solution and yeast will produce ethanol (alcohol) and carbon dioxide. This process is called fermentation and is the basis of the beer and wine making industries.
Baking	Enzymes present in yeast	This also depends on the fermentation process. The carbon dioxide produced helps the bread dough rise. The ethanol evaporates during the baking process.
Washing using biological washing powders	Proteases	These enzymes break down proteins found in stains (e.g. blood, egg) on clothing.
Making cheese	Lipases	These enzymes speed up the ripening of cheese.

- Increasing the temperature of a reaction will usually increase its rate. This is not the case in reactions where an enzyme is involved. The protein structure of an enzyme is affected by temperature. Above a certain temperature the protein becomes **denatured** and it will cease to function as a catalyst.

- Enzymes are also sensitive to **pH**. Inside cells, most enzymes work best in neutral conditions, around pH 7. However, the enzymes in the stomach work best at about pH 2.

> ⚡ **A* EXTRA**
>
> ▸ Enzymes are protein molecules with an active site where the reaction occurs. The active site has a certain shape and will only accommodate the shape of a particular molecule (sometimes referred to as the 'lock and key' model).
> ▸ This active site can be caused to lose its shape by changes in pH or temperature. If this happens it will no longer 'hold' the reacting molecule.

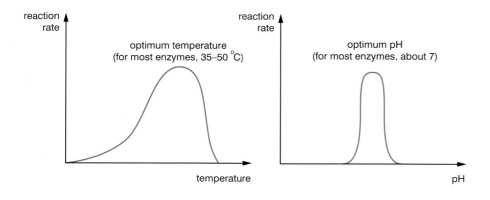

reaction rate — optimum temperature (for most enzymes, 35–50 $^{\circ}$C) — temperature

reaction rate — optimum pH (for most enzymes, about 7) — pH

The effect of temperature and pH on the rate of a reaction involving enzymes.

⌷ How enzymes work

■ How enzymes work can best be understood by using a simple model. The enzyme provides a surface for the reaction to take place on. The surface of the enzyme molecule contains a cavity known as an **active site**. Reactant molecules become 'trapped' in the active site and so collide more frequently, resulting in more effective collisions and a greater rate of reaction.

■ This model also explains why enzymes cease to function above a certain temperature. The protein molecule is a long folded chain. As the temperature is increased the folded chain jostles and reforms and so the shape of the active site changes. Above a certain temperature the active site has changed so much that it is no longer able to 'trap' reactant molecules. Such an enzyme is said to be **denatured**.

CHECK YOURSELF QUESTIONS

Q1 What is an enzyme?

Q2 In fermentation, glucose ($C_6H_{12}O_6$) is broken down to ethanol (C_2H_5OH) and carbon dioxide (CO_2).

  a What is used as a source of enzymes for this reaction?

  b Which two major industries make use of this reaction?

  c The optimum temperature for this reaction is about 40°C. Why isn't a higher temperature used?

  d Write a word equation for the reaction.

  e Write a balanced symbol equation for the reaction.

Q3 a What is an active site?

  b Use the active site model to explain why enzymes usually only act as catalysts for one reaction.

Answers are on page 244.

■ Reversible reactions ■

⟳ Types of reversible reaction

■ Carbon burns in oxygen to form carbon dioxide:

carbon	+	oxygen	→	carbon dioxide
$C(s)$	+	$O_2(g)$	→	$CO_2(g)$

Carbon dioxide cannot be changed back into carbon and oxygen. The reaction cannot be reversed.

■ When blue copper(II) sulphate crystals are heated a white powder is formed (anhydrous copper(II) sulphate) and water is lost as steam. If water is added to this white powder, blue copper(II) sulphate is re-formed. The reaction is **reversible**:

copper(II) sulphate crystals	⇌	anhydrous copper(II) sulphate	+	water
$CuSO_4.5H_2O(s)$	⇌	$CuSO_4(s)$	+	$5H_2O(l)$

When copper(II) sulphate crystals are heated they turn from blue to white.

The reaction can then be reversed by adding water.

■ A reversible reaction can go from left to right or from right to left – notice the double-headed '⇌' arrow used when writing these equations.

■ Another reversible reaction is the reaction between ethene and water to make ethanol. This is one of the reactions used industrially to make ethanol:

ethene	+	water	⇌	ethanol
$C_2H_4(g)$	+	$H_2O(g)$	⇌	$C_2H_5OH(g)$

If ethene and water are heated in the presence of a catalyst in a sealed container ethanol is produced.

■ As the ethene and water are used up, the rate of the forward reaction decreases. As the amount of ethanol increases the rate of the back reaction (the decomposition of ethanol) increases. Eventually the rate of formation of ethanol will be exactly equal to the rate of decomposition of ethanol. The amounts of ethene, water and ethanol will be constant. The reaction is said to be in **equilibrium**.

> ### ⚡ A* EXTRA
>
> A chemical equilibrium is an example of a dynamic equilibrium (a moving equilibrium). Reactants are constantly forming products and products are constantly reforming the reactants. Equilibrium is reached when the rates of the forward and backward reactions are the same.

⟳ Changing the position of equilibrium

- Reversible reactions can be a nuisance to an industrial chemist. You want to make a particular product but as soon as it forms it starts to change back into the reactants! Fortunately scientists have found ways of increasing the amount of product that can be obtained (the **yield**) in a reversible reaction by moving the position of balance to favour the products rather than the reactants.

- The position of equilibrium or yield can be changed in the following ways:
  - changing **concentrations**
  - changing **pressure**
  - changing **temperature**.

⟳ The Haber process

- Ammonia is used to make nitrogen-containing fertilisers.

- It is manufactured in the **Haber process** from nitrogen and hydrogen. The conditions include an iron catalyst, a temperature of 450°C and 200 times atmospheric pressure.

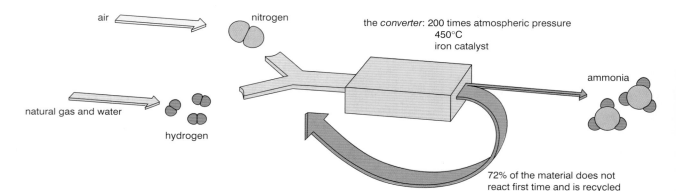

The Haber Process for making ammonia. The reactants have to be recycled to increase the amount of ammonia produced.

nitrogen	+	hydrogen	⇌	ammonia
$N_2(g)$	+	$3H_2(g)$	⇌	$2NH_3(g)$

- The temperature of 450°C is a compromise between rate and equilibrium requirements. If it were lower more ammonia would be formed, but the reaction would be much slower. The catalyst is used to increase the rate of the reaction – it does not change the yield.

⊡ The contact process

■ Sulphuric acid is a very important starting material in the chemical industry. It is used in the manufacture of many other chemicals, from fertilisers to plastics.

■ It is manufactured in a process known as the **contact process** – sulphur dioxide is oxidised to sulphur trioxide, then water is added to make sulphuric acid.

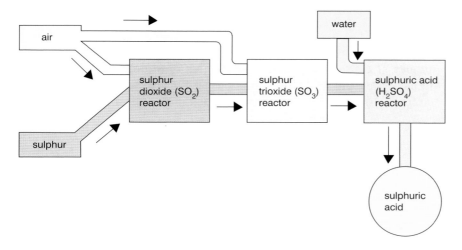

The conversion of sulphur dioxide to sulphur trioxide takes place at 450°C in the presence of a vanadium(V) oxide catalyst.

sulphur dioxide	+	oxygen	⇌	sulphur trioxide
$2SO_2(g)$	+	$O_2(g)$	⇌	$2SO_3(g)$

■ The temperature of 450°C is a compromise between rate and equilibrium requirements. A catalyst is used to increase the rate of the reaction. High pressure is not used as this would be costly and, as 98% conversion can be achieved at normal atmospheric pressure, it is unnecessary.

⚡ A* EXTRA

▸ Low temperature often gives a good conversion of reactant into product but a very slow rate of reaction.
▸ The temperature chosen in an industrial process is often a compromise between one that favours the forward reaction (rather than the backward reaction) and one that gives a suitable rate of reaction.

CHECK YOURSELF QUESTIONS

Q1 When a chemical reaction is in equilibrium what does this mean?

Q2 What effect does a catalyst have on:
  a the rate of reaction
  b the yield of a reaction?

Q3 In the Haber process for making ammonia the forward reaction is favoured by a low temperature. Why is a temperature as high as 450°C used?

Answers are on page 245.

REVISION SESSION 1

Organising the elements

How are elements classified?

- Elements are the building blocks from which all materials are made. Over 100 elements have been identified so far and each element has its own properties and reactions. The elements are arranged in the **periodic table**, which puts elements with similar reactions and properties close together.

- The periodic table arranges the elements in order of **increasing atomic number**. The atomic number is the number of protons in the atom. As atoms are neutral, the atomic number also gives the number of electrons. The elements are then arranged in **periods** and **groups**.

groups	1	2											3	4	5	6	7	8(0)
periods																		
1								H hydrogen 1										He helium 2
2	Li lithium 3	Be beryllium 4											B boron 5	C carbon 6	N nitrogen 7	O oxygen 8	F fluorine 9	Ne neon 10
3	Na sodium 11	Mg magnesium 12				transition metals							Al aluminium 13	Si silicon 14	P phosphorus 15	S sulphur 16	Cl chlorine 17	Ar argon 18
4	K potassium 19	Ca calcium 20	Sc scandium 21	Ti titanium 22	V vanadium 23	Cr chromium 24	Mn manganese 25	Fe iron 26	Co cobalt 27	Ni nickel 28	Cu copper 29	Zn zinc 30	Ga gallium 31	Ge germanium 32	As arsenic 33	Se selenium 34	Br bromine 35	Kr krypton 36
5	Rb rubidium 37	Sr strontium 38	Y yttrium 39	Zr zirconium 40	Nb niobium 41	Mo molybdenum 42	Tc technetium 43	Ru ruthenium 44	Rh rhodium 45	Pd palladium 46	Ag silver 47	Cd cadmium 48	In indium 49	Sn tin 50	Sb antimony 51	Te tellurium 52	I iodine 53	Xe xenon 54
6	Cs caesium 55	Ba barium 56	La lanthanum 57	Hf hafnium 72	Ta tantalum 73	W tungsten 74	Re rhenium 75	Os osmium 76	Ir iridium 77	Pt platinum 78	Au gold 79	Hg mercury 80	Tl thallium 81	Pb lead 82	Bi bismuth 83	Po polonium 84	At astatine 85	Rn radon 86

metal	non metal	transition metal	metalloid

Part of the modern periodic table showing periods and groups.

QUESTION SPOTTER

Questions commonly ask you to label the parts of the periodic table where the metals/ non-metals/transition metals are found.

Periods

- Rows of elements arranged in increasing atomic number from left to right. They are numbered from 1 to 7.

- The first period contains only two elements, hydrogen and helium.

- The elements in the middle block of the periodic table in periods 4, 5 and 6 are called the **transition metals**.

Groups

- Columns of elements with the atomic number increasing down the column. They are numbered from 1 to 8 (group 8 is often referred to as group 0).

- Elements in a group have similar properties – they are a 'chemical family'.

- Some groups have family names – the **alkali metals** (group 1), the **halogens** (group 7) and the **noble gases** (group 8/0).

- The fact that elements in the same group have similar reactions can be explained in terms of the electron structures of their atoms (see Unit 8). If elements have the same number of electrons in their outer shells they will have similar chemical properties. The relationship between the group number and the number of electrons in the outer electron shell of the atom is shown in the table.

Group number									
	I	2	3	4	5	6	7	0 (8)	
Electrons in the outer electron shell	I	2	3	4	5	6	7	2 or 8 (full)	

Metals and non-metals

- Most elements can be classified as either **metals** or **non-metals**. In the periodic table the metals are arranged on the left-hand side and in the middle, the non-metals are on the right-hand side.

- **Metalloid** elements are close to the boundary between metals and non-metals, and have some properties of metals and some of non-metals. Examples are silicon and germanium.

- Metals and non-metals have quite different physical and chemical properties.

Good conductors of electricity

High melting point

Good conductors of heat

Shiny

Typical properties of metals

Sonorous
rings when struck

Malleable
can be hammered into shape

Ductile
can be drawn into a wire

Exceptions:

- the alkali metals have low melting points and are not sonorous
- mercury has a low melting point

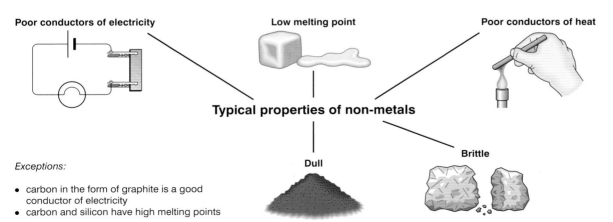

Poor conductors of electricity

Low melting point

Poor conductors of heat

Typical properties of non-metals

Brittle

Dull

Exceptions:

- carbon in the form of graphite is a good conductor of electricity
- carbon and silicon have high melting points

- The **oxides** of elements can often be made by heating the element in air or oxygen. For example, a metal such as magnesium burns in oxygen to form magnesium oxide:

$$\text{magnesium} + \text{oxygen} \rightarrow \text{magnesium oxide}$$
$$2Mg(s) + O_2(g) \rightarrow 2MgO(s)$$

- The magnesium oxide forms as a white ash. If distilled water is added to the ash and the mixture is tested with universal indicator the pH will be greater than 7 – the oxide has formed an **alkaline** solution.

- If sulphur is burned in oxygen, sulphur dioxide gas is formed:

$$\text{sulphur} + \text{oxygen} \rightarrow \text{sulphur dioxide}$$
$$S(s) + O_2(g) \rightarrow SO_2(g)$$

- If this is dissolved in water and then tested with universal indicator solution the pH will be less than 7 – the oxide has formed an **acidic** solution.

- The oxides of most elements can be classified as **basic oxides** or **acidic oxides**. Some elements form **neutral oxides**, for example water is a neutral oxide. Basic oxides or bases that dissolve in water are called **alkalis**.

- Bases and alkalis react with acids to form salts in reactions known as **neutralisation** reactions. A typical neutralisation reaction occurs when sodium hydroxide (an alkali) reacts with hydrochloric acid. The salt formed is sodium chloride, common salt:

$$\text{alkali} + \text{acid} \rightarrow \text{salt} + \text{water}$$
$$\text{sodium hydroxide} + \text{hydrochloric acid} \rightarrow \text{sodium chloride} + \text{water}$$
$$NaOH(aq) + HCl(aq) \rightarrow NaCl(aq) + H_2O(l)$$

A* EXTRA

▸ Salts are formed when the hydrogen of an acid is replaced by a metal.
▸ Hydrochloric acid forms salts called chlorides, sulphuric acid forms salts called sulphates and nitric acid forms salts called nitrates.

Oxide	Type of oxide	pH of solution	Other reactions of the oxide
Metal oxide	basic	more than 7 (alkaline)	reacts with an acid to form a salt + water
Non-metal oxide	acidic	less than 7 (acidic)	reacts with a base to form a salt + water

Q1 Look at the diagram representing the periodic table. The letters stand for elements.

a Which element is in group 4?
b Which element is in the second period?
c Which element is a noble gas?
d Which element is a transition metal?
e Which element is a metalloid?
f Which elements are non-metals?
g Which element is most likely to be a gas?

Q2 Why do elements in the same group react in similar ways?

Q3 Look at the table of experimental results at the end of the question.
a Which of the oxides is/are acidic? Explain how you decided.
b Which of the oxides is/are basic? Explain how you decided.
c Copper(II) oxide reacts with sulphuric acid (H_2SO_4).
  i What is the name given to this type of reaction?
  ii Write a word equation for the reaction.
  iii Write a symbol equation for the reaction.
  iv Which oxide A to D is most likely to be copper(II) oxide?

Oxide of element	pH of solution	Does it react with an acid?	Does it react with an alkali?
A	7	✓	✗
B	3	✗	✓
C	7	✗	✗
D	10	✓	✗

Answers are on page 245.

The metals

Group I elements become more reactive as you go further down the group.

Most elements are metals. Some metals are highly reactive whilst others are almost completely unreactive. These types of metals are found in different parts of the periodic table.

Group 1 – the alkali metals

■ These very reactive metals all have only **one electron** in their outer electron shell. This electron is readily given away when the metal reacts with non-metals. The more electrons a metal atom has to lose in a reaction, the more energy is needed to start the reaction. This is why the group 2 elements are less reactive – they have to lose two electrons when they react (see Chapter 8).

■ **Reactivity increases down the group** because, as the atom gets bigger, the outer electron is further away from the nucleus and so is removed more easily.

Properties of group 1 metals

■ **Soft to cut**.

■ **Shiny when cut**, but quickly tarnish in the air.

■ **Very low melting points** compared with most metals.

■ **Very low densities** compared with most metals (lithium, sodium and potassium will float on water).

■ **React very easily** with air, water and other elements such as chlorine. The alkali metals are so reactive that they are stored in oil to prevent reaction with air and water.

Reaction	Observations	Equations
Air or oxygen	The metals burn easily with coloured flames: • lithium – red • sodium – orange • potassium – lilac A white solid oxide is formed.	lithium + oxygen → lithium oxide $4Li(s) + O_2(g) \rightarrow 2Li_2O(s)$ sodium + oxygen → sodium oxide $4Na(s) + O_2(g) \rightarrow 2Na_2O(s)$ potassium + oxygen → potassium oxide $4K(s) + O_2(g) \rightarrow 2K_2O(s)$

Reaction	Observations	Equations
Water	The metals react vigorously. They float on the surface; moving around rapidly; the heat of the reaction melts the metal so it forms a sphere; effervescence occurs and a gas is given off; the metal rapidly dissolves. With the more reactive metals (e.g. potassium) the hydrogen gas produced burns. The resulting solution is alkaline.	lithium + water → lithium hydroxide + hydrogen $2Li(s) + 2H_2O(l) \rightarrow 2LiOH(aq) + H_2(g)$ sodium + water → sodium hydroxide + hydrogen $2Na(s) + 2H_2O(l) \rightarrow 2NaOH(aq) + H_2(g)$ potassium + water → potassium hydroxide + hydrogen $2K(s) + 2H_2O(l) \rightarrow 2KOH(aq) + H_2(g)$
Chlorine	The metals react easily burning in the chlorine to form a white solid.	lithium + chlorine → lithium chloride $2Li(s) + Cl_2(g) \rightarrow 2LiCl(s)$ sodium + chlorine → sodium chloride $2Na(s) + Cl_2(g) \rightarrow 2NaCl(s)$ potassium + chlorine → potassium chloride $2K(s) + Cl_2(g) \rightarrow 2KCl(s)$

Uses for group 1 metals

- The compounds of the alkali metals are widely used:
  - lithium carbonate – in light sensitive lenses for glasses
  - lithium hydroxide – removes carbon dioxide in air conditioning systems
  - sodium chloride – table salt
  - sodium carbonate – a water softener
  - sodium hydroxide – used in paper manufacture
  - mono-sodium glutamate – a flavour enhancer
  - sodium sulphite – a preservative
  - potassium nitrate – a fertiliser also used to make explosives.

The transition metals

- The transition metals are listed in the centre of the periodic table.

- All the transition metals have **more than one electron in their outer electron shell**, which is why they are much less reactive than the alkali metals and so are more 'everyday' metals. They have much higher melting points and densities. Iron, cobalt and nickel are the only magnetic elements. They react much more slowly with water and with oxygen. Some, like iron, will react with dilute acids – others, like copper, show no reaction.

- They are widely used as construction metals (particularly iron), and they are frequently used as **catalysts** in the chemical industry.

Property	Group I metal	Transition metal
Melting point	low	high
Density	low	high
Colours of compounds	white	coloured
Reactions with water/air	vigorous	slow or no reaction
Reactions with acid	violent (dangerous)	slow or no reaction

■ The **compounds** of the transition metals are usually **coloured**. Copper compounds are usually blue or green; iron compounds tend to be either green or brown. If sodium hydroxide solution is added to the solution of a transition metal compound, a precipitate of the metal hydroxide will be formed. The colour of the precipitate will help to identify the metal. For example:

$$\begin{array}{c} \text{copper} \\ \text{sulphate} \end{array} + \begin{array}{c} \text{sodium} \\ \text{hydroxide} \end{array} \rightarrow \begin{array}{c} \text{copper(II)} \\ \text{hydroxide} \end{array} + \begin{array}{c} \text{sodium} \\ \text{sulphate} \end{array}$$

$$CuSO_4(aq) + 2NaOH(aq) \rightarrow Cu(OH)_2(s) + Na_2SO_4(aq)$$

■ This can be written as an ionic equation (see Unit 7):

$$Cu^{2+}(aq) + 2OH^-(aq) \rightarrow Cu(OH)_2(s)$$

Colour of metal hydroxide	Likely metal present
blue	copper
green	nickel
green turning to brown	iron
greenish/blue	chromium

■ Transition metal compounds and other metal compounds produce characteristic colours in **flame tests**.

Metal ion	Flame colour
lithium	red
sodium	orange
potassium	lilac
copper	turquoise
calcium	brick red
strontium	crimson
barium	green

The colour of the flame can be used to identify the metal ions present.

CHECK YOURSELF QUESTIONS

Q1 This question is about the group 1 elements.
  a Which is the most reactive of the elements?
  b Why are the elements stored in oil?
  c Which element will be the easiest to cut?
  d Why do the elements tarnish quickly when they are cut?
  e Why is the group known as the alkali metals?
  f Why does sodium float when added to water?
  g Write word equations and symbol equations for the following reactions:
      i rubidium and oxygen
      ii caesium and water
      iii potassium and chlorine.

Q2 This question is about the transition metals.
  a Give two differences in the physical properties of the transition metals compared with the alkali metals.
  b Transition metals are used as catalysts. What is a catalyst?
  c Suggest why the alkali metals are more reactive than the transition metals.

Q3 Look at the table of observations below.

Compound tested	Colour of compound	Colour produced in a flame test	Effect of adding sodium hydroxide solution to a solution of the compound
A	white	orange	no change
B	green	turquoise	blue precipitate formed
C	white	brick red	white precipitate formed

  a Identify the metal present in each of the three compounds.
  b Explain why C could not contain a metal from group 1 of the periodic table.
  c Write an ionic equation for the reaction of a solution of B with sodium hydroxide solution.

Answers are on page 246.

The non-metals

There are only about 20 non-metal elements. There is a wide range of reactivity between different groups of non-metals. The most reactive non-metals are found in group 7, the least reactive are found in the next group, group 0.

F
fluorine
9

Cl
chlorine
17

Br
bromine
35

I
iodine
53

At
astatine
85

INCREASING REACTIVITY

The elements become more reactive as you go further up the group.

Group 7 – The halogens

- The term 'halogen' means 'salt-maker' and the halogens react with most metals to make salts.

- The halogen elements have **seven electrons in their outermost electron shell**, which means they only need to gain one electron to obtain a full outer electron shell and so are **very reactive**. The halogens react with metals, gaining an electron and forming a singly charged negative ion (see ionic bonding in Unit 8).

- The reactivity of the elements **decreases down the group** because as the atom gets bigger the extra electron will be further from the attractive force of the nucleus. This means it is harder for this electron to be gained.

Differences between the group 7 elements

- **Appearance**: fluorine is a pale yellow gas; chlorine is a yellow/green gas; bromine is a brown liquid; iodine is a black solid.

Similarities between the group 7 elements

- All have **7 electrons** in their outermost electron shell.

- All exist as **diatomic** molecules (molecules containing two atoms – e.g. F_2, Cl_2, Br_2, I_2).

- All react with water and react quickly with metals to form **salts**.

- All undergo **displacement** reactions.

⚡ **A* EXTRA**

A more reactive halogen will displace a less reactive halogen from a solution of one of its salts – for example, chlorine will displace bromine from sodium bromide solution. The ionic equation is: $Cl_2(aq) + 2Br^-(aq) \rightarrow 2Cl^-(aq) + Br_2(aq)$

Reaction	Observations	Equations
Water	The halogens dissolve in water and also react with it forming solutions that behave as bleaches. Chlorine solution is pale yellow. Bromine solution is brown. Iodine solution is brown.	chlorine + water → hydrochloric acid + hypochlorous acid (bleach) $Cl_2(g) + H_2O(l) \rightarrow HCl(aq) + HClO(aq)$
Metals	The halogens will form salts with all metals. For example, gold leaf will catch fire in chlorine without heating. With a metal such as iron, brown fumes of iron(III) chloride form.	iron + chlorine → iron (III) chloride $2Fe(s) + 3Cl_2(g) \rightarrow 2FeCl_3(s)$ Fluor*ine* forms salts called fluor*ides* Chlor*ine* forms salts called chlor*ides* Brom*ine* forms salts called brom*ides* Iod*ine* forms salts called iod*ides*

Reaction	Observations	Equations
Displacement chlorine gas → potassium iodide solution iodine being formed	A more reactive halogen will displace a less reactive halogen from a solution of a salt. Chlorine displaces bromine from sodium bromide solution. The colourless solution (sodium bromide) will turn brown as the chlorine is added due to the formation of bromine. Chlorine displaces iodine from sodium iodide solution. The colourless solution (sodium iodide) will turn brown as the chlorine is added due to the formation of iodine.	chlorine + sodium bromide → sodium chloride + bromine $Cl_2(g) + 2NaBr(aq) \rightarrow 2NaCl(aq) + Br_2(aq)$ chlorine + sodium iodide → sodium chloride + iodine $Cl_2(g) + 2NaI(aq) \rightarrow 2NaCl(aq) + I_2(aq)$

Uses of halogens

- The halogens and their compounds have a wide range of uses:
  - fluorides – in toothpaste help to prevent tooth decay
  - fluorine compounds – make plastics like Teflon (the non-stick surface on pans)
  - chloro-fluorocarbons – propellants in aerosols (now being phased out due to their effect on the ozone layer)
  - chlorine – a bleach
  - chlorine compounds – kill bacteria in drinking water and are used in antiseptics
  - hydrochloric acid – widely used in industry
  - bromine compounds – make pesticides
  - silver bromide – the light sensitive film coating in photography
  - iodine solution – an antiseptic.

Group 0 – The noble gases

- This is a group of **very unreactive** non-metals. They used to be called the inert gases as it was thought that they didn't react with anything! Scientists have more recently managed to produce fluorine compounds of some of the noble gases. As far as the school laboratory is concerned, however, they are completely unreactive.

- This can be explained in terms of their electronic structures. The atoms all have **complete outer electron shells**. They don't need to lose electrons (as metals do), or gain electrons (as most non-metals do).

Name	Symbol
Helium	He
Neon	Ne
Argon	Ar
Krypton	Kr
Xenon	Xe
Radon	Rn

Similarities of the noble gases

- Full outer electron shells.
- Very unreactive.
- Gases.
- Exist as single atoms – they are **monatomic** (He, Ne, Ar, Kr, Xe, Rn).

How are the noble gases used?

- Helium – in balloons.
- Neon – in 'red lights'.
- Argon – in light bulbs.
- Krypton – in some lasers.

CHECK YOURSELF QUESTIONS

Q1 This question is about the group 7 elements.
 a Which is the most reactive of the elements?
 b Which of the elements exists as a liquid at room temperature and pressure?
 c Which of the elements exists as a solid at room temperature and pressure?
 d Why are halogens such reactive elements?
 e Write word and symbol equations for the following reactions:
  i sodium and chlorine
  ii magnesium and bromine
  iii hydrogen and fluorine.

Q2 The table below records the results of some reactions.

	sodium chloride	sodium bromide	sodium iodide
chlorine	✗		✓
bromine		✗	✓
iodine			✗

a ✓ indicates a reaction occurred, a ✗ indicates no reaction occurred.)
 a What are the colours of the following solutions:
  i aqueous chlorine (chlorine water)
  ii aqueous bromine
  iii aqueous iodine
  iv aqueous sodium bromide?
 b What would be observed in the reaction between aqueous chlorine and sodium bromide solution?
 c Complete the table of results. Use a ✓ or ✗ as appropriate.
 d Write a word equation and symbol equation for the reaction between bromine and sodium iodide.

Q3 Explain why the noble gases are so unreactive.

Answers are on page 247.

UNIT 13: CHEMICAL CALCULATIONS

REVISION SESSION 1 ▰▰ Atomic masses and the mole ▰▰

⌑ Working out the mass of atoms

■ Atoms are far too light to be weighed. Instead scientists have developed a **relative atomic mass** scale. Initially the hydrogen atom, the lightest atom, was chosen as the unit that all other atoms were weighed in terms of.

■ On this scale, a carbon atom weighs the same as 12 hydrogen atoms, so carbon's relative atomic mass was given as 12.

■ Using this relative mass scale you can see, for example, that:

- 1 atom of magnesium has 24 × the mass of 1 atom of hydrogen
- 1 atom of magnesium has 2 × the mass of 1 atom of carbon
- 1 atom of copper has 2 × the mass of 1 atom of sulphur.

	Hydrogen	Carbon	Oxygen	Magnesium	Sulphur	Calcium	Copper
Symbol	H	C	O	Mg	S	Ca	Cu
Relative atomic mass	1	12	16	24	32	40	64

■ Recently, the reference point has been changed to carbon and the relative atomic mass is defined as:

the mass of an atom on a scale where the mass of a carbon atom is 12 units.

■ This change does not really affect the work that is done at GCSE. The relative atomic masses are not changed.

⌑ Moles of atoms

■ The **mole** is a very large number, approximately 6×10^{23}. That is 600 000 000 000 000 000 000 000.

■ 6×10^{23} atoms of hydrogen have a mass of 1 g.

■ 6×10^{23} atoms of carbon have a mass of 12 g.

■ 6×10^{23} atoms of magnesium have a mass of 24 g.

■ So the relative atomic mass (RAM) of an element expressed in grams contains one mole of atoms. This means that the number of atoms of an element can be worked out by weighing.

these all
contain
1 mole of
atoms:

| 12 g | 24 g | 32 g | 56 g | 64 g |
| Carbon | Magnesium | Sulphur | Iron | Copper |

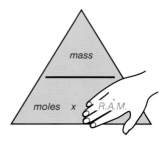

■ Calculations can be done using the simple equation:

$$\text{moles of atoms} = \frac{\text{mass}}{\text{RAM}}$$

WORKED EXAMPLES

1 How many moles of atoms are there in 72 g of magnesium? (RAM of magnesium = 24)

Write down the formula:	$\text{moles} = \frac{\text{mass}}{\text{RAM}}$
Rearrange if necessary:	(None needed)
Substitute the numbers:	$\text{moles} = \frac{72}{24}$
Write the answer and units:	moles = 3 moles

2 What is the mass of 0.1 moles of carbon atoms? (RAM of carbon = 12)

Write down the formula:	$\text{moles} = \frac{\text{mass}}{\text{RAM}}$
Rearrange if necessary:	mass = moles × RAM
Substitute the numbers:	mass = 0.1 × 12
Write the answer and units:	mass = 1.2 g

Put your finger over the quantity you are trying to work out. The triangle will then tell you whether to multiply or divide the other quantities.

QUESTION SPOTTER

Calculation questions are very common. You will be asked to convert moles into mass in grams and vice versa. You will need to remember the equation moles of atoms = mass/RAM.

⬚ How do we work out chemical formulae?

■ A chemical formula shows the number of atoms of each element that combine together. For example:

H_2O A water molecule contains 2 hydrogen atoms and 1 oxygen atom.

Alternatively:

H_2O 1 mole of water molecules is made from 2 moles of hydrogen atoms and 1 mole of oxygen atoms.

■ The formula of a compound can be calculated if the number of moles of the combining elements are known.

1 What is the simplest formula of a hydrocarbon that contains 60 g of carbon combined with 20 g of hydrogen? (RAMs: H = 1, C = 12)

	C	H
Write down the mass of each element:	60	20
Work out the number of moles of each element:	$\frac{60}{12} = 5$	$\frac{20}{1} = 20$
Find the simplest ratio (divide by the smaller number):	$\frac{5}{5} = 1$	$\frac{20}{5} = 4$
Write the formula showing the ratio of atoms:		CH_4

2 What is the simplest formula of calcium carbonate if it contains 40% calcium, 12% carbon and 48% oxygen? (C = 12, O = 16, Ca = 40)

	Ca	C	O
Write down the mass of each element:	40	12	48
Work out the number of moles of each element:	$\frac{40}{40} = 1$	$\frac{12}{12} = 1$	$\frac{48}{16} = 3$
Find the simplest ratio:	(Already in the simplest ratio)		
Write the formula showing the ratio of atoms:	$CaCO_3$		

Moles of molecules

- You can also refer to a mole of molecules. A mole of water molecules will be 6×10^{23} water molecules. The **relative molecular mass** of a molecule can be worked out by simply adding up the relative atomic masses of the atoms in the molecule. For example:

Water, H_2O (H = 1, O = 16)

The relative molecular mass (RMM) = 1 + 1 + 16 = 18.

Carbon dioxide, CO_2 (C = 12, O = 16)

The RMM = 12 + 16 + 16 = 44.

(Note: The '2' only applies to the oxygen atom.)

- A similar approach can be used for any formula, including ionic formulae. As ionic compounds do not exist as molecules the **relative formula mass** (RFM) can be worked out.

WORKED EXAMPLES

Sodium chloride, NaCl (Na = 23, Cl = 35.5)

The relative formula mass (RFM) = 23 + 35.5 = 58.5

Potassium nitrate, KNO_3 (K = 39, N = 14, O = 16)

RFM = 39 + 14 + 16 + 16 + 16 = 101

(Note: The '3' only applies to the oxygen atoms.)

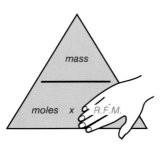

Put your finger over the quantity you are trying to work out.

Calcium hydroxide, $Ca(OH)_2$ $(Ca = 40, O = 16, H = 1)$

$RFM = 40 + (16 + 1)2 = 40 + 34 = 74$

(Note: The '2' applies to everything in the bracket.)

Magnesium nitrate, $Mg(NO_3)_2$ $(Mg = 24, N = 14, O = 16)$

$RFM = 24 + (14 + 16 + 16 + 16)2 = 24 + (62)2 = 24 + 124 = 148$

■ An equation can be written that can be used with atoms, molecules and ionic compounds.

$$\text{number of moles} = \frac{\text{mass}}{\text{RFM}}$$

CHECK YOURSELF QUESTIONS

Q1 Calculate the number of moles in the following:

a 56 g of silicon (Si = 28)
b 3.1 g of phosphorus (P = 31)
c 11 g of carbon dioxide, CO_2 (C = 12, O = 16)
d 50 g of calcium carbonate, $CaCO_3$ (Ca = 40, C = 12, O = 16)

Q2 Calculate the mass of the following:

a 2 moles of magnesium atoms (Mg = 24)
b 2 moles of hydrogen molecules, H_2 (H = 1)
c 0.1 moles of sulphuric acid, H_2SO_4 (H = 1, O = 16, S = 32)

Q3 Titanium chloride contains 25% titanium and 75% chlorine by mass.
Work out the simplest formula of titanium chloride. (Ti = 48, Cl = 35.5)

Answers are on page 248.

Equations and reacting masses

⊡ Linking reactants and products

- Chemical equations allow quantities of **reactants** and **products** to be linked together. They tell you how much of the products you can expect to make from a fixed amount of reactants.

- In a balanced equation the numbers in front of each symbol or formula indicate the number of moles represented. The number of moles can then be converted into a mass in grams.

- For example, when magnesium (RAM 24) reacts with oxygen (RAM 16):

Write down the balanced equation:	$2Mg(s)$	+	$O_2(g)$	→	$2MgO(s)$
Write down the number of moles:	2	+	1	→	2
Convert moles to masses:	48 g	+	32 g	→	80 g

So when 48 g of magnesium reacts with 32 g of oxygen, 80 g of magnesium oxide is produced. From this you should be able to work out the mass of magnesium oxide produced from any mass of magnesium. All you need to do is work out a **scaling factor**.

WORKED EXAMPLES

1 What mass of magnesium oxide can be made from 6 g of magnesium? (O = 16, Mg = 24.)

Equation:	$2Mg(s)$	+	$O_2(g)$	→	$2MgO(s)$
Moles:	2		1		2
Masses:	48 g		32 g		80 g

Instead of **48 g** of magnesium, the question asks about **6 g**. We can scale down all the quantities by dividing them by 8. Therefore $\frac{48}{8}$ g = 6 g of magnesium would make $\frac{80}{8}$ g =10 g of magnesium oxide.

Note: In this example, there was no need to work out the mass of oxygen needed. It was assumed that there would be as much as was necessary to convert all the magnesium to magnesium oxide.

2 What mass of ammonia can be made from 56 g of nitrogen? (H = 1, N = 14)

Equation:	$N_2(g)$	+	$3H_2(g)$	→	$2NH_3(g)$
Moles:	1		3		2
Masses:	28 g		6 g		34 g

In this case we need to multiply the mass of nitrogen by 2 to get the amount asked about in the question. Use the same scaling factor on the other quantities. So 28 g × 2 = 56 g of nitrogen makes 34 g × 2 = 68 g of ammonia.

Note: In this example there was no need to work out the mass of hydrogen required.

QUESTION SPOTTER

▸ You should be able to use equations and relative atomic masses to work out calculations like those shown here.
▸ Sometimes the question will refer to tonnes rather than grams. The method is just the same.

Each of these contains 1 mole
(6×10^{23}) of molecules.

Moles of gases

■ In reactions involving gases it is often more convenient to measure the **volume** of a gas rather than its mass.

■ One mole of any gas occupies the same volume under the same conditions of temperature and pressure. The conditions chosen are usually room temperature (20°C) and normal atmospheric pressure.

1 mole of any gas occupies 24 000 cm^3 (24 litres) at room temperature and pressure.

■ The following equation can be used to convert moles and volumes:

$$\text{moles} = \frac{\text{volume in } cm^3}{24000}$$

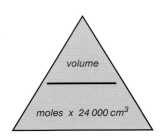

The triangle can be used as before to work out whether to multiply or divide the quantities.

WORKED EXAMPLE

What volume of hydrogen is formed at room temperature and pressure when 4 g of magnesium is added to excess dilute hydrochloric acid? (H = 1, Mg = 24)

Equation:	Mg(s)	+	2HCl(aq)	→	MgCl₂(aq)	+	H₂(g)
Moles:	1		2		1		1
Masses/volumes:	24 g						24 000 cm^3

Now work out the scaling factor needed and use the same scaling factor on the other quantities. Here we divide 24 g by 6 to get 4 g of magnesium. This produces $\frac{24\,000}{6}$ cm^3 = 4000 cm^3 of hydrogen gas.

Note: The hydrochloric acid is in excess. This means that there is enough to react with all the magnesium.

Moles of solutions

■ A solution is made when a **solute** dissolves in a **solvent**. The concentration of a solution depends on how much solute is dissolved in how much solvent. The concentrations of a solution are defined in terms of moles per litre (1000 cm^3) and are referred to as the **molarity** of the solution.

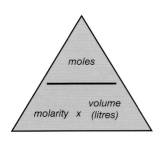

This triangle will help you to calculate concentrations of solutions.

1 mole of solute dissolved to make 1000 cm^3 of solution produces a 1 molar (1 M) solution

2 moles dissolved to make a 1000 cm^3 solution produces a 2 M solution

0.5 moles dissolved to make a 1000 cm^3 solution produces a 0.5 M solution

1 mole dissolved to make a 500 cm^3 solution produces a 2 M solution

1 mole dissolved to make a 250 cm^3 solution produces a 4 M solution.

■ If the same amount of solute is dissolved to make a smaller amount of solution the solution will be more concentrated.

WORKED EXAMPLE

How much sodium chloride can be made from reacting 100 cm³ of
1 M hydrochloric acid with excess sodium hydroxide solution?
(Na = 23, Cl = 35.5)

Equation:	HCl(aq) + NaOH(aq)	→ NaCl(aq) + H₂O(l)

Equation: $HCl(aq) + NaOH(aq) \rightarrow NaCl(aq) + H_2O(l)$

Moles: 1   1   1   1

Masses/volumes: (1000 cm³ 1 M)   58.5 g

Now work out the scaling factor and use the same scaling factor
on the other quantities. In this case we divide by 10 to get 100
cm³ of reactant, which means we get $\frac{58.5}{10}$ g = 5.85 g of product.

Note: 100 cm³ of 1 M solution is equal to 0.1 mole.

A* EXTRA

The concentration of a solution
is often expressed in terms of
moles/dm³. A 1 molar (1 M)
solution contains 1 mole of
solute dissolved to make 1 dm³
(1000 cm³) of solution.

CHECK YOURSELF QUESTIONS

Q1 What mass of sodium hydroxide can be
made by reacting 2.3 g of sodium with
water? (H = 1, O = 16, Na = 23)

$2Na(s) + 2H_2O(l) \rightarrow 2NaOH(aq) + H_2(g)$

Q2 Iron(III) oxide is reduced to iron by
carbon monoxide.
(C = 12, O = 16, Fe = 56)

$Fe_2O_3(s) + 3CO(g) \rightarrow 2Fe(s) + 3CO_2(g)$

a Calculate the mass of iron that could
be obtained by the reduction of 800
tonnes of iron(III) oxide.

b What volume of carbon dioxide would
be obtained by the reduction of 320 g
of iron(III) oxide?

Q3 What mass of barium sulphate can be
produced from 50 cm³ of
0.2 M barium chloride solution and excess
sodium sulphate solution?
(O = 16, S = 32, Ba = 137)

$BaCl_2(aq) + Na_2SO_4(aq) \rightarrow$
$\qquad\qquad\qquad BaSO_4(s) + 2NaCl(aq)$

Answers are on page 248.

UNIT 14: ELECTRICITY

Electric circuits

energy transferred from charge to lamp and then to surroundings

same current flows into and out of lamp

battery transfers energy to charge and pushes charge around circuit

In this simple circuit the arrows show the direction of the current.

What does electricity do?

- You cannot see electricity but you can see the effects it has. It is very good at **transferring energy**, and can:
  - make things **hot** – as in the heating element of an electric fire
  - make things **magnetic** – as in an electromagnet
  - produce **light** – as in a light bulb
  - **break down** certain compounds and solutions – as in electrolysis.

A simple model of an electrical circuit

- The battery in an electrical circuit can be thought of as pushing electrical charge round the circuit to make a current. It also transfers energy to the electrical charge. The **voltage** of the battery is a measure of how much 'push' it can provide and how much energy it can transfer to the charge.

- Scientists now know that electric current is really a **flow of electrons** around the circuit from negative to positive. Unfortunately, early scientists guessed the direction of flow incorrectly. Consequently all diagrams were drawn showing the current flowing from positive to negative. This way of showing the current has not been changed and so the **conventional current** that everyone uses gives the direction that positive charges would flow.

free electron   positive ion

positive ion and nearby electron

The electrons move down the wire   ELECTRON FLOW

CONVENTIONAL CURRENT

It is as if the positive ions move up the wire

Conventional current is drawn in the opposite direction to electron flow.

- There are two different ways of connecting two lamps to the same battery. Two very different kinds of circuit can be made. These circuits are called **series** and **parallel** circuits.

	Series	Parallel
Circuit diagram		
Appearance of the lamps	Both lamps have the same brightness, both lamps are dim.	Both lamps have the same brightness, both lamps are bright.
Battery	The battery is having a hard time pushing the same charge first through one bulb, then another. This means less charge flows each second, so there is a low current and energy is slowly transferred from the battery.	The battery pushes the charge along two alternative paths. This means more charge can flow around the circuit each second, so energy is quickly transferred from the battery.
Switches	The lamps cannot be switched on and off independently.	The lamps can be switched on and off independently by putting switches in the parallel branches.
Advantages/ disadvantages	A very simple circuit to make. The battery will last longer. If one lamp 'blows' then the circuit is broken so the other one goes out too.	The battery won't last as long. If one lamp 'blows' the other one will keep working.
Examples	Christmas tree lights are often connected in series.	Electric lights in the home are connected in parallel.

Charge, current and potential difference

- Electric charge is measured in **coulombs** (C). Electric current is measured in **amperes** (A).

- The electric current is the amount of charge flowing every second – the number of coulombs per second:

$$I = \frac{Q}{t}$$

I = current in amperes (A)
Q = charge in coulombs (C)
t = time in seconds (s)

- The charge flowing round a circuit has some **potential energy**. As charge flows around a circuit it transfers energy to the various components in the circuit. For example, when the charge flows through a lamp it transfers some of its energy to the lamp.

- The amount of energy that a unit of charge (a coulomb) transfers between one point and another (the number of joules per coulomb) is called the **potential difference** (p.d.). Potential difference is measured in **volts** and so it is often referred to as **voltage**:

$$V = \frac{E}{Q}$$

V = potential difference in volts
E = energy transferred in joules
Q = charge in coulombs

⚡ A * EXTRA

▸ In a conductor the charge carriers are electrons and flow round the circuit from negative to positive.
▸ In an electrolyte (e.g. sulphuric acid in a car battery) the charge carriers are ions. The negative ions (anions) move to the anode and the positive ions (cations) move to the cathode.

QUESTION SPOTTER

You will be expected to remember the equation that links current, charge and time and carry out calculations which use it. Don't forget that charge is measured in coulombs and current in amps.

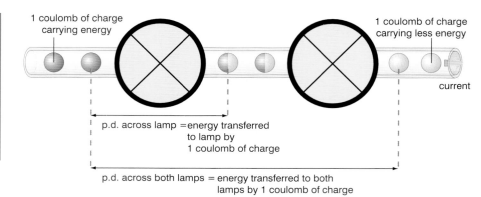

1 coulomb of charge carrying energy

1 coulomb of charge carrying less energy

current

p.d. across lamp = energy transferred to lamp by 1 coulomb of charge

p.d. across both lamps = energy transferred to both lamps by 1 coulomb of charge

Potential difference (p.d.) is the difference in energy of a coulomb of charge between two parts of a circuit.

Measuring electricity

- Potential difference is measured using a **voltmeter.** If you want to measure the p.d. across a component then the voltmeter must be connected **in parallel** to that component. Testing with a voltmeter does not interfere with the circuit at all.

- A voltmeter can be used to show how the potential difference varies in different parts of a circuit. In a series circuit you get different values of the voltage depending on where you attach the voltmeter. You can assume that energy is only transferred when the current passes through

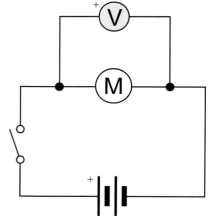

The voltmeter can be added after the circuit has been made.

p.d. = 6 V
6 joules transferred from each coulomb

power = 2 coulombs per second, of 6 joules each
12 joules per second

p.d. = 3 V
= 3 J/C

power = 2 C/s × 3 J/C
= 6 J/s

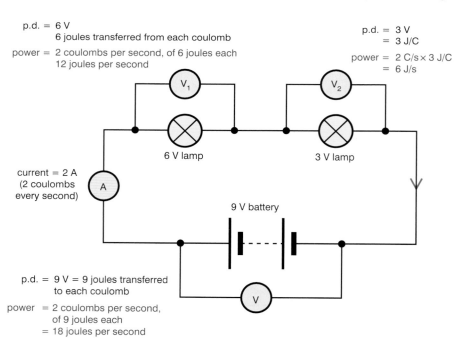

V_1

V_2

6 V lamp

3 V lamp

current = 2 A
(2 coulombs every second)

A

9 V battery

V

p.d. = 9 V = 9 joules transferred to each coulomb

power = 2 coulombs per second, of 9 joules each
= 18 joules per second

The potential difference across the battery equals the sum of the potential differences across each lamp. That is $V = V_1 + V_2$.

electrical components such as lamps and motors – the energy transfer as the current flows through copper connecting wire is very small. It is only possible therefore to measure a p.d. or voltage across a component.

■ The current flowing in a circuit can be measured using an **ammeter**. If you want to measure the current flowing through a particular component, such as a lamp or motor, the ammeter must be connected **in series** with the component. In a series circuit the current is the same no matter where the ammeter is put. This is not the case with a parallel circuit.

In this series circuit the current will be the same throughout the circuit so the readings $A_1 = A_2 = A_3$.

The current flow splits between the two branches of the parallel circuit so the readings $A_1 = A_2 + A_3$.

The circuit has to be broken to include the ammeter.

Direct and alternating currents

■ A battery produces a steady current. The electrons are constantly flowing from the negative terminal of the battery round the circuit and back to the positive terminal. This produces a **direct current** (d.c.).

■ The mains electricity used in the home is quite different. The electrons in the circuit move backwards and forwards. This kind of current is called **alternating current** (a.c.). Mains electricity moves forwards and backwards 50 times each second, that is, with a frequency of 50 hertz (Hz).

■ The advantage of using an a.c. source of electricity rather than a d.c. source is that it can be transmitted from power stations to the home at very high voltages, which reduces the amount of energy that is lost in the overhead cables (see Unit 15).

Q1 Look at the following circuit diagrams. They show a number of ammeters and in some cases the readings on these ammeters. All the lamps are identical.

circuit X

circuit Y

a For circuit X, what readings would you expect on ammeters A_1 and A_2?

b For circuit Y, what readings would you expect on ammeters A_3 and A_4?

Q2 Look at the circuit diagram. It shows how three voltmeters have been added to the circuit. What reading would you expect on V_1?

Q3 a A charge of 10 coulombs flows through a motor in 30 seconds. What is the current flowing through the motor?

b A heater uses a current of 10 A. How much charge flows through the lamp in:

i 1 second, **ii** 1 hour?

Answers are on page 249.

What affects resistance?

⊡ Ohm's Law

■ The relationship between voltage, current and resistance in electrical circuits is given by **Ohm's law**:

	V is the voltage in volts (V)
$V = I\,R$	I is the current in amps (A)
	R is the resistance in ohms (Ω)

■ It is important to be able to rearrange this equation when performing calculations. Use the triangle on the right to help you.

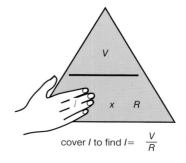

cover I to find $I = \dfrac{V}{R}$

WORKED EXAMPLES

1 Calculate the resistance of a heater element if the current is 10 A when it is connected to a 230 V supply.

Write down the formula in terms of R:	$R = \dfrac{V}{I}$
Substitute the values for V and I:	$R = \dfrac{230}{10}$
Work out the answer and write down the unit:	$R = 23\ \Omega$

2 A 6 V supply is applied to 1000 Ω resistor. What current will flow?

Write down the formula in terms of I:	$I = \dfrac{V}{R}$
Substitute the values for V and R:	$I = \dfrac{6}{1000}$
Work out the answer and write down the unit:	$I = 0.006\ \text{A}$

> ### ☼ QUESTION SPOTTER
>
> Calculations involving Ohm's Law are very common. You will need to remember the equation and be able to change the subject. Marks will usually be given for the correct units.

⊡ Effect of material on resistance

■ Substances that allow an electric current to flow through them are called **conductors**. Those which do not are called **insulators**.

■ Metals are conductors. In a metal structure the metal atoms exist as ions surrounded by an electron cloud. If a potential difference is applied to the metal the electrons in this cloud are able to move and a current flows.

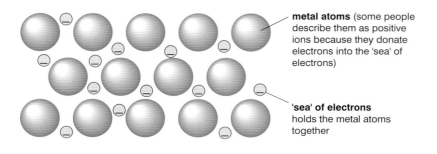

metal atoms (some people describe them as positive ions because they donate electrons into the 'sea' of electrons)

'sea' of electrons holds the metal atoms together

In a metal structure metal ions are surrounded by a cloud or 'sea' of electrons.

■ When the electrons are moving through the metal structure they bump into the metal ions and this causes **resistance** to the electron flow or current. In different conductors the ease of flow of the electrons is different and so the conductors have different resistances. For instance, copper is a better conductor than iron.

⌷Effects of length and cross-sectional area

■ For a particular conductor the resistance is **proportional to length.** The longer the conductor, the further the electrons have to travel, the more likely they are to collide with the metal ions and so the greater the resistance.

Two wires in series are like one long wire, because the electrons have to travel twice as far.

■ Resistance is **inversely proportional to cross–sectional area.** The greater the cross-sectional area of the conductor, the more electrons there are available to carry the charge along the conductor's length and so the lower the resistance.

Two wires in parallel are like one thick wire, so the electrons have more routes to travel along the same distance.

■ The amount of current flowing through a circuit can be controlled by changing the resistance of the circuit using a **variable resistor** or **rheostat.** Adjusting the rheostat changes the length of the wire the current has to flow through.

wire-wrapped variable resistor

slider

terminals

long wire with high resistance

variable resistor made from carbon ring

metal slider

carbon ring

terminals

symbol for a variable resistor (rheostat)

control (turn to move slider)

Variable resistors are commonly used in electrical equipment, for example in the speed controls of model racing cars or in volume controls on radios and hi-fi systems.

Effect of temperature on resistance

- If the resistance of a conductor remains constant a graph of voltage against current will give a **straight line.** The gradient of the line will be the resistance of the conductor.

- The resistance of most conductors becomes higher if the temperature of the conductor increases. As the temperature rises the metal ions vibrate more and provide greater resistance to the flow of the electrons. For example, the resistance of a filament lamp becomes greater as the voltage is increased and the lamp gets hotter.

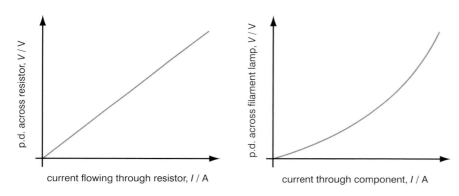

p.d. across resistor, V / V

current flowing through resistor, I / A

p.d. across filament lamp, V / V

current through component, I / A

In an 'ohmic' resistor, such as carbon, Ohm's law applies and the voltage is directly proportional to the current – a straight line is obtained. In a filament lamp, Ohm's law is not obeyed because the heating of the lamp changes its resistance.

- In some substances, increasing the temperature actually **lowers** the resistance. This is the case with **semiconductors** such as silicon. Silicon has few free electrons and so behaves more like an insulator than a conductor. But if silicon is heated, more electrons are removed from the outer electron shells of the atoms producing an increased electron cloud. The released electrons can move throughout the structure, creating an electric current. This effect is large enough to outweigh the increase in resistance that might be expected from the increased movement of the silicon ions in the structure as the temperature increases.

> **QUESTION SPOTTER**
>
> You will often be shown graphs of potential difference against current and asked to explain how the current varies with the p.d.

■ Semiconducting silicon is used to make **thermistors**, which are used as temperature sensors, and **light-dependent resistors** (LDRs), which are used as light sensors.

A light-dependent resistor, (top left) conducts better when light shines on it. A thermistor (top right) conducts better when it is hot. A diode (bottom left) only conducts in one direction. An ordinary (ohmic) resistor is shown bottom right.

■ In LDRs it is light energy that removes electrons from the silicon atoms, increasing the electron cloud.

■ Silicon **diodes** also use resistance as a means of controlling current flow in a circuit. In one direction the resistance is very high, effectively preventing current flow, in the other direction the resistance is relatively low and current can flow. Diodes are used to **protect** sensitive electronic equipment that would be damaged if a current flowed in the wrong direction.

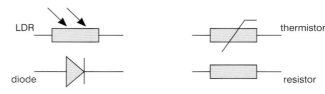

LDR

thermistor

diode

resistor

CHECK YOURSELF QUESTIONS

Q1 a Draw a circuit diagram to show how you could measure the resistance of a piece of nichrome wire. Explain how you would calculate the resistance of the wire.
b How would the resistance of the wire change if: **i** its length was doubled, **ii** its cross-sectional area was doubled?

Q2 Use Ohm's law to calculate the following:
a The voltage required to produce a current of 2 A in a 12 Ω resistor.
b The voltage required to produce a current of 0.1 A in a 200 Ω resistor.
c The current produced when a voltage of 12 V is applied to a 100 Ω resistor.
d The current produced when a voltage of 230 V is applied to a 10 Ω resistor.
e The resistance of a wire which under a potential difference of 6 V allows a current of 0.1 A to flow.
f The resistance of a heater which under a potential difference of 230 V allows a current of 10 A to flow.

Q3 A graph of current against voltage is plotted for a piece of wire. The graph is shown below.

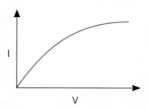

a Describe how the resistance of the wire changes as the voltage is increased.
b Suggest an explanation for this change.

Answers are on page 249.

Power in electrical circuits

⊡ Calculating power ratings

- All electrical equipment has a **power rating**, which indicates how many joules of energy are supplied each second. The unit of power used is the **watt** (W). Light bulbs often have power ratings of 60 W or 100 W. Electric kettles have ratings of about 2 kilowatts (2 kW = 2000 W). A 2 kW kettle supplies 2000 J of energy each second.

- The power of a piece of electrical equipment depends on the voltage and the current:

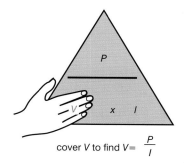

cover V to find V= $\frac{P}{I}$

	P = power in watts (W)
$P = V I$	V = voltage in volts (V)
	I = current in amps (A)

WORKED EXAMPLES

1 What is the power of an electric toaster if a current of 7 A is obtained from a 230V supply?

Write down the formula in terms of P:	$P = V I$
Substitute the values:	$P = 230 \times 7$
Work out the answer and write down the unit:	$P = 1610\,W$

2 An electric oven has a power rating of 2 kW. What current will flow when the oven is used with a 230 V supply?

Write down the formula in terms of I:	$I = \dfrac{P}{V}$
Substitute the values:	$I = \dfrac{2000}{230}$
Work out the answer and write down the unit:	$I = 8.7\,A$

> **QUESTION SPOTTER**
>
> Questions on the equation $P = V I$ are very common. You will need to be able to change the subject of the equation and give the units for P, V and I.

⊡ How do suppliers charge for electricity?

- Electricity meters in the home and in industry measure the amount of energy used in **kilowatt-hours** (kWh). 1 kilowatt-hour (1 kWh) is the amount of energy transferred by a 1 kW device in 1 hour.

  1 kWh = 3600000 J.

Calculate the energy transferred by a 3 kW electrical immersion heater which is used for 30 minutes.

Write down the formula:	Energy = power (kW) × time (h)
Substitute the values:	Energy = 3 × 0.5
Work out the answer and write down the unit:	Energy = 1.5 kWh

An off-peak white meter has two displays. The lower display shows the number of kWh units used at the standard rate. The upper display shows the units used at off-peak rate.

Balancing supply and demand

- Because they can't close the power stations at night when demand is lower, the electricity companies sell electricity at two different rates.

- **Standard rate** applies to electricity used during the day.

- **Off-peak rate** electricity is used at night, and costs less than half standard rate electricity. Users need a special meter for this type of electricity. Off-peak electricity is usually available from midnight until 7 a.m. – hence it is sometimes called '**Economy 7**' electricity.

WORKED EXAMPLE

A 3 kW night storage heater is switched on full power for 7 hours one night. The rate on the Economy 7 tariff is 4p per unit. Calculate the cost of using the heater.

Write down the formula:	Units = power (kW) × time (h)
Substitute the values:	Units = 3 × 7 = 21
Include cost of each unit:	Cost = units × 4p = 21 × 4 = 84p

Using electricity safely

- Electrical appliances can be damaged if the current flowing through them is too high. The electric current usually has to pass through the **fuse** in the plug before it reaches the appliance. If there is a sudden surge in the current the wire in the fuse will heat up and melt – it 'blows'. This breaks the circuit and stops any further current flowing.

- The fuse must have a value above the normal current that the appliance needs but should be as small as possible. The most common fuses are rated at 3 A, 5 A and 13 A. Any electrical appliance with a heating element in it should be fitted with a 13 A fuse.

The fuse fits between the live brown wire and the pin. The brown live wire and the blue neutral wire carry the current. The green and yellow striped earth wire is needed to make metal appliances safer.

1 What fuse should be fitted in the plug of a 2.2 kW electric kettle used with a supply voltage of 230 V?

Calculate the normal current: $I = \frac{P}{V} = \frac{2000}{230} = 9.6$ A.

Choose the fuse with the smallest rating bigger than the normal current: the fuse must be 13 A.

2 What fuse should be fitted to the plug of a reading lamp which has a 60 W lamp and a supply of 230 V?

Calculate the normal current: $I = \frac{P}{V} = \frac{60}{230} = 0.26$ A.

Choose the fuse with the smallest rating bigger than the normal current: the fuse must be 3 A.

Other safety measures

- **Circuit breakers** spring open ('trip') a switch if there is an increase in current in the circuit. They can be reset easily once the fault in the circuit has been corrected.

- Metal-cased appliances must have an **earth wire** as well as a fuse. If the live wire worked loose and came into contact with the metal casing, the casing would become live and the user could be electrocuted. The earth wire provides a very low resistance route to the 0 V earth – usually water pipes buried deep underground. This low resistance means that a large current passes from the live wire to earth, causing the fuse to melt and break the circuit.

- Appliances that are made with plastic casing do not need an earth wire. The plastic is an insulator and so can never become live. Appliances like this are said to be **double insulated.**

The earth wire and fuse work together to make sure that the metal outer casing of this appliance can never become live and electrocute someone.

CHECK YOURSELF QUESTIONS

Q1 A hairdryer works on mains electricity of 230V and takes a current of 4 A. Calculate the power of the hairdryer.

Q2 **a** An iron has a power rating of 1000 W. Calculate the cost of using the iron for 3 hours if electricity costs 8p per kilowatt-hour.
   b The power of a television set is 200 W. Calculate how much it costs to watch the television for 5 hours. A unit (kWh) of electricity costs 8p.

Q3 A 3 kW immersion heater transfers energy to water for 10 minutes. How much energy does the heater transfer in 10 minutes?

Answers are on page 250.

■ Static electricity ■

⌂ What is static electricity?

■ Electric charge doesn't flow in an insulator. However, when two insulators are rubbed together electrons from the atoms on the surface of one insulator are transferred to the surface of the other. This leaves an excess of electrons – a negative charge – on one insulator and a shortage of electrons – a positive charge – on the other insulator. The charge is fixed in place – it is **static electricity.**

Charging up a plastic ruler.

wool

polythene

fewer electrons therefore positive

more electrons therefore negative

electrons repelled away from surface

ceiling

negative balloon

The balloon induces a charge on the ceiling's surface.

■ Static charges interact in a simple way: **like charges repel – unlike charges attract**. For example, when a balloon is rubbed against clothing it will 'stick' to a wall or ceiling. This is because of **electrostatic induction**. The balloon 'sticks' because of the attraction between the negative charges on the balloon and the induced positive charges on the ceiling.

⌂ What problems can static electricity cause?

■ Air currents in thunderclouds, rub past water molecules and charge them up. The bottom of the cloud is left with a negative charge, which induces a positive charge in buildings and trees on the ground and creates a strong electric field in the air between the cloud and the ground. A short burst of electric current can occur in the air – **lightning**.

■ The sudden discharge of electricity caused by friction between two insulators can cause **shocks in everyday situations** – for example:
- combing your hair
- pulling clothes over your head
- walking on synthetic carpets
- getting out of a car.

■ Sparks can also cause **explosions** and so great care has to be taken when emptying fuel tankers at service stations and airports or in grain silos or flour factories.

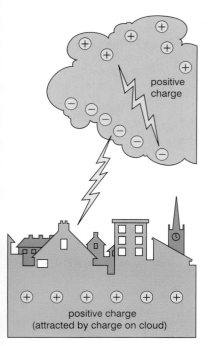

positive charge

positive charge (attracted by charge on cloud)

Thunderclouds have a high concentration of negative charge at the bottom. They have very high voltages. They ionise the air so that it conducts electricity. Lightning is caused by a burst of electric current through the air.

QUESTION SPOTTER

A common question will ask you to explain how a flash of lightning occurs. It is easier to explain if you include a diagram showing the build up of charges.

⌷ Uses of static electricity

- ■ The properties of static electricity are put to good effect in **ink-jet printers** and **photocopiers**.

1 high voltage wire charges drum

2 drum is charged evenly

3 light removes charge from parts that are not to be printed

In a photocopier, charged particles attract the toner. Light is used to remove charge from parts that are not to be printed.

4 charged parts attract toner particles

5 toner rolled onto paper

6 toner melted on to paper by heating

In inkjet printers, uncharged ink droplets do not reach the paper. This is how the spaces between words are made.

? CHECK YOURSELF QUESTIONS

Q1 A plastic rod is rubbed with a cloth.
   a How does the plastic become positively charged?
   b The charged plastic rod attracts small pieces of paper. Explain why this attraction occurs.

Q2 a A car stops and one of the passengers gets out. When she touches a metal post she feels an electric shock. Explain why she feels this shock.
   b Write down two other situations where people might get this type of shock.

Q3 Give two examples of where static electricity can be dangerous.

Answers are on page 250.

Electromagnetism

Magnetic fields are created around any wire that carries a current.

⬚ What is electromagnetism?

■ An electric current flowing through a wire creates a magnetic field in the region of the wire. Magnetism created in this way is known as **electromagnetism.** The magnetic field is stronger if the wire is made into a coil. It is even stronger if the coil is wrapped around a piece of magnetic material such as iron.

■ The strength of the electromagnet can be increased by:
  • increasing the number of coils in the wire
  • increasing the current flowing through the wire
  • placing a soft iron core inside the coils.

⬚ How do relay switches work?

■ **Electromagnets** produce magnetic fields that can be turned on and off at will. A **relay** is an electromagnetic switch. It has the advantage of using a small current from a low-voltage circuit to switch on a higher current in a higher-voltage circuit.

■ A relay switch operates the **starter motor** of a car. Thin low-current wires are used in the circuit that contains the ignition switch operated by the driver. Much thicker wires are used in the circuit containing the battery and the high-current starter motor. Turning the ignition key causes a current to flow through the relay coil. This creates a magnetic field which attracts the armature to the core. The armature pivots and connects the starter motor to the car battery.

A relay circuit used to switch on a starter motor.

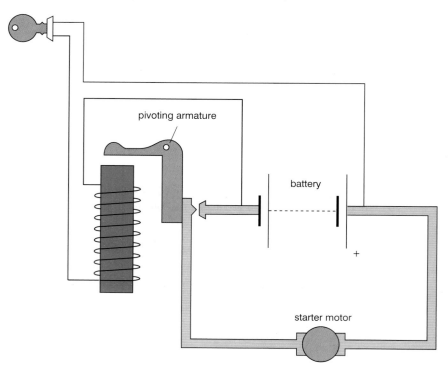

pivoting armature

battery

+

starter motor

⎑ D.C. Motors

■ An **electric motor** transfers electrical energy to kinetic energy. It is made from a coil of wire positioned between the poles of two permanent magnets. When a current flows through the coil of wire, it creates a magnetic field, which interacts with the magnetic field produced by the two permanent magnets. The two fields exert a force that pushes the wire at right angles to the permanent magnetic field.

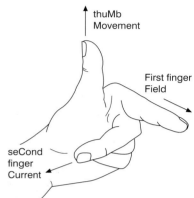

Fleming's left-hand rule predicts the direction of the force on a current carrying wire.

■ A motor coil as set up in the diagram will be forced round as indicated by the arrows (1 and 2 below). The split-ring commutator ensures that the motor continues to spin. Without the commutator, the coil would rotate 90° and then stop. This would not make a very useful motor! The commutator reverses the direction of the current at just the right point (3) so that the forces on the coil flip around and continue the rotating motion (4).

⚡ A* EXTRA

Fleming's left-hand rule relates the movement of a coil to the direction of the permanent magnetic field and the direction of the current flowing in the coil.

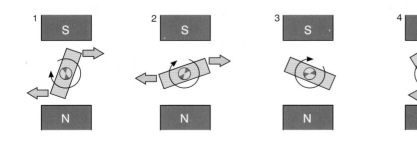

Q1 In a recycling plant an electromagnet separates scrap metal from household rubbish.

a Can this method be used to separate aluminium drinks cans from other household rubbish? Explain your answer.

b How can the operator drop the scrap metal into the skip?

Q2 The diagram shows a simple electromagnet made by a student.

Suggest two ways in which the electromagnet can be made to pick up more nails.

Q3 The diagram shows an electric bell.

Explain how the bell works when the switch is closed.

Answers are on page 251.

REVISION SESSION 2

Electromagnetic induction

⟦⟧ Generating electricity

■ Michael Faraday was the first person to generate electricity from a magnetic field using **electromagnetic induction**. The large generators in power stations generate the electricity we need using this process.

■ Current is created in a wire when:
- the wire is moved through a magnetic field ('cutting' the field lines)
- the magnetic field is moved past the wire (again 'cutting' the field lines)
- the magnetic field around the wire changes strength.

■ Current created in this way is said to be **induced**.

■ The faster these changes, the larger the current.

⟦⟧ Dynamos and generators

■ A **dynamo** is a simple current generator. A dynamo looks very like an electric motor. Turning the permanent magnet near to the coil induces a current in the wires. The split-ring commutator ensures that the current generated flows in only one direction.

In a bicycle dynamo the magnet rotates and the coil is fixed.

■ Power station generators don't have a commutator, so they produce **alternating current**. Power stations use electromagnets rather than permanent magnets.

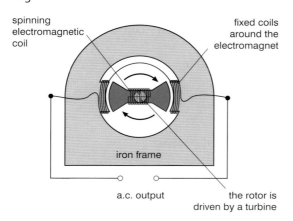

The generator rotates at 50 times per second, producing a.c. at 50 hertz.

⬚ Transformers

- A **transformer** consists of two coils of insulated wire wound on a piece of iron. If an alternating voltage is applied to the first (primary) coil the alternating current produces a changing magnetic field in the core. This changing magnetic field induces an alternating current in the second (the secondary) coil.

- If there are more turns on the secondary coil than on the primary coil, then the voltage in the secondary coil will be greater than the voltage in the primary coil. The exact relationship between turns and voltage is:

$$\frac{\text{primary coil voltage (Vp)}}{\text{secondary coil voltage (Vs)}} = \frac{\text{number of primary turns (Np)}}{\text{number of secondary turns (Ns)}}$$

- When the secondary coil has more turns than the primary coil, the voltage increases in the same proportion. This is a **step–up transformer**.

- A transformer with fewer turns on the secondary coil than on the primary coil is a **step–down transformer**, which produces a smaller voltage in the secondary coil.

step-down transformer
ratio of number of turns is 2:1
voltage ratio is 2:1

step-up transformer
ratio of number of turns is 1:4
voltage ratio is 1:4

Transformers are widely used to change voltages. They are frequently used in the home to step down the mains voltage of 230V to 6V or 12V.

WORKED EXAMPLE

Calculate the output voltage from a transformer when the input voltage is 230 V and the number of turns on the primary coil is 2000 and the number of turns on the secondary coil is 100.

Write down the formula:	$\dfrac{V_P}{V_S} = \dfrac{N_P}{N_S}$
Substitute the values known:	$\dfrac{230}{V_S} = \dfrac{2000}{100} = 20$
Rewrite this so that Vs is the subject:	$V_S = \dfrac{230}{20}$
Work out the answer and write down the unit:	$V_S = 11.5\,V$

A* EXTRA

In dynamos and transformers changing the magnetic field around a coil of wire can create or induce an electric current in the coil. The direction of this induced current can be predicted using Fleming's right-hand rule.

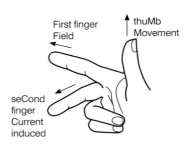

First finger Field

thuMb Movement

seCond finger Current induced

Fleming's right-hand rule predicts the direction of the current induced in a moving wire.

QUESTION SPOTTER

Calculations involving transformers are very common. Most often you will have to calculate output voltages from input voltages. Remember the equation because it will not be given in the examination.

⚟ Transmitting electricity

- Most power stations **burn fuel** to heat water into high-pressure steam, which is then used to drive a **turbine**. The turbine turns an a.c. generator, which produces the electricity.

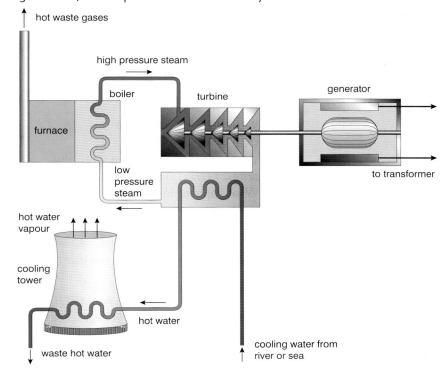

The most common fuels used in power stations are still coal, oil and gas.

- The **National Grid** links all the power stations to all parts of the country. To minimise the power loss in transmitting electricity around the grid the current has to be kept as low as possible. The higher the current the more the transmission wires will be heated by the current and the more energy is wasted as heat.

- This is where transformers come in useful. This is also the reason that mains electricity is generated as alternating current. When a transformer steps up a voltage it also steps down the current and vice versa. Power stations generate electricity with a voltage of 25 000 V. Before this is transmitted on the grid it is converted by a step-up transformer to 400 000 V. This is then reduced by a series of step-down transformers to 230 V before it is supplied to homes.

Mains electricity is a.c. so that it can be easily stepped up and down. High-voltage/low-current transmission lines waste less energy than low-voltage/high-current lines.

Q1 Two students are using the equipment shown in the diagram.

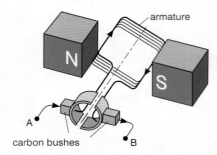

The students cannot decide whether it is an electric motor or a generator. Explain how you would know which it is.

Q2 The diagram shows a transformer.

a What material is used for the transformer core?

b What happens in the core when the primary coil is switched on?

c What happens in the secondary coil when the primary coil is switched on?

d If the primary coil has 12 turns and the secondary coil has 7 turns, what will the primary voltage be if the secondary voltage is 14 V?

Q3 Explain why electricity is transmitted on the National Grid at very high voltages.

Answers are on page 251.

UNIT 16: FORCES AND MOTION

▰▰ The effects of forces ▰▰

▢ How do forces act on objects?

■ It is very unusual for a single force to be acting on an object. Usually there will be two or more. The size and direction of these forces determine whether the object will move and the direction it will move in.

■ Forces are measured in **newtons**. They take many forms and have many effects including pushing, pulling, bending, stretching, squeezing and tearing. Forces can:
  - **change the speed** of an object
  - **change the direction** of movement of an object
  - **change the shape** of an object.

▢ What is friction?

■ **Friction** is a very common force. It is the force that tries to stop movement between touching surfaces by opposing the force that causes the movement.

■ In many situations friction can be a disadvantage, e.g. friction in the bearings of a bicycle wheel. In other situations friction can be an advantage, e.g. between brake pads and a bicycle wheel.

▢ The effects of weight

■ **Weight** is another common force. It is also measured in **newtons**. The weight of an object depends on its **mass** and **gravity**. Any mass near the Earth has weight due to the Earth's gravitational pull.

■ On the Moon, your mass will be the same as on Earth, but your weight will be less. This is because the gravity on the Moon is about one-sixth of that on the Earth, and so the force of attraction of an object to the Moon is about one-sixth of that on the Earth.

Earth

mass = 90 kg

weight = 900 N

Moon

mass = 90 kg

weight = 150 N

Who cares how much you weigh? It's your mass that people really care about.

Balanced forces

- Usually there are at least two forces acting on an object. If these two forces are **balanced** then the object will either be stationary or moving at a constant speed.

- A spacecraft in deep space will have no forces acting on it – no air resistance (no air!), no force of gravity – and because there is no need to produce a forward force from its rockets it will travel at a constant speed.

Unbalanced forces

- For an object's speed or direction of movement to change the forces acting on it must be **unbalanced**.

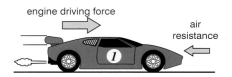

Acceleration. The force provided by the engine is greater than the force provided by air resistance and so the car increases its speed.

Deceleration. The engine is now providing no forward force. The 'drag' force provided by the parachute will slow the car down.

- As a gymnast first steps on to a trampoline, his weight is much greater than the opposing supporting force of the trampoline, so he moves downwards, stretching the trampoline. As the trampoline stretches, its supporting force increases until the supporting force is equal to the gymnast's weight. When the two forces are balanced the trampoline stops stretching. If an elephant stood on the trampoline it would break because it could never produce a supporting force equal to the elephant's weight.

A trampoline stretches until it supports the weight on it.

gymnast moves down
pulled by his own weight

gymnast stops moving
when trampoline's supporting
force equals his weight

- As a skydiver jumps from a plane, the force of gravity will be much greater than the opposing force caused by air resistance. The skydiver's speed will increase rapidly – and the force caused by the air resistance increases as the skydiver's speed increases. Eventually it will exactly match the force of gravity, the forces will be balanced and the speed of the skydiver will remain constant. This speed is known as the **terminal speed**.

- If the skydiver spreads out so that more of his or her surface is in contact with the air, the resistive force will be greater and the terminal speed will be lower than if he or she adopted a more compact shape. A parachute has a very large surface, and produces a very large resistive force, so the terminal speed of a parachutist is quite low. This means that he or she can land relatively safely.

CHECK YOURSELF QUESTIONS

Q1 Look at the diagrams A, B and C. In each case describe the effect the forces would have on the object.

A · Stationary wooden block

20N ← → 20N

B

2000N ← → 6000N

C

ice skater (moving)

400N ← → 400N

Q2 Skiers can travel at very high speeds. A friction force acts on the skis.

a Use the diagram to show the direction of the friction force acting on the skier.
b Explain why it is important for the friction forces to be as small as possible.
c Describe one way the skier could reduce the friction force.

Q3 The diagram shows the stages in the descent of a skydiver.

1 · 600N

2 · 600N / 600N

3 · 1000N / 600N

4 · 600N / 600N

5 · 600N / 600N

a Describe and explain the motion of the skydiver in each case.
b In stage 5 explain why the parachutist doesn't sink into the ground.

Answers are on page 252.

Velocity and acceleration

Both cars have the same speed. Car A has a velocity of +10m/s, car B has a velocity of −10m/s.

⊡ Are speed and velocity the same?

■ The **speed** of an object can be calculated using the following formula:

$$speed = \frac{distance}{time}$$

v = speed in m/s
s = distance in m
t = time in s

$$v = \frac{s}{t}$$

■ **Velocity** is almost the same as speed. It has a **size** (called speed) and a **direction**.

WORKED EXAMPLES

1 Calculate the average speed of a motor car that travels 500 m in 20 seconds.

Write down the formula:	$v = \frac{s}{t}$
Substitute the values for s and t:	$v = \frac{500}{20}$
Work out the answer and write down the units:	$v = 25$ m/s

Cover speed to find that
$$speed = \frac{distance}{time}$$

2 A horse canters at an average speed of 5 m/s for 2 minutes. Calculate the distance it travels.

Write down the formula in terms of s:	$s = v \times t$
Substitute the values for v and t:	$s = 5 \times 2 \times 60$
Work out the answer and write down the units:	$s = 600$ m

⊡ What is acceleration?

■ How much an object's **speed or velocity changes** in a certain time is its **acceleration**. Acceleration can be calculated using the following formula:

$$acceleration = \frac{change\ in\ speed}{time\ taken}$$

a = acceleration

$$a = \frac{(v - u)}{t}$$

v = final speed in m/s
u = starting speed in m/s
t = time in s

■ The units of acceleration m/s/s (metres per second per second) are sometimes written as m/s^2 (metres per second squared).

:☀: **QUESTION SPOTTER**

Calculation questions involving $v = \frac{s}{t}$ are very common. You will need to remember the equation and be able to change the subject of the equation to match the question.
(For example, write $s = v \times t$.) Don't forget to include the correct units.

WORKED EXAMPLE

Calculate the acceleration of a car that travels from 0 m/s to 28 m/s in 10 seconds.

Write down the formula: $a = \dfrac{(v - u)}{t}$

Substitute the values for v, u and t: $a = \dfrac{(28 - 0)}{10}$

Work out the answer and write down the units: $a = 2.8$ m/s/s

QUESTION SPOTTER

Calculations of acceleration are very common. The equation will not be given in the exam so you will need to remember it. The questions usually will ask for a unit for the acceleration (e.g. *m/s/s*).

⌂ Using graphs to study motion

- Journeys can be summarised using **graphs**. The simplest type is a **distance–time graph** where the distance travelled is plotted against the time of the journey.

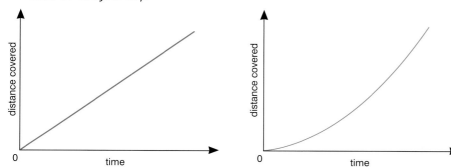

Steady speed is shown by a straight line. Steady acceleration is shown by a smooth curve.

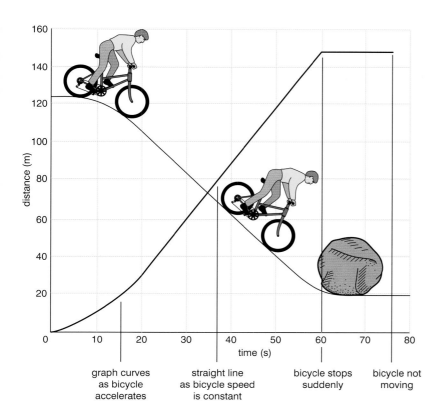

A distance–time graph for a bicycle travelling down a hill. The graph slopes when the bicycle is moving. The slope gets steeper when the bicycle goes faster. The slope is straight (has a constant gradient) when the bicycle's speed is constant. The line is horizontal when the bicycle is at rest.

graph curves as bicycle accelerates

straight line as bicycle speed is constant

bicycle stops suddenly

bicycle not moving

- A **speed–time graph** provides information on speed, acceleration and distance travelled.

Steady speed is shown by a horizontal line. Steady acceleration is shown by a line sloping up.

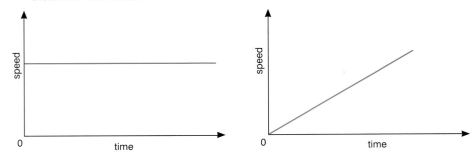

- The graph shows a car travelling between two sets of traffic lights. It can be divided into three regions.

A speed–time graph for a car travelling between two sets of traffic lights.

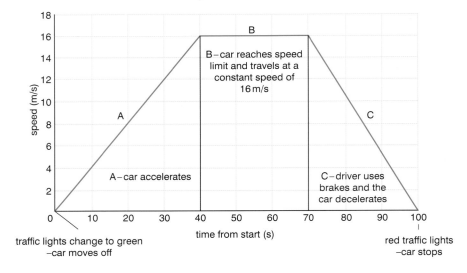

QUESTION SPOTTER

You are likely to be asked to interpret distance/time and speed/time graphs. This will involve describing in words the movement of the object at different times during its journey. If the graph has a number of different regions then explain what is happening region by region.

- In region A, the car is **accelerating at a constant rate** (the line has a constant positive gradient). The distance travelled by the car can be calculated:

average velocity = $\dfrac{(16 + 0)}{2}$ = 8 m/s

time = 40 s

so distance = $v \times t$ = 8 × 40 = 320 m

This can also be calculated from the area under the line ($\frac{1}{2}$ base × height = $\frac{1}{2}$ × 40 × 16 = 320 m).

- In region B, the car is travelling at a **constant speed** (the line has a gradient of zero). The distance travelled by the car can be calculated:

velocity = 16 m/s

time = 30 s

so, distance = $v \times t$ = 16 × 30 = 480 m

This can also be calculated from the area under the line (base × height = 30 × 16 = 480 m).

- In region C, the car is **decelerating at a constant rate** (the line has a constant negative gradient). The distance travelled by the car can be calculated:

average velocity $= \dfrac{(16 + 0)}{2} = 8$ m/s

time = 30 s

so, distance $= v \times t = 8 \times 30 = 240$ m

This can also be calculated from the area under the line
($\frac{1}{2}$ base $\times$ height $= \frac{1}{2} \times 30 \times 16 = 240$ m).

⌷ Thinking, braking and stopping distances

- When a car driver has to brake it takes time for him or her to react. During this time the car will be travelling at its normal speed. The distance it travels in this time is called the **thinking distance**.

- The driver then puts on the brakes. The distance the car travels while it is braking is called the **braking distance**. The overall stopping distance is made up from the thinking distance and the braking distance.

- The thinking distance can vary from person to person and from situation to situation – the braking distance can vary from car to car.

Factors affecting thinking distance	Factors affecting braking distance
speed	speed
tiredness	condition of tyres (amount of tread)
alcohol	condition of brakes
medication, drugs	road conditions (dry, wet, icy, gravel, etc.)
level of concentration and distraction	mass of the car

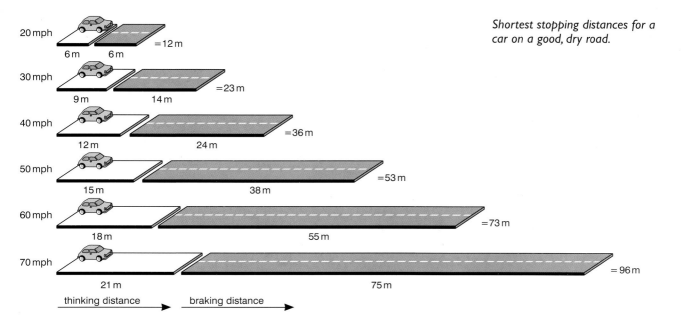

Shortest stopping distances for a car on a good, dry road.

20 mph — 6 m — 6 m = 12 m
30 mph — 9 m — 14 m = 23 m
40 mph — 12 m — 24 m = 36 m
50 mph — 15 m — 38 m = 53 m
60 mph — 18 m — 55 m = 73 m
70 mph — 21 m — 75 m = 96 m

thinking distance ⟶ braking distance ⟶

⬚ How are mass, force and acceleration related?

- The acceleration of an object depends on its **mass** and the **force** that is applied to it. The relationship between these factors is given by the formula:

force = mass × acceleration	F = force in newtons
$F = m\,a$	m = mass in kg
	a = acceleration in m/s/s

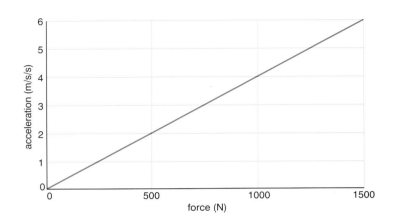

Acceleration is directly proportional to force. Acceleration is inversely proportional to mass.

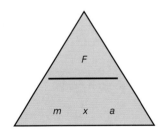

WORKED EXAMPLES

1 What force would be required to give a mass of 5 kg an acceleration of 10 m/s/s?

Write down the formula:	$F = m\,a$
Substitute the values for m and a:	$F = 5 \times 10$
Work out the answer and write down the units:	$F = 50$ N

2 A car has a resultant driving force of 6000 N and a mass of 1200 kg. Calculate the car's initial acceleration.

Write down the formula in terms of a:	$a = \dfrac{F}{m}$
Substitute the values for F and m:	$a = \dfrac{6000}{1200}$
Work out the answer and write down the units:	$a = 5$ m/s/s

CHECK YOURSELF QUESTIONS

Q1 The graph shows a distance–time graph for a journey.

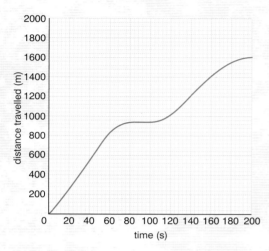

a What does the graph tell us about the speed of the car between 20 and 60 seconds?

b How far did the car travel between 20 and 60 seconds?

c Calculate the speed of the car between 20 and 60 seconds.

d What happened to the car between 80 and 100 seconds?

Q2 Look at the velocity–time graph for a toy tractor.

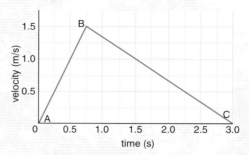

a Calculate the acceleration of the tractor from A to B.

b Calculate the total distance travelled by the tractor from A to C.

Q3 The manufacturer of a car gave the following information:
Mass of car 1000 kg. The car will accelerate from 0 to 30 m/s in 12 seconds.

a Calculate the average acceleration of the car during the 12 seconds.

b Calculate the force needed to produce this acceleration.

Answers are on page 252.

UNIT 17: ENERGY

Where does our energy come from

☐ Sources of energy

■ Most of the energy we use is obtained from **fossil fuels** – coal, oil and natural gas.

■ Once supplies of these fuels have been used up they cannot be replaced – they are **non-renewable.**

■ At current levels of use, oil and gas supplies will last for about another 40 years, and coal supplies for about a further 300 years. The development of **renewable** sources of energy is therefore becoming increasingly important.

☐ Renewable energy sources

■ **Solar power** is energy from the Sun. The Sun's energy is trapped by solar panels and transferred into electrical energy or, as with domestic solar panels, is used to heat water. The cost of installing solar panels is high, and the weather limits the time when the panels are effective.

■ The **wind** is used to turn windmill-like turbines which generate electricity directly from the rotating motion of their blades. Modern wind turbines are very efficient but several thousand would be required to equal the generating capacity of a modern fossil-fuel power station.

■ The motion of **waves** can be used to move large floats and generate electricity. A very large number of floats are needed to produce a significant amount of electricity.

■ Dams on tidal estuaries trap the water at high tide. When the water is allowed to flow back at low tide, **tidal power** can be generated. This obviously limits the use of the estuary.

A 'pumped storage' hydroelectric power station.

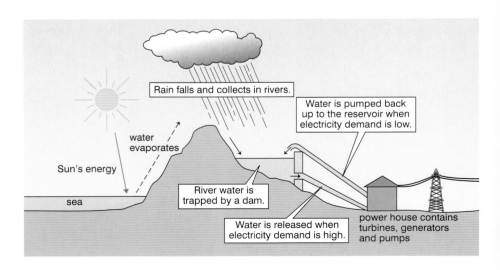

Rain falls and collects in rivers.

Water is pumped back up to the reservoir when electricity demand is low.

water evaporates

Sun's energy

River water is trapped by a dam.

sea

Water is released when electricity demand is high.

power house contains turbines, generators and pumps

- Dams can be used to store **water** which is allowed to fall in a controlled way that generates electricity. This is particularly useful in mountainous regions for generating **hydroelectric power**. When demand for electricity is low, electricity can be used to pump water back up into the high dam for use in times of high demand.

- **Plants** use energy from the Sun in photosynthesis. Plant material can then be used as a **biomass fuel** – either directly by burning it or indirectly. A good example of indirect use is to ferment sugar cane to make ethanol, which is then used as an alternative to petrol. Waste plant material can be used in 'biodigesters' to produce methane gas. The methane is then used as a fuel.

- **Geothermal power** is obtained using the heat of the Earth. In certain parts of the world, water forms hot springs which can be used directly for heating. Water can also be pumped deep into the ground to be heated.

CHECK YOURSELF QUESTIONS

Q1
a What is meant by a non-renewable energy source?
b Name three non-renewable energy sources.
c Which non-renewable energy source is likely to last the longest?

Q2 Look at the graph, which shows the amount of energy from different sources used in the UK in 1955, 1965, 1975 and 1985.

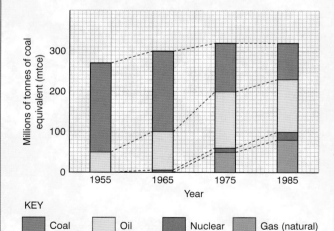

KEY

■ Coal   ☐ Oil   ■ Nuclear   ■ Gas (natural)

a Describe the trend in the total energy used in this period.
b Describe the main changes in the sources of this energy.

Q3 A site has been chosen for a wind farm (a series of windmill-like turbines).
a Give two important factors in choosing the site.
b Give one advantage and one disadvantage of using wind farms to generate electricity.

Answers are on page 253.

REVISION SESSION 2

Transferring energy

Conduction in a solid. Particles in a hot part of a solid (top) vibrate further and faster than particles in a cold part (bottom). The vibrations are passed on through the bonds from particle to particle.

Conduction plays an important part in cooking food.

☐ How is energy transferred?

■ Energy flows from high temperatures to low temperatures – this is called **thermal transfer**. Thermal energy can be transferred in four main ways:
  • **conduction**
  • **convection**
  • **radiation**
  • **evaporation**.

☐ Conduction

■ Materials that allow thermal energy to transfer through them quickly are called **conductors**. Those that do not are called **insulators**.

■ If one end of a conductor is heated the atoms that make up its structure start to vibrate more vigorously. As the atoms in a solid are linked together by chemical bonds the increased vibration can be passed on to other atoms. The energy of movement (kinetic energy) passes through the whole material.

■ **Metals** are particularly good conductors because they contain freely moving electrons which transfer energy very rapidly. **Air** is a good insulator. As air is a gas there are no bonds between the particles and so energy can only be transferred by the particles colliding with each other. Conduction cannot occur when there are no particles present, so a vacuum is a perfect insulator.

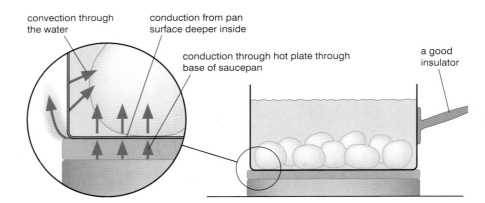

convection through the water

conduction from pan surface deeper inside

conduction through hot plate through base of saucepan

a good insulator

☐ Convection

■ Convection occurs in **liquids** and **gases** because these materials flow (they are 'fluids'). The particles in a fluid move all the time. When a fluid is heated, energy is transferred to the particles, causing them to move faster and further apart. This makes the heated fluid less dense than the unheated fluid. The less dense warm fluid will rise above the more dense colder fluid, causing the fluid to circulate. This **convection current** is how the thermal energy is transferred.

- If a fluid's movement is restricted, then energy cannot be transferred. That is why many insulators, such as ceiling tiles, contain trapped air pockets. Wall cavities in houses are filled with fibre to prevent air from circulating and transferring thermal energy by convection.

Radiation

- Radiation, unlike conduction and convection, **does not need particles** at all. Radiation can travel through a vacuum.

- All objects take in and give out infrared radiation all the time. Hot objects radiate more infrared than cold objects. The amount of radiation given out or absorbed by an object depends on its temperature and on its surface.

Type of surface	As an emitter of radiation	As an absorber of radiation	Examples
Dull black	Good	Good	Cooling fans on the back of a refrigerator are dull black to radiate away more energy.
Bright shiny	Poor	Poor	Marathon runners wrap themselves in shiny blankets to prevent thermal transfer by radiation. Fuel storage tanks are sprayed with shiny silver paint to reflect radiation from the Sun.

Evaporation

- When particles break away from the surface of a liquid and form a vapour, the process is known as evaporation.

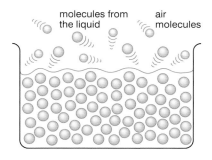

The more energetic molecules of the liquid escape from the surface. This reduces the average energy of the molecules remaining in the liquid and so the liquid cools down.

- Evaporation causes cooling. The evaporation of sweat helps to keep a body cool in hot weather. The cooling obtained in a refrigerator is also due to evaporation.

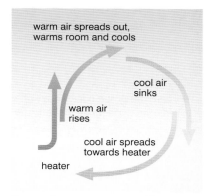

Convection currents caused by a room heater.

A vacuum flask has a hollow glass lining. The absence of air in the lining prevents thermal transfer by conduction and convection. The insides of the lining are silvered to reduce thermal transfer by radiation. The flask will therefore keep hot drinks hot, or cold drinks cold, for hours.

⚡ A * EXTRA

Convection currents in gases and liquids are caused by changes in density.
- When a liquid is heated the particles move more quickly and move further apart, making that part of the liquid less dense than cooler parts.
- The less dense part then rises and the cooler or denser liquid takes its place.

⊡ How can we keep our energy costs low?

- Heating a house can account for over 60% of a family's total energy bill. Reducing thermal energy transfer from the house to the outside can greatly reduce the amount of energy that is being used and save a lot of money.

There are a number of ways of reducing wasteful energy transfer.

curtains reduce radiation

loft insulation

porch to reduce warm air loss

double-glazed windows insulate

draught excluder on door

wall cavity filled with insulation

carpet underlay acts as insulation

QUESTION SPOTTER

Questions on insulation techniques frequently ask how the technique prevents energy transfer by conduction, convection or radiation.

Source of energy wastage	% of energy wasted	Insulation technique
Walls	35	*Cavity wall insulation.* Modern houses have cavity walls, that is, two single walls separated by an air cavity. The air reduces energy transfer by conduction but not by convection as the air is free to move within the cavity. Fibre insulation is inserted into the cavity to prevent the air from moving and so reduces convection.
Roof	25	*Loft insulation.* Fibre insulation is placed on top of the ceiling and between the wooden joists. Air is trapped between the fibres, reducing energy transfer by conduction and convection.
Floors	15	*Carpets.* Carpets and underlay prevent energy loss by conduction and convection. In some modern houses foam blocks are placed under the floors.
Draughts	15	*Draught excluders.* Cold air can get into the home through gaps between windows and doors and their frames. Draught excluder tape can be used to block these gaps.
Windows	10	*Double glazing.* Energy is transferred through glass by conduction and radiation. Double glazing has two panes of glass with a layer of air between the panes. It reduces energy transfer by conduction but not by radiation. Radiation can be reduced by drawing the curtains.

Means of insulation	Approximate pay-back time (years)
Cavity wall	5
Loft	2
Carpets	10
Draught excluders	1
Double glazing	20

- One thing to consider when insulating a house is the balance of the cost of the insulation against the potential saving in energy costs. The **pay-back time** is the time it takes for the savings to repay the costs of installation. The different methods of insulation have very different pay-back times.

- The pay-back time is not the only thing to think about when considering different means of insulation. For instance, glazing reduces noise and condensation inside the home, and carpets provide increased comfort.

⊡ Efficiency of energy transfers

- Energy transfers can be summarised using simple **energy transfer diagrams** or **Sankey diagrams**. The thickness of each arrow is drawn to scale to show the amount of energy.

- Energy is always conserved – the total amount of energy after the transfer must be the same as the total amount of energy before the transfer. Unfortunately, in nearly all energy transfers some of the energy will end up as 'useless' heat.

- In a power station only some of the energy originally produced from the fuel is transferred to useful electrical output. Energy **efficiency** can be calculated from the following formula:

$$\text{efficiency} = \frac{\text{useful energy output} \times 100\%}{\text{energy input}}$$

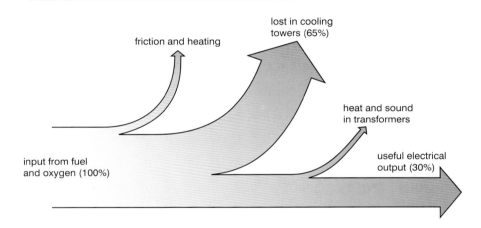

In a power station as much as 70% of the energy transfers do not produce useful energy. The power station is only 30% efficient.

> ## QUESTION SPOTTER
>
> You may be asked to label or complete a Sankey diagram like the one shown. Remember that the thickness of each section is directly related to its percentage contribution.

- Many power stations are now trying to make use of the large amounts of energy 'lost' in the cooling towers.

CHECK YOURSELF QUESTIONS

Q1 Why are several thin layers of clothing more likely to reduce thermal transfer than one thick layer of clothing?

Q2 Hot water in an open container transfers energy by evaporation. Explain how the loss of molecules from the surface of the liquid causes the liquid to cool.

Q3 The diagram shows a cross-section of a steel radiator positioned in a room next to a wall.

Describe how energy from the hot water reaches the wall behind the radiator.

Answers are on page 254.

Work, power and energy

In this position the gymnast is not doing any work against his body weight – he is not moving (he will be doing work pumping blood around his body though!).

The gymnast is doing work. He is moving upwards against the force of gravity. Energy is being transferred as he does the work.

⊏⊐ Work

■ **Work** is done when the application of a force results in movement. Work can only be done if the object or system has energy. When work is done energy is transferred.

■ Work done can be calculated using the following formula:

work done = force × distance moved

$W = F\,s$

W = work done in joules (J)

F = force in newtons (N)

s = distance moved in the direction of the force in metres (m)

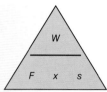

WORKED EXAMPLES

1 A cyclist pedals along a flat road. She exerts a force of 60 N and travels 150 m. Calculate the work done by the cyclist.

Write down the formula:	$W = F\,s$
Substitute the values for F and s:	$W = 60 \times 150$
Work out the answer and write down the unit:	$W = 9000$ J

2 A person does 3000 J of work in pushing a supermarket trolley 50 m across a level car park. What force was the person exerting on the trolley?

Write down the formula with F as the subject:	$F = \dfrac{W}{s}$
Substitute the values for W and s:	$F = \dfrac{3000}{50}$
Work out the answer and write down the unit:	$F = 60$ N

⊏⊐ Power

■ **Power** is defined as the rate of doing work or the rate of transferring energy. The more powerful a machine is the quicker it does a fixed amount of work or transfers a fixed amount of energy.

■ Power can be calculated using the formula:

$$\text{power} = \frac{\text{work done}}{\text{time taken}} = \frac{\text{energy transfer}}{\text{time taken}}$$

$P = \dfrac{W}{t}$

P = power in joules per second or watts (W)

W = work done in joules (J)

t = time taken in seconds (s)

WORKED EXAMPLES

1 A crane does 20 000 J of work in 40 seconds. Calculate its power over this time.

Write down the formula:	$P = \dfrac{W}{t}$
Substitute the values for W and t:	$P = \dfrac{20000}{40}$
Work out the answer and write down the unit:	$P = 500 \text{ W}$

2 A student with a weight of 600 N runs up the flight of stairs shown in the diagram (right) in 4 seconds. Calculate the student's power.

Write down the formula for work done:	$W = F\,s$
Substitute the values for F and s:	$W = 600 \times 5 = 3000 \text{ J}$
Write down the formula for power:	$P = \dfrac{W}{t}$
Substitute the values for W and t:	$P = 3000/4 = 750 \text{ W}$

The student is lifting his body against the force of gravity, which acts in a vertical direction. The distance measured must be in the direction of the force (that is, the vertical height).

⬚ Potential energy

- Stored, or hidden, energy is called **potential energy** (P.E.). If a spring is stretched the spring will have potential energy. If a load is raised above the ground it will have **gravitational potential energy**. If the spring is released or the load moves back to the ground the stored potential energy is transferred to movement energy, which is called **kinetic energy** (K.E.).

- Gravitational potential energy can be calculated using the following formula:

gravitational potential energy = mass × gravitational field strength × height
P.E. = $m\,g\,h$
P.E. = gravitational potential energy in joules (J)
m = mass in kilograms (kg)
g = gravitational field strength of 10 N/kg
h = height in metres (m)

WORKED EXAMPLE

A skier has a mass of 70 kg and travels up a ski lift a vertical height of 300 m. Calculate the change in the skier's gravitational potential energy.

Write down the formula:	P.E. = $m\,g\,h$
Substitute values for m, g and h:	P.E. = $70 \times 10 \times 300$
Work out the answer and write down the unit:	P.E. = 210 000 J or 210 kJ

The kinetic energy given to the stone when it is thrown is transferred to potential energy as it gains height and slows down. At the top of its flight practically all the kinetic energy will have been converted into gravitational potential energy. A small amount of energy will have been lost due to friction between the stone and the air.

⊡ Kinetic energy

- The kinetic energy of an object depends on its mass and its velocity. The kinetic energy can be calculated using the following formula:

kinetic energy $= \tfrac{1}{2} \times$ mass $\times$ velocity^2

$$\text{K.E.} = \tfrac{1}{2} mv^2$$

K.E. = kinetic energy in joules (J)
m = mass in kilograms (kg)
v = velocity in m/s

WORKED EXAMPLE

An ice skater has a mass of 50 kg and travels at a velocity of 5 m/s. Calculate the ice-skater's kinetic energy.

Write down the formula:	$\text{K.E.} = \tfrac{1}{2}mv^2$
Substitute the values for m and v:	$\text{K.E.} = \tfrac{1}{2} \times 50 \times 5 \times 5$
Work out the answer and write down the unit:	$\text{K.E.} = 625 \text{ J}$

? CHECK YOURSELF QUESTIONS

Q1 50 000 J of work are done as a crane lifts a load of 400 kg. How far did the crane lift the load? (Gravitation field strength, g, is 10 N/kg.)

Q2 A student is carrying out a personal fitness test.

She steps on and off the 'step' 200 times. She transfers 30 J of energy each time she steps up.
a Calculate the energy transferred during the test.
b She takes 3 minutes to do the test. Calculate her average power.

Q3 A child of mass 35 kg climbed a 30 m high snow-covered hill.
a Calculate the change in the child's potential gravitational energy.
b The child then climbed onto a lightweight sledge and slid down the hill. Calculate the child's maximum speed at the bottom of the hill. (Ignore the mass of the sledge.)
c Explain why the actual speed at the bottom of the hill is likely to be less than the value calculated in part (b).

Answers are on page 254.

UNIT 18: WAVES

The properties of waves

There are two types of waves

- **Longitudinal waves.** This type of wave can be shown by pushing and pulling a spring. The spring stretches in places and squashes in others. The stretching produces regions of **rarefaction**, whilst the squashing produces regions of **compression**. Sound is an example of a longitudinal wave.

- **Transverse waves.** In a transverse wave the vibrations are at right angles to the direction of motion. Light, radio and other electromagnetic waves are transverse waves. Water waves are often used to demonstrate the properties of waves because the **wavefront** of a water wave is easy to see. A wavefront is the moving line that joins all the points on the crest of a wave.

QUESTION SPOTTER

You will often be asked to label a transverse wave showing features such as crest, trough, amplitude and wavelength.

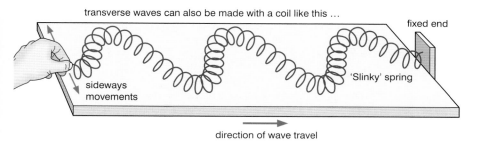

transverse waves can also be made with a coil like this …

fixed end

sideways movements

'Slinky' spring

direction of wave travel

Transverse and longitudinal waves are made by vibrations

longitudinal waves

backwards and forwards movements

rarefaction   compression

What features do all waves have?

- The speed a wave travels at depends on the substance or **medium** it is passing through.

- Waves have a **repeating shape** or pattern.

- Waves **carry energy** without moving material along.

- Waves have a wavelength, frequency and amplitude.
  - **Wavelength** – the length of the repeating pattern.
  - **Frequency** – the number of repeated patterns that go past any point each second.
  - **Amplitude** – the maximum displacement of the medium's vibration. In transverse waves, this is half the crest-to-trough height.

transverse

longitudinal

- **The speed of a wave in a given medium is constant.** If you change the wavelength the frequency *must* change as well. Speed, frequency and wavelength of a wave are related by the equation:

wave speed = frequency × wavelength

$v = f \times \lambda$

v = wave speed, usually measured in metres/second (m/s)

f = frequency, measured in cycles per second or hertz (Hz)

λ = wavelength, usually measured in metres (m)

WORKED EXAMPLES

1 A loudspeaker makes sound waves with a frequency of 300 Hz. The waves have a wavelength of 1.13 m. Calculate the speed of the sound waves.

Write down the formula:	$v = f \times \lambda$
Substitute the values for f and λ:	$v = 300 \times 1.13$
Work out the answer and write down the unit:	$v = 339$ m/s

2 A radio station broadcasts on a wavelength of 250 m. The speed of the radio waves is 3×10^8 m/s. Calculate the frequency.

Write down the formula with f as the subject:	$f = \dfrac{v}{\lambda}$
Substitute the values for v and λ:	$f = \dfrac{3 \times 10^8}{250}$
Work out the answer and write down the unit:	$f = 12000000$ Hz or 12000 kHz

⊡ Reflection, refraction and diffraction

- When a wave hits a barrier the wave will be **reflected**. If it hits the barrier at an angle then the angle of reflection will be equal to the angle of incidence. Echoes are a common consequence of the reflection of sound waves.

Waves hit a barrier. The angle between a wavefront and the barrier is the angle of incidence.

The waves bounce off.

The angle of reflection is the same as the angle of incidence.

- When a wave moves from one medium into another, it will either speed up or slow down. When a wave **slows down**, the wavefronts crowd together – the **wavelength gets smaller**. When a wave **speeds up**, the wavefronts spread out – the **wavelength gets larger**.

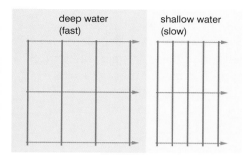

When waves slow down, their wavelength gets shorter.

- If a wave enters a new medium at an angle then the wavefronts also change direction. This is known as **refraction**. Refraction happens whenever there is a change in wave speed. Water waves are slower in shallower water than in deep water, so water waves will refract when the depth changes.

QUESTION SPOTTER

Calculations involving the wave equation are very common. You will need to be able to remember the equation and change its subject if required.

If waves cross into a new medium at an angle, their wavelength and direction changes.

- Wavefronts change shape when they pass the edge of an obstacle or go through a gap. This process is known as **diffraction**. Diffraction is strong when the width of the gap is similar in size to the wavelength of the waves.

- Diffraction is a problem in communications when radio and television signals are transmitted through the air in a narrow beam. Diffraction of the wavefront means that not all the energy transmitted with the wavefront reaches the receiving dishes. On the other hand, diffraction allows long-wave radio waves to spread out and diffract around buildings and hills.

Diffraction is most noticeable when the size of the gap equals the wavelength of the waves.

⌷ Seismic waves

- Earthquakes make waves that travel right through the Earth. These waves are called **seismic waves**. There are longitudinal waves called **P-waves** (primary) and transverse waves called **S-waves** (secondary).

- The waves travel through rock and are partially reflected at the boundaries between different types of rock. Instruments called **seismometers** detect the waves. Monitoring these seismic waves after earthquakes has provided geologists with evidence that the Earth is made up of layers and that part of the core is liquid.

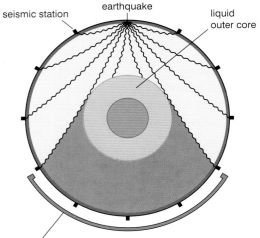

seismic station · earthquake · liquid outer core

S-waves can travel through solid rock but not through liquid. P-waves can travel through solid and liquid rock. Only the P-waves from an earthquake, not the S-waves, are received at seismic stations on the opposite side of the world.

sideways (transverse) waves are not received here

CHECK YOURSELF QUESTIONS

Q1 The diagram shows a trace of a sound wave obtained on a cathode ray oscilloscope.

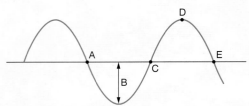

a Which letter shows the crest of the wave?

b The wavelength is the distance between which two letters?

c Which letter shows the amplitude?

d The frequency of the wave is 512 Hz. How many waves are produced each second?

Q2 Radio waves of frequency 900 MHz are used to send information to and from a portable phone. The speed of the waves is 3×10^8 m/s. Calculate the wavelength of the waves. (1 MHz = 1 000 000 Hz, 3×10^8 = 300 000 000.)

Q3 The speed of sound is approximately 340 m/s. Calculate the wavelength of middle C, which has a frequency of 256 Hz.

Answers are on page 254.

The electromagnetic spectrum

☐ Electromagnetic waves

■ The **electromagnetic spectrum** is a family of different kinds of waves. Electromagnetic waves all travel at the same speed in a vacuum, i.e. the speed of light, 300 000 000 m/s.

■ **White light** is a mixture of different colours and can be split by a prism into the **visible spectrum**. All the different colours of light travel at the same speed in a vacuum but they have different frequencies and wavelengths. When they enter glass or perspex they all slow down, but by different amounts. The different colours are therefore refracted through different angles. Violet is refracted the most, red the least.

■ The visible spectrum is only a small part of the full electromagnetic spectrum.

A prism splits white light into the colourful spectrum of visible light.

The complete electromagnetic spectrum.

Type of wave	gamma rays	X rays	ultraviolet	visible	infrared	microwaves	TV and radio waves
frequency	high						low
wavelength	low						high
use	killing cancer cells	to look at bones	sun tan beds	photography	TV remote controls	cooking	transmission of TV and radio

☐ The waves you can't see

■ **X-rays** are produced when high-energy electrons are fired at a metal target. Bones absorb more X-rays than other body tissue. If a person is placed between the X-ray source and a photographic plate, the bones appear to be white on the developed photographic plate compared with the rest of the body. X-rays have very high energy and can damage or destroy body cells. They may also cause cancer. Cancer cells absorb X-rays more readily than normal healthy cells and so X-rays are also used to treat cancer.

■ **Gamma rays** have even higher energy than X-rays. Gamma rays are frequently used in radiotherapy to kill cancer cells. Radioactive substances that emit gamma rays are used as **tracers** (see Unit 20).

■ **Ultraviolet radiation** (UV) is the component of the Sun's rays that gives you a suntan. UV is also created in fluorescent light tubes by exciting the atoms in a mercury vapour. The UV radiation is then absorbed by the coating on the inside of the fluorescent tube and re-emitted as visible light. Fluorescent tubes are more efficient than light bulbs because they don't depend on heating and so more energy is available to produce light.

QUESTION SPOTTER

Questions often require you to remember which waves in the electromagnetic spectrum have the greatest frequency or greatest wavelength.

⚡ A* EXTRA

The energy associated with an electromagnetic wave depends on its frequency. The waves with the higher frequencies are potentially the more hazardous.

- All objects give out **infrared radiation** (IR). The hotter the object is, the more radiation it gives out. Thermograms are photographs taken to show the infrared radiation given out from objects. Infrared radiation grills and cooks our food in an ordinary oven and is used in remote controls to operate televisions and videos.

- **Microwaves** are high-frequency radio waves. They are used in radar in finding the position of aeroplanes and ships. Metal objects reflect the microwaves back to the transmitter, enabling the distance between the object and the transmitter to be calculated. Microwaves are also used for cooking. Water particles in food absorb the energy carried by microwaves. They vibrate more and get much hotter. Microwaves penetrate several centimetres into the food and so speed up the cooking process.

- **Radio waves** have the longest wavelengths and lowest frequencies. **UHF** (ultra-high frequency) waves are used to transmit television programmes to homes. **VHF** (very high frequency) waves are used to transmit local radio programmes. **Medium** and **long** radio waves are used to transmit over longer distances because their wavelengths allow them to diffract around obstacles such as buildings and hills. Communication satellites above the Earth receive signals carried by high-frequency (**short-wave**) radio waves. These signals are amplified and re-transmitted to other parts of the world.

CHECK YOURSELF QUESTIONS

Q1 This is a list of types of wave:

*gamma   infrared   light   microwaves
radio   ultraviolet   X-rays*

Choose from the list the type of wave that best fits each of these descriptions.

a Stimulates the sensitive cells at the back of the eye.
b Necessary for a suntan.
c Used for *rapid* cooking in an oven.
d Used to take a photograph of the bones in a broken arm.
e Emitted by a video remote control unit.

Q2 Gamma rays are part of the electromagnetic spectrum. Gamma rays are useful to us but can also be very dangerous.

a Explain how the properties of gamma rays make them useful to us.
b Explain why gamma rays can cause damage to people.
c Give one difference between microwaves and gamma rays.
d Microwaves travel at 300 000 000 m/s. What speed do gamma rays travel at?

Answers are on page 255.

Light reflection and refraction

⎡⎤ Light reflects

■ Light rays are reflected from mirrors in such a way that

angle of incidence (*i*) = angle of reflection (*r*)

The angles are measured to an imaginary line at 90° to the surface of the mirror. This line is called the **normal**. With a curved mirror it is difficult to measure the angle between the ray and the mirror.

■ When you look in a plane mirror you see an **image** of yourself. The image is said to be **laterally inverted** because if you raise your right hand your image raises its left hand. The image is formed as far behind the mirror as you are in front of it and is the same size as you. The image cannot be projected onto a screen. It is known as a **virtual image**.

⎡⎤ Uses of mirrors

■ In a plane mirror the image is always the same size as the object. Examples of plane mirrors include household 'dressing' mirror, dental mirror for examining teeth, security mirror for checking under vehicles, periscope.

■ Close to a **concave mirror** the image is **larger** than the object – these mirrors **magnify**. They are used in torches and car headlamps to produce a beam of light, make-up and shaving mirrors, satellite dishes.

■ The image in a **convex mirror** is always **smaller** than the object Examples are a car driving mirror, shop security mirror.

⎡⎤ Light refracts

■ Light waves **slow down** when they travel from air into glass. If they are at an angle to the glass they bend towards the normal. When the light rays travel out of the glass into the air, their speed increases and they bend away from the normal.

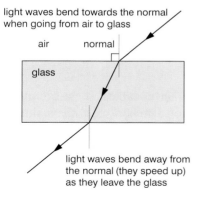

light waves bend towards the normal when going from air to glass

air   normal

glass

light waves bend away from the normal (they speed up) as they leave the glass

■ Refraction is observed when a triangular prism (a glass or plastic block) is used to obtain the visible spectrum (see page 193). Lenses also refract light rays.

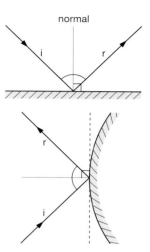

The angles of incidence and reflection are the same when a mirror reflects light. This type of curved mirror is known as a convex mirror.

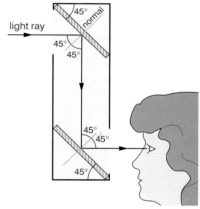

light ray   45° normal 45° 45°

45° 45°

45°

A periscope uses reflection to allow you to see above your normal line of vision – or even round corners.

- **Convex (converging, positive) lenses** cause parallel rays of light to **converge** to the principal focus. They are used in magnifying glasses, cameras, telescopes, binoculars, microscopes, film projectors and spectacles.

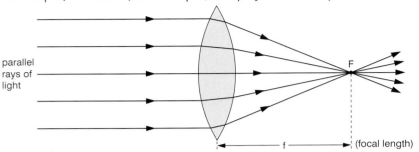

parallel rays of light

F

f (focal length)

- **Concave (diverging, negative) lenses** make parallel rays of light **diverge** as if they were coming from the principal focus. You see concave lenses in spectacles, telescopes and correcting lenses in all optical equipment.

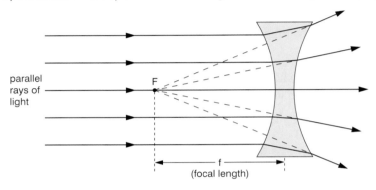

parallel rays of light

F

f (focal length)

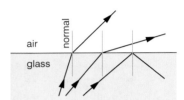

air

glass

normal

Total internal reflection occurs when a ray of light tries to leave the glass. If the angle of incidence equals or is greater than the critical angle the ray will be totally internally reflected.

light beam

Light does not escape from the fibre because it always hits it at an angle greater than the critical angle and is internally reflected.

QUESTION SPOTTER

Questions on total internal reflection are common. Typically you will have to draw or interpret simple ray diagrams in objects such as binoculars, periscopes, bicycle reflectors or endoscopes.

⟲ Total internal reflection

- When rays of light pass from a **slow medium** to a **faster medium** they move **away** from the normal.

- As the angle of incidence increases, an angle is reached at which the light rays will have to leave with an angle of refraction greater than 90°! These rays cannot refract, so they are entirely reflected back inside the medium. This process is known as **total internal reflection**.

- The angle of incidence at which all refraction stops is known as the **critical angle** for the material. The critical angle of glass is 42°, the critical angle of water is 49°.

- Total internal reflection is used in **fibre-optic cables**. These are made up of large numbers of very thin, glass fibres. The light continues along the fibres by being constantly internally reflected. Fibre-optic cables are used in medical endoscopes for internal examination of the body.

- Telephone and TV communications systems are increasingly relying on fibre optics instead of the more traditional copper cables. Fibre-optic cables do not use electricity and the signals are carried by infrared rays. The signals are very clear as they don't suffer from electrical interference. Other advantages are that they are cheaper than the copper cables and can carry thousands of different signals down the same fibre at the same time.

CHECK YOURSELF QUESTIONS

Q1 a Rays of light can be reflected and refracted. State one difference between reflection and refraction.

b The diagram shows a glass block and two rays of light.

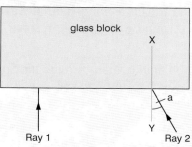

glass block

X

a

Y

Ray 1   Ray 2

i Complete the paths of the two rays as they pass into and then out of the glass block.

ii What name is given to the angle marked a?

iii What name is given to the line marked XY?

Q2 a Tom looks into the mirror. E is his eye and X an object.

E

X

Complete the ray diagram to show clearly how Tom sees an image of X.

b Jane uses two mirrors to look at the back of her head. Explain how this works.

Q3 The diagram shows light entering a prism. Total internal reflection takes place at the inner surfaces of the prism.

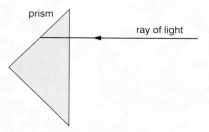

prism

ray of light

a Complete the path of the ray.

b Suggest one use for a prism like this.

c Complete the table about total internal reflection. Use T for total internal reflection or R for refraction.

angle of incidence/ degrees	total internal reflection (T) or refraction (R)
36	
42 (critical angle)	
46	

Answers are on page 255.

■ Sound waves ■

⊡ Properties of sound waves

■ Sound waves travel at about 340 m/s in the air – much slower than the speed of light. This explains why you almost always see the flash of lightning before hearing the crash of the thunder.

■ Sound is caused by vibrations and travels as **longitudinal waves**. The compressions and rarefactions of sound waves result in small differences in air pressure.

■ Sound waves travel faster through liquids than through air. Sound travels fastest through solids. This is because particles are linked most strongly in solids.

■ High-**pitch** sounds have a high frequency whereas low-pitch sounds have a low frequency. The human ear can detect sounds with pitches ranging from 20 Hz to 20 000 Hz. Sound with frequencies above this range is known as **ultrasound**.

■ Loud sounds have a high amplitude whereas quiet sounds have a low amplitude. Sound amplitude is measured in **decibels**.

⊡ How do we use ultrasound?

■ Ultrasound is used in echo sounding or SONAR (SOund NAvigation and Ranging). An echo sounder on a ship sends out ultrasonic waves which reflect off the bottom of the sea. The depth of the water can be calculated from the time taken for the echo to be received and the speed of sound in water.

a short burst of ultrasonic waves travel to the sea bed

the reflected waves arrive at the echosounder 2.0 s later

WORKED EXAMPLE

A ship sends out an ultrasound wave and receives an echo in 2 seconds. If the speed of sound in water is 1500 m/s, how deep is the water?

Write down the formula:	speed = distance/time or $v = s/t$
Rearrange to make s the subject:	$s = v \times t$
Substitute the values for v and t:	$s = 1500 \times 2 = 3000$ m

This is the distance travelled by the sound wave.
Therefore the depth of the water must be half this. Depth = 1500 m.

■ Ultrasound is used in medicine. Dense material, such as bone, reflects more ultrasound waves than less dense material, such as skin and tissue. Ultrasound waves have lower energy than X-rays and so are less likely to damage healthy cells.

⚡ A* EXTRA

▸ Ultrasound waves are reflected from the different layers of tissues in the body and so can produce quite clear images. They have lower energy than X-rays and so are less hazardous.

▸ However, they can be used to break down solid material such as kidney stones when they are highly focused.

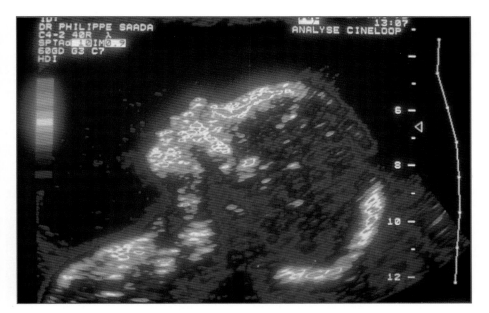

The fetus reflects the ultrasound waves more than the surrounding amniotic fluids.

? CHECK YOURSELF QUESTIONS

Q1 **a** **i** What causes a sound? **ii** Explain how sound travels through the air.
   b Astronauts in space cannot talk directly to each other. They have to speak to each other by radio. Explain why this is so.
   c Explain why sound travels faster through water than through air.

Q2 Ultrasonic waves are longitudinal waves.
   a What does the word 'ultrasonic' mean?
   b What does the word 'longitudinal' mean?
   c The waves travel through carbon dioxide more slowly than through air. How do the frequency and wavelength change when ultrasonic waves pass from air to carbon dioxide?

Q3 A fishing boat was using echo sounding to detect a shoal of fish. Short pulses of ultrasound were sent out from the boat. The echo from the shoal was detected 0.5 seconds later. How far away from the boat was the shoal of fish? (Sound waves travel through water at a speed of 1500 m/s.)

Answers are on page 256.

REVISION SESSION 1 ■■■ ## The solar system ■■■

⌑ What makes up the solar system?

■ The **solar system** is made up of the Sun and its planets. The planets are **satellites** of the Sun and are kept in **orbit** by the gravitational pull from the Sun. The orbits of the planets are slightly oval or elliptical.

INNER SOLAR SYSTEM

INNER SOLAR SYSTEM

Saturn, 1427 million kilometres from the Sun

Uranus, 2870 million kilometres from the Sun

Neptune, 4497 million kilometres from the Sun

Pluto, 5900 million kilometres from the Sun

Mars, 228 million kilometres from the Sun

Earth, 149.6 million kilometres from the Sun

Sun

Venus, 107.5 million kilometres from the Sun

Mercury, 58 million kilometres from the Sun

Jupiter, 778 million kilometres from the Sun

Nine planets orbit the Sun.

■ **Asteroids** are fragments of rock, up to 1000 km in diameter, that orbit the Sun between the four inner planets and the five outer planets. The asteroids were formed at the same time as the Solar System.

■ **Comets** go round the Sun like planets but their orbits are much more elliptical. Comets spend much of their time too far away from the Sun to be seen. They are thought to be made from ice and rock. When they get close to the Sun some of the solid turns into gas, forming a 'tail' which points away from the Sun.

tail always points away from the Sun

elongated eliptical orbit

comet moves slow here

comet moves fast here

A comet moves round the Sun in an elliptical orbit.

⌂ Centripetal force

- Natural and artificial satellites orbit the Earth in a circle for the same reason that the planets orbit the Sun – **gravitational pull**.

- To keep an object moving in a circle, you have to constantly pull it towards the centre of that circle. A force that constantly pulls towards a centre is called a **centripetal force**.

- Near the Earth, gravity exerts a force that always acts towards its centre and keeps satellites like the Moon moving in a near-circular orbit around the Earth. Artificial satellites orbit the Earth for the same reason – and as they don't need motors or rockets to stay in such orbits, they can stay there for decades.

- At the right distance from the Earth, an unpowered orbit takes exactly 24 hours. This means that an artificial satellite orbiting above the Earth's equator and moving in the same direction as the Earth's spin, will appear to be flying over the same spot.

⌂ Galaxies

- The Sun is part of a group of stars called the Milky Way **galaxy**. The Milky Way is in the shape of a spiral.

- We can see other galaxies through telescopes. These other galaxies are so far away that it is difficult to see the individual stars, so earlier astronomers called them **nebulae** (singular: nebula) meaning 'a bright cloudy spot'. These days, we can see these galaxies properly, and the word nebula now usually means a cloud of gas where stars are being born. Many nebulae are formed by stars exploding.

⌑ Life-cycle of a star

Birth (thousands of millions of years)	Life (tens of millions of years)	Death (millions of years)
• The star starts as a huge cloud of hydrogen gas and dust. • Gravity pulls the hydrogen atoms closer together. • The gas gets hotter as the cloud gets smaller and more concentrated. • In the very high temperatures created, the hydrogen atoms join together to form helium atoms in a process called nuclear fusion. Large amounts of energy are released in this process. • The core sends out light and other radiation and the cool, outer layers are blown away, sometimes forming planets around the new star.	• Huge gravitational forces pull the outer parts of the star towards its core. • The energy produced by the nuclear fusion ensures that the gases on the outside are very hot. • The pressure exerted by the hot gases exactly balances the force of gravity. • This balance continues for millions of years until all the hydrogen has been used up and the nuclear reactions stop. • Some stars appear red-orange but hotter stars appear blue-white.	• The hydrogen in the star's core gets used up and the core starts to cool. • The star then starts to collapse and the core gets hotter again very quickly, enabling other nuclear fusion reactions to start. • A sudden surge of radiation is produced and the star expands to form a red giant or red supergiant. • In a medium-sized star like the Sun, the nuclear fusion reactions finish and the core collapses under gravity and the red giant forms a white dwarf star. • In a large star, when the core collapses there is a sudden explosion and the red supergiant forms a supernova. A supernova is brighter than a whole galaxy of stars. A very dense core is left behind becoming a neutron star and, if it is very small and dense, a black hole.

QUESTION SPOTTER

Questions on the life cycle of a star will usually require an extended written answer and be worth 3 marks or more. Divide your answer into three parts: birth, life and death. Remember that what happens at the death of the star will depend on its size.

CHECK YOURSELF QUESTIONS

Q1 How does a normal star produce energy?

Q2 The list contains the stages in the life cycle of a star. Arrange them in the correct order.
*supernova   clouds of hydrogen gas
red supergiant   blue star*

Q3 a A satellite moves around the Earth at a constant speed in a circular orbit.
i What force is acting on the satellite and **ii** what is the direction of the force?
b Some satellites travel in geostationary orbits. Explain what is meant by a geostationary orbit.

Answers are on page 257.

REVISION SESSION 2 — How did the Universe begin?

⌑ Red shift

- If a star is moving away from the Earth, light waves will reach the Earth with a lower frequency than that emitted by the star. This change in frequency is called a **red shift**.

- Light from all the distant galaxies shows a red shift, so it follows that all these galaxies are moving away from us. In fact, **all galaxies are moving away from each other.** The Universe is expanding.

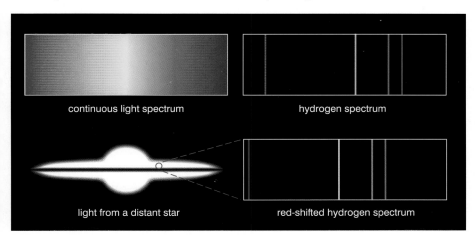

continuous light spectrum

hydrogen spectrum

light from a distant star

red-shifted hydrogen spectrum

The top picture shows the spectrum of white light. The second picture shows the spectrum produced by hydrogen when it glows. The bottom picture shows the spectrum of hydrogen from a star seen through a telescope. The pattern is shifted towards the red end. This red shift shows that the star is moving away from us.

⌑ The Big Bang theory

One explanation for the Universe expanding is that everything in the Universe originated from the same point, which exploded in the **Big Bang**. Since this explosion, the Universe has been expanding and cooling. Calculations suggest that the Big Bang could have occurred between 11 and 18 billion years ago. There are three main possibilities as to what will happen to the Universe:

1 **The Universe will keep on expanding.** The galaxies move fast enough to overcome the forces of gravity acting between them.

2 **The expansion will slow down and stop.** The galaxies will remain in a fixed position. The gravitational forces will exactly balance the 'expansion forces'.

3 **The Universe will start to contract.** The force of gravity between the galaxies will overcome the forces causing expansion and pull them back together again.

? CHECK YOURSELF QUESTIONS

Q1 What is the red shift?

Q2 What is the evidence that supports the Big Bang theory?

Answers are on page 257.

UNIT 20: RADIOACTIVITY

Unstable atoms

⌂ Inside the atom

- Inside the atom the central **nucleus** of positively charged **protons** and neutral **neutrons** is surrounded by shells, or orbits, of **electrons**. Most nuclei are very stable, but some 'decay' and break apart into more stable nuclei. This breaking apart is called **nuclear fission**. Atoms whose nuclei do this are **radioactive**.

- When a nucleus decays it emits:
  - **alpha (α) particles**
  - **beta (β) particles**
  - **gamma (γ) rays.**

- A stream of these rays is referred to as **ionising radiation** (often called nuclear radiation, or just 'radiation' for short).

QUESTION SPOTTER

You will often have to describe the differences between α, β and γ rays. You will be asked what the rays are, what materials they can penetrate and if they can be deflected.

alpha radiation

beta radiation

gamma radiation

| skin or sheet of paper | 2 mm of aluminium | thick lead or concrete |

	alpha (α)	**beta (β)**	**gamma (γ)**
Description	A positively charged particle, identical to a helium nucleus (two protons and two neutrons)	A negatively charged particle, identical to an electron	Electromagnetic radiation. Uncharged
Penetration	4–10 cm of air. Stopped by a sheet of paper	About 1 m of air. Stopped by a few mm of aluminium	No limit in air. Stopped by several cm of lead or several metres of concrete
Effect of electric and magnetic fields	Deflected	Deflected considerably	Unaffected – not deflected

How was the 'nuclear' atom discovered?

- In the 19th century, many scientists believed that atoms were just spheres of positive charge embedded with specks of negative charge (electrons).

- In a crucial experiment in 1911, a stream of alpha particles was aimed at a piece of gold foil a few atoms thick. Most of the alpha particles passed through the foil undeflected, showing that most of the atom is empty space. Some alpha particles passed through but were deflected and a few bounced back as if they had done a U-turn.

- The deflections meant that the atom's mass and charge isn't spread out but must be clustered together.

- The very small number of U-turns must have been caused by 'head-on' collisions with a concentration of mass and positive charge. This meant that such clusters were very small.

- Altogether, this showed that an atom has a tiny cluster of positive charge – a **nucleus**.

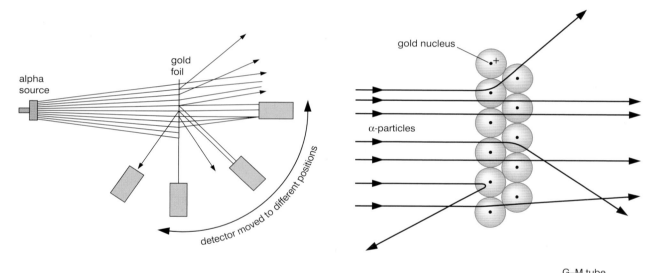

Background radiation

- All ionising radiation is invisible to the naked eye, but it affects photographic plates. Individual particles of ionising radiation can be detected using a Geiger–Müller tube.

- There is *always* ionising radiation present. This is called **background radiation**. Background radiation is caused by radioactivity in soil, rocks and materials like concrete, radioactive gases in the atmosphere and cosmic rays from the Sun.

Radioactivity is measured using a Geiger–Müller tube linked to a counter.

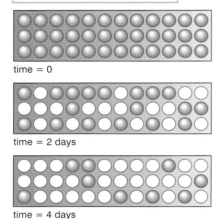

The half-life is 2 days. Half the number of radioactive atoms decays in 2 days.

Half-life

■ The **activity** of a radioactive source is the number of ionising particles it emits each second. Over time, fewer nuclei are left in the source to decay, so the activity drops. The time taken for half the radioactive atoms to decay is called the **half-life**.

■ Starting with a pure sample of radioactive atoms, after one half-life half the atoms will have decayed. The remaining undecayed atoms still have the same chance of decaying as before, so after a second half-life half of the remaining atoms will have decayed. After two half-lives a quarter of the atoms will remain undecayed.

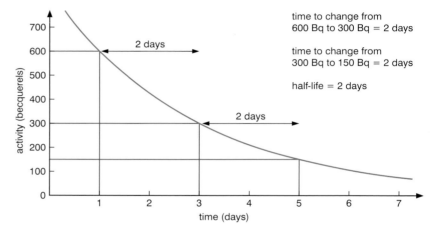

time to change from 600 Bq to 300 Bq = 2 days

time to change from 300 Bq to 150 Bq = 2 days

half-life = 2 days

WORKED EXAMPLE

A radioactive element is detected by a Geiger–Müller tube and counter as having an activity of 400 counts per minute. Three hours later the count is 50 counts per minute. What is the half-life of the radioactive element?

> Write down the activity and progressively halve it. Each halving of the activity is one half-life:
>
> | | |
> |---|---|
> | 0 | 400 counts |
> | 1 half-life | 200 counts |
> | 2 half-lives | 100 counts |
> | 3 half-lives | 50 counts |
>
> 3 hours therefore corresponds to 3 half-lives and 1 hour therefore corresponds to 1 half-life.

Nuclear equations

■ You can write down nuclear changes as **nuclear equations**. Each nucleus is represented by its chemical symbol with two extra numbers written before it. Here is the symbol for Radium-226:

the top number is the **mass number** (the total number of protons and neutrons)

the bottom number is the **atomic number** (the number of protons)

$$^{226}_{88}\text{Ra}$$

■ The mass numbers and atomic numbers must balance on both sides of a nuclear equation.

Alpha decay – the nucleus emits an α-particle (2 protons and 2 neutrons)

radium-226 (parent nucleus)   radon-222 (daughter nucleus)

alpha particle

$^{226}_{88}Ra \rightarrow ^{222}_{86}Rn + ^{4}_{2}\alpha$

Beta decay – a neutron changes into a proton in the the nucleus

polonium-218 (parent nucleus)   astatine-218 (daughter nucleus)

beta particle

$^{218}_{84}Po \rightarrow ^{218}_{85}At + ^{0}_{-1}\beta$

? CHECK YOURSELF QUESTIONS

Q1 The diagram shows some of the results of an experiment using some very thin gold foil that was carried out by the scientist Sir Ernest Rutherford.

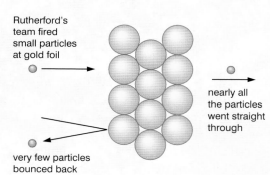

Rutherford's team fired small particles at gold foil

nearly all the particles went straight through

very few particles bounced back

  a What type of radioactive particle did Rutherford use?

  b What did Rutherford deduce from the observation that most of the particles passed straight through the foil?

  c What did Rutherford deduce from the observation that some particles bounced back from the foil?

Q2 The graph shows how a the activity of a sample of sodium-24 changes with time. Activity is measured in becquerels (Bq).

  a Sodium-24 has an atomic number of 11 and a mass number of 24. What is the composition of the nucleus of a sodium-24 atom?

  b Use the graph to work out the half-life of the sodium-24.

Q3 The following equation shows what happens when a nucleus of sodium-24 decays.

$$^{24}_{11}Na \rightarrow ^{x}_{y}Mg + ^{0}_{-1}\beta$$

  a What type of nuclear radiation is produced?

  b What are the numerical values of x and y?

Answers are on page 257.

Uses and dangers of radioactivit

⌐⌐ Radioactivity is dangerous

- Alpha, beta and gamma radiation can all damage living cells. Alpha particles, due to their strong ability to ionise other particles, are particularly dangerous to human tissue. Gamma radiation is dangerous because of its high penetrating power. Nevertheless, radiation can be very useful – it just needs to be used *safely*.

⌐⌐ Uses of radioactivity

- Gamma rays can be used to kill bacteria. This is used in **sterilising** medical equipment and in preserving food. The food can be treated after it has been packaged.

Sheet thickness control.

- A **smoke alarm** includes a small radioactive source that emits alpha radiation. The radiation produces ions in the air which conduct a small electric current. If a smoke particle absorbs the alpha particles, it reduces the number of ions in the air, and the current drops. This sets off the alarm.

- Beta particles are used to monitor the **thickness** of paper or metal. The number of beta particles passing through the material is related to the thickness of the material.

- A gamma source is placed on one side of a weld and a photographic plate on the other side. Weaknesses in the weld will show up on the photographic plate.

- In **radiotherapy** high doses of radiation are fired at cancer cells to kill them.

Tracers detect leaks.

- **Tracers** are radioactive substances with half-lives and radiation types that suit the job they are used for. The half-life must be long enough for the tracer to spread out and to be detected after use but not so long that it stays in the system and causes damage.
  - **Medical tracers** are used to detect blockages in vital organs. A gamma camera is used to monitor the passage of the tracer through the body.
  - **Agricultural tracers** monitor the flow of nutrients through a plant.
  - **Industrial tracers** can measure the flow of liquid and gases through pipes to identify leakages.

⌐⌐ Radioactive dating

- Igneous rock contains small quantities of uranium-238 – a type of uranium that decays with a half-life of 4500 million years, eventually forming lead. The ratio of lead to uranium in a rock sample can be used to calculate the age of the rock. For example, a piece of rock with equal numbers of uranium and lead atoms in it must be 4500 million years old – but this would be unlikely as the Earth is only 4000 million years old!

- Carbon in living material contains a constant, small amount of the radioactive isotope **carbon–14**, which has a half life of 5700 years. When the living material dies the carbon-14 atoms slowly decay. The ratio of carbon-14 atoms to the non-radioactive carbon-12 atoms can be used to calculate the age of the plant or animal material. This method is called **radioactive carbon dating**.

Nuclear fission

- In a nuclear power station atoms of **uranium–235** are bombarded with neutrons and split into two smaller atoms (barium and krypton). This fission of the atoms releases energy, other neutrons and gamma rays.

- The products of the fission are radioactive and so need to be disposed of very carefully.

- The amount of energy produced is considerable – a single kilogram of uranium-235 produces approximately the same amount of energy as 2 000 000 kg of coal!

- Don't confuse this process with the nuclear reactions taking place in the Sun. In the Sun, small atoms combine together to form larger atoms in a process known as **nuclear fusion**. This process also produces huge amounts of energy.

This woman's body was preserved in a bog in Denmark. Radioactive carbon-14 dating showed that she had been there for over 2000 years.

CHECK YOURSELF QUESTIONS

Q1 What type of radiation is used in
- **a** smoke detectors,
- **b** thickness measurement,
- **c** weld checking?

Q2 This question is about tracers.
- **a** What is a tracer?
- **b** The table below shows the half-life of some radioactive isotopes.

Radioactive isotope	Half-life
lawrencium-257	8 seconds
sodium-24	15 hours
sulphur-35	87 days
carbon-14	5700 years

Using the information in the table only, state which one of the isotopes is most suitable to be used as a tracer in medicine. Give a reason for your choice.

Q3 **a** When uranium-238 in a rock sample decays what element is eventually produced?
- **b** Explain how the production of this new element enables the age of the rock sample to be determined.

Answers are on page 258.

Exam tips

- Read each question carefully; this includes looking in detail at any **diagrams**, **graphs** or **tables**. Remember that any information you are given is there to help you to answer the question. Underline or circle the **key words** in the question and **make sure you answer the question that is being asked** rather than the one you wish had been asked!

- Make sure that you understand the meaning of the **'command words'** in the questions. For example:
  - **'Describe'** is used when you have to give the main feature(s) of, for example, a process or structure;
  - **'Explain'** is used when you have to give reasons, e.g. for some experimental results;
  - **'Suggest'** is used when there may be more than one possible answer, or when you will not have learnt the answer but have to use the knowledge you do have to come up with a sensible one;
  - **'Calculate'** means that you have to work out an answer in figures.

- Look at the **number of marks** allocated to each question and also the **space provided** to guide you as to the length of your answer. You need to make sure you include at least as many points in your answer as there are marks, and preferably more. If you really do need more space to answer than provided, then use the nearest available space, e.g. at the bottom of the page, making sure you write down which question you are answering. **Beware of continually writing too much because it probably means you are not really answering the questions.**

- Don't spend so long on some questions that you don't have time to finish the paper. You should spend approximately **one minute per mark**. If you are really stuck on a question, leave it, finish the rest of the paper and come back to it at the end. Even if you eventually have to guess at an answer, you stand a better chance of gaining some marks than if you leave it blank.

- In short answer questions, or multiple-choice type questions, **don't write more than you are asked for**. In some exams, examiners apply the rule that they only mark the first part of the answer written if there is too much. This means that the later part of the answer will not be looked at. In other exams you would not gain any marks, even if the first part of your answer is correct, if you've written down something incorrect in the later part of your answer. This just shows that you haven't really understood the question or are guessing.

- **In calculations always show your working.** Even if your final answer is incorrect you may still gain some marks if part of your attempt is correct. If you just write down the final answer and it is incorrect, you will get no marks at all. Also in calculations you should write down your answers to as many **significant figures** as are used in the question. You may also lose marks if you don't use the correct **units**.

- In some questions, particularly short answer questions, answers of only one or two words may be sufficient, but in longer questions you should aim to use **good English** and **scientific** language to make your answer as clear as possible.

- If it helps you to answer clearly, don't be afraid to also use **diagrams** or **flow charts** in your answers.

- When you've finished your exam, **check through** to make sure you've answered all the questions. Cover over your answers and read through the questions again and check your answers are as good as you can make them.

Biology

1 Your skin plays a vital role in protecting you from infection and in controlling your temperature.
The diagram shows a section through human skin.

pore — hair follicle

nerves —

sweat gland

— blood capillaries

a) Name two places on the diagram where bacteria might gain entry. (2)

pore ✓

hair follicle ✓

b) i) Name the body defence system which recognises that bacteria are not part of the body and should be destroyed. (1)

White blood cells ✓

ii) Explain why the body can react more quickly to infection if it has been previously infected by the same type of bacteria. (2)

The white blood cells remember how to make the right kind of antibodies ✓

c) Some of the structures shown help to control body temperature. For each one listed below, explain how it responds to cold conditions, and how this response helps to keep the body warm. (6)

i) sweat glands. sweat evaporates cooling the skin ✗

ii) hair. Muscles pull the hairs flat so they don't trap a layer of insulating air ✗

iii) blood capillaries. Blood capillaries get smaller so they carry less blood so the skin is paler and cooler ✓

d) 'Signals' to control responses in the skin may be sent either by the nervous system or by the hormone system. Describe the main differences in the way these two systems work. (3)

The nervous system sends signals along nerves but the hormone system sends signals by hormones in the blood. ✓

Signals travel faster along nerves. ✓

⑦/14

(Total 14 marks)

OCR

How to score full marks

a) **If you are provided with information in a question, it will be there to help you to answer the question. If it tells you to use the information, you may not gain full marks if you do not use it.**

In this case you have to name two places 'on the diagram' so if the candidate had for example written 'mouth', which is a place where bacteria could enter, they would not have gained a mark.

b) i) An acceptable answer. 'Immune system' would be better.

ii) The candidate gains one mark for the idea that antibodies can be made quickly. One mark would also have been given for stating that the antibodies would recognise or attack the bacteria and another mark (up to a maximum total of two) would have been given for explaining that some antibodies could remain from the previous infection.

c) i) The candidate has not read the question carefully. The correct answer would have been that less sweat would be produced (one mark) so there would be less evaporation cooling the skin (one mark).

ii) **Make sure you read the question carefully.** This question has been misread. The correct answer would have been that the hairs stand up (one mark) trapping a layer of air as insulation (one mark).

iii) One mark has been gained for explaining that less blood is flowing through the skin because the capillaries contract. The second mark would have been awarded for explaining that this means less heat loss through the skin.

d) **Always look at the number of marks available for an answer.** The candidate should have given three differences to gain full marks. There were two other answers worth one mark each: that nerve signals are electrical and hormonal signals are chemical, and that nerve signals tend to go to one part of the body but hormones travel through the whole body.

● This candidate has gained 7 marks out of a possible 14. A grade C candidate should have gained at least 9 marks.

Exam question and student's answers (Higher Tier)

2 Red-green colour blindness is a sex-linked inherited characteristic. The allele (gene) n for colour-blindness is recessive to the allele N for normal vision. The allele n is carried only on the X chromosome.
Different combinations of alleles produce different characteristics.

a) Describe the characteristics (phenotypes) produced by these combinations. (4)

sex	female ✓	
vision	normal ✓	
sex	male ✓	
vision	colour blind ✓	

b) In a family, Arthur could not understand why he was red-green colour blind when his brother Colin and his parents had normal vision. Use the symbols shown above to explain how this was possible. (4)

mum X X ✔   X Y dad ✔
N   n   N

X Y   X Y ✔

normal = colin N   n   colourblind = arthur

You need only one n gene to be colourblind if you are male. The mum has normal vision because she also has an N gene. ✓

(8/8)

(Total 8 marks)

OCR

⌷ How to score full marks

a) Full marks have been awarded. The candidate correctly identified XX as female and XY as male. As the allele N for normal vision is dominant, the female, who is Nn, has normal vision. Normally you would have to have two copies of a recessive allele to show the recessive condition but in this case the male only needs one copy of the n allele to be red–green colour blind. This is because there is no corresponding part of the Y chromosome to carry a dominant allele. Therefore it is much more likely that more males will show the recessive condition than females. This is why red–green colour blindness is described as a sex-linked condition. If you do not know about sex-linked characteristics **all the information you need is in the start of the question. Always read very carefully all the information you are given in a question** – it is there to help you.

All the necessary points have been identified and the candidate has gained full marks. One mark each has been gained for identifying the genotypes of the parents. As Arthur is red–green colour blind he must have one copy of the n allele. His father has normal vision and as males only carry one allele his father must have one N allele. Therefore the n must have come from his mother, but she too has normal vision so she must have the genotype Nn. The third mark is for showing Arthur's genotype and phenotype and the fourth mark is for showing how Arthur had inherited his genotype.

Parts of the diagram have been missed out, but it seems clear that the candidate understands what is going on, so marks have not been lost for these omissions. As a general rule, **make sure you set out your diagrams like this in full.** The chromosomes can be shown as in the answer but there are acceptable alternatives such as: $X^N X^n$ for the mother, $X^N Y$ for the father and $X^n Y$ for Arthur. Full marks could also have been gained for a labelled Punnett Square instead.

b) The candidate has used the word 'gene' when the term 'allele' would have been correct. On this occasion the candidate has gained full marks, but this might not always happen. **Always try to use scientific terms in your answers – but make sure you use them correctly.**

● This candidate has gained 8 marks out of a possible 8. This is the mark that a grade A or B candidate might be expected to get.

1 This question is about the digestive system.

Look at this diagram of three types of food molecules found in the small intestine.

X   Y   Z

FOUNDATION

a) Which type of food molecule will get into the blood most easily? (1)

b) How do food molecules get into the blood? Write down the name of the process. (1)

c) Why do food molecules need to get into the blood? (1)

d) Chemical substances produced in the intestine digest food.
   i) Write down the name of these chemical substances. (1)
   ii) Explain how they digest food. (1)

OCR

2 The figure below represents the nitrogen cycle.

HIGHER

a) Bacteria play an important part in the nitrogen cycle.

   i) Denitrifying bacteria are anaerobic. Explain why plants growing in waterlogged soil may show signs of nitrogen deficiency. (3)
   ii) Why might a nitrogen deficient soil limit the growth of the plants? (2)

b) Explain why a good crop of wheat would require the addition of a fertiliser containing nitrogen compounds, while a crop of clover grown in the same field would not need the addition of nitrate fertiliser. (4)

c) Why are artificial fertilisers normally applied directly to crops in the **spring** but manure is added to the soil in **autumn**? (4)

OCR

Answers are on pages 258–259.

⌂ Exam question and student's answers (Foundation Tier)

I a) Crude oil was formed in the Earth from marine (sea) deposits over millions of years. Possible conditions are listed below. Tick the two conditions which are needed to change the deposits into crude oil. (2)

low temperatures	
water	
high temperatures	✓
air	
high pressures	✓
a magnetic field	

✓
✓

b) The diagram shows how crude oil can be separated into useful products. (6)

crude oil in

----

kerosene (paraffin out)

fuel oil out

↑ Heat ↑

i) Name the process of separation shown in the diagram.

<u>fractional distillation</u> ✓ ✓

ii) Write the names of TWO more products in the correct spaces in the diagram.

iii) Two elements are present in compounds in all the products obtained. Name these elements.

<u>carbon</u> ✓   and <u>hydrogen</u> ✓

c) When oil has been refined in this way there is often too much fuel oil. The larger molecules of fuel oil can be broken down into smaller, more useful molecules. This is shown in the diagram below.

FUEL OIL	→ PROCESS **X** →	COMPOUNDS WITH SMALLER MOLECULES

(3)

i) What is the name of process X?

<u>cracking</u> ✓

ii) Give TWO conditions used in process X.

heating to high temperature ✓

high pressure ✗ (4)

d) Diesel fuel has a much higher boiling point than petrol.
   i) Which of these fuels is more **volatile**?

   ii) Which of these fuels has larger molecules?

   diesel ✓

   iii) Which fuel poses the greater fire hazard? Explain your answer.

   petrol – it has the smallest molecules and a lower boiling point ✓

10/15 (Total 15 marks)
Edexcel

⌑ How to score full marks

a) The correct responses have been chosen.

b) i) The correct response has been given. **Notice that 2 marks have been awarded.** One for fractional and one for distillation.

   ii) **The candidate has missed this altogether. This often happens when answers have to be written on a chart or diagram given previously.** The lower boiling point liquids (or molecules with the smaller size) are found higher up the column. Hence petrol could have been written on the top line, diesel on the lower line.

   iii) The candidate has correctly appreciated that the compounds are hydrocarbons.

c) i) The correct answer has been given.

   ii) Only one of the conditions is correct, i.e. high temperature. The condition missed is that a catalyst is required. You would not be expected to give the name of the catalyst.

d) i) **The candidate left this part blank. Not a policy to be recommended, especially as there was a 50:50 chance of gaining the mark.** Always have a go. The word volatile means 'readily forms a vapour'. The fuel with the smaller molecules will be the more volatile, i.e. petrol.

   ii) The correct answer was given here.

   iii) Petrol is the correct answer. One mark has been gained for the reason given relating to boiling point. (A similar answer in terms of it having a higher volatility would have been even better.) For the second mark the candidate needed to say that vapour mixes more readily with oxygen than liquid does.

● A mark of 10 out of 15 corresponds to a grade C on this foundation tier question.

2 A student was investigating the effects of acid rain on marble statues. The student found out that the acid rain contains two acids. One of these acids is dilute nitric acid.

The student set up the following apparatus.

Look at the diagram.

gas syringe

dilute nitric acid —

— marble

The student measured the volume of carbon dioxide formed every minute.

The results are shown on the graph.

At the end of the reaction there will be some marble present in the flask.

a) The equation for the reaction taking place is written below.

calcium carbonate + nitric acid → calcium nitrate + water + carbon dioxide

Look at the table. It shows the chemical formula of each substance in the reaction.

Substance	Formula
calcium carbonate	$CaCO_3$
nitric acid	HNO_3
calcium nitrate	$Ca(NO_3)_2$
water	H_2O
carbon dioxide	CO_2

Write down a balanced equation for the reaction. (1)

$CaCO_3 + HNO_3 \rightarrow Ca(NO_3)_2 + H_2O + CO_2$ ✗

b) What was the total volume of carbon dioxide formed after 2 minutes? (1)

Answer 35 ✓ cm^3

c) The experiment was repeated.

The only change was that marble powder was used instead of pieces.

Draw on the graph the curve you would expect. (2)

d) The experiment was repeated a second time.

This time the only change was that warm nitric acid was used instead of cold nitric acid.

Describe and explain, using ideas about reacting particles, the changes you would expect in the reaction. (4)

The reaction of the marble with warm nitric acid would be quicker than the reaction with cold nitric acid. This is because ✓ *the hydrogen ions in the acid will be moving faster and have more energy.* ✓

(5/8)

(Total 8 marks)

OCR

How to score full marks

a) The chemical formulae have been written down correctly to match the word equation but the candidate has not balanced the equation. The equation should have been:

$$CaCO_3(s) + 2HNO_3(aq) \rightarrow Ca(NO_3)_2(aq) + H_2O(l) + CO_2(g)$$

b) The intercept from the graph has been read correctly. **Always take care in reading data from a graph.** In this question the unit was given. If the unit had not been given the candidate would be expected to give the unit as well.

c) The curve has been drawn correctly. One mark is given for drawing the curve steeper (with a greater gradient) than the original curve. This is because the rate of reaction with the powder will be greater due to its increased surface area. The second mark is given for drawing the curve with the same final volume of carbon dioxide. The marble is in excess and so the volume of carbon dioxide depends on the amount of acid used. This remains constant.

d) The candidate has described and explained the changes as the question asks. **Always check what the command words are – in this case 'describe' and 'explain'.** However, only two of the four marks have been scored: one for saying that the reaction would be quicker with the warm acid; one for explaining that this is due to the hydrogen ions in the acid having more energy. The key points missed are: there will be more collisions each second (greater collision frequency) (1 mark) resulting in more effective collisions each second (1 mark).

● Note: The candidate has shown a good understanding of the reaction and has correctly referred to **hydrogen ions** in the acid rather than simply **acid particles. Always use the correct scientific terms.**

● A mark of 5/8 corresponds to a good grade C answer on this higher tier question.

1 Ammonia is used in the manufacture of fertilisers. Ammonia is made in the Haber process.
The equation shows the reaction that takes place in the Haber process.

hydrogen + nitrogen ⇌ ammonia

$$3H_2 \,(g) + N_2 \,(g) \rightleftharpoons 2NH_3 \,(g)$$

a) What does the sign ⇌ represent? (1)

b) The rate of the reaction makes a lot of difference to the cost of making ammonia.
The greater the rate of reaction the cheaper it is to make ammonia.
Suggest **two** ways of increasing the rate of reaction. (2)

c) The large scale manufacture of ammonia by the Haber process has a number of economic, social and environmental effects.
Write about some of the local and global economic, social and environmental effects. (4)

d) The percentage of ammonia formed in the Haber process depends on the pressure and the temperature.
Look at the graphs.

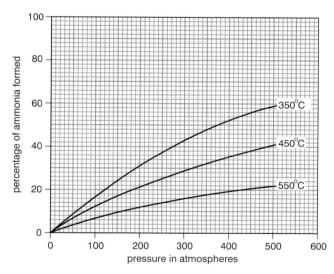

i) What is the percentage of ammonia formed at 350°C and 200 atmospheres pressure? (1)

ii) How does the percentage of ammonia change as the temperature is increased? (1)

iii) How does the percentage of ammonia change as the pressure is increased? (1)

OCR

2 Use your periodic table and your knowledge of more familiar elements to **suggest** answers to the following questions.

You are not expected to **know** about the chemistry of rubidium, iodine and selenium.

a) Rubidium, Rb, has the atomic number 37.
   i) In what group of the periodic table is rubidium? (1)
   ii) Name the two products you would expect when rubidium reacts with water. (2)
   iii) Suggest TWO observations you might SEE during the reaction. (2)

b) Iodine, I, has the atomic number 53. It reacts with hydrogen to form a gas, hydrogen iodide.

$$H_2 + I_2 \rightarrow 2HI$$

Hydrogen iodide is very soluble in water.
   i) Name a common laboratory liquid you would expect to behave like hydrogen iodide solution. (1)
   ii) What TWO products would you expect to be formed when magnesium reacts with hydrogen iodide solution? (2)
   iii) Suggest TWO observations you might SEE during the reaction. (2)

c) Selenium, Se, has the atomic number 34. Selenium trioxide reacts with water to form a new compound.

$$H_2O(l) + SeO_3(s) \rightarrow H_2SeO_4(aq)$$

   i) What effect would the solution have on universal indicator? (1)
   ii) Suggest TWO observations you might SEE when this solution was added to sodium carbonate. (2)
   iii) Name one of the compounds formed in the reaction with sodium carbonate. (1)

Edexcel

Answers are on pages 259–260.

Physics

I A skier is pulled up a slope by holding a handle attached to a moving cable.

The cable passes round pulleys at the top and bottom of the slope.

The pulleys are driven by an electric motor.

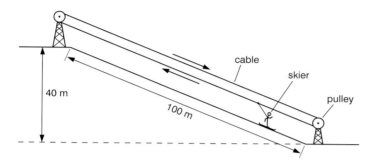

a) The skier weighs 550 N. She travels 100 m along the slope and rises a vertical height of 40 m.

   i) Calculate the useful work done just to lift the skier to the top of the slope. (3)

   Work done   = Force x distance ✓
               = 550 x (100)
               = 55000 J   ✗

   ii) The skier takes 50 s to travel up the slope.

   Use the equation, power = $\dfrac{\text{work done}}{\text{time taken}}$

   to calculate the power needed just to lift her to the top of the slope. (3)

   Power = $\dfrac{55000}{50}$ = 1100

   error carried forward

   Power: 1100 ✓ ✓   unit: watts ✓

b) The power output of the motor is greater than the power needed to just lift the skier to the top of the slope.

   Give two reasons for this. ✓ (2)

   energy is wasted due to friction in the pulleys and between the skis
   and the snow. ✓

(Total 8 marks)

OCR

How to score full marks

a) i) One mark has been given for using the correct formula. However, the incorrect distance has been substituted. The distance must be in a vertical direction as this is the direction the force must act to overcome the gravity. The calculation should have been: work = F s = 550 × 40 = 22000 J

ii) The correct method has been used to calculate the power and the candidate has not been penalised again for the incorrect answer in part (i). **Always carry on with a calculation – you can get marks even if your answer is wrong.** The correct units for power have been given. The correct calculation should have been: power = 22000/50 = 440 W.

b) Both marks have been scored. I mark for appreciating that energy will be transferred due to friction in the pulleys and the second mark for appreciating that friction will also occur between the skis and the snow.

● A mark of 6/8 corresponds to a good grade C on this common question between foundation and higher tiers.

Exam question and student's answers (Higher Tier)

2 a) A student wanted to know what happened to the current flowing in a resistor when the voltage changed. She used the circuit shown in the diagram below. The readings she took are shown in the table.

Voltage in volts	Current in amps
2.0	0.4
4.0	0.8
6.0	1.2
8.0	1.6
10.0	2.0
12.0	2.2
14.0	2.3

i) Plot a graph of her results. (3)

✓
✓
✓

ii) What voltage is needed to get a current of 1.8 A? (1)

9 volts ✓

b) What is the resistance of the resistor she is using? Include in your answer the equation you are going to use. Show clearly how you are going to get your final answer and give the unit. (3)

$V = IR$ ✔ $9 = 1.8 \times R$ $R = 9/1.8$ ✔

$R = 5\ ohms$ ✔

c) Explain why the results she obtained did **not** result in a straight line graph. (3)

Ohm's law ($V = IR$) applies only to certain resistors, in this case current is not directly proportional to voltage and so a curve is formed. ✔

(8/10)

(Total 10 marks)

AQA

⌷ How to score full marks

a) i) All of the points have been plotted correctly (2 marks) and a line through the points has been drawn accurately. **Always take extra care when transferring data from a table to a graph.** As the first set of points are clearly in a straight line, this part of the curve can be drawn with a ruler.

ii) The straight line part of the graph has been correctly used to align a current of 1.8 A with 9 volts. The student has sensibly marked on the graph how this alignment has been done. The mark would not have been awarded if the unit had been missed. **Always give the unit.**

b) Full marks have been awarded. The equation has been given (1 mark), the substitution has been done correctly (1 mark) and the answer worked out correctly. The final mark is only given because the correct units have been given also. **Always write the equation down first.**

c) The candidate has only scored 1 mark here for stating that according to Ohm's law current is directly proportional to voltage. Insufficient explanation has been given to score further marks. **Always look at the number of marks – this will tell you the number of scoring points.** Marks were available for any two of the following points: stating that as the voltage increases the temperature increases (1 mark); this increases the resistance of the resistor (1 mark) causing non-proportionality between voltage and current at the higher voltages (1 mark). This idea is commonly tested on Higher Tier papers.

● A mark of 8/10 corresponds to a grade A on this higher tier question.

I Diagrams A, B, C and D show oscilloscope traces of four different sounds.

FOUNDATION

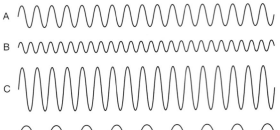

A

B

C

D

time

a) Which diagram, A, B, C or D, represents:
   i) the loudest sound? (1)
   ii) the sound with the highest pitch? (1)

b) The sound labelled C has a frequency of 500 Hz and a speed of 340 m/s.
   Calculate the wavelength of this sound.
   Show your working. (3)

c) The drawing shows how the speed of P-waves change as they travel through the Earth.

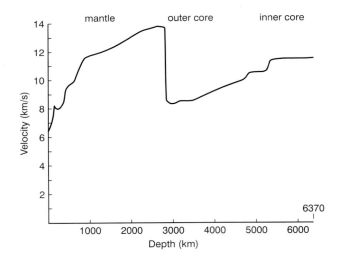

   i) Explain why the speed of the waves falls at a depth of 3000km. (2)
   ii) Explain what evidence the speed of the P-waves through the Earth has given scientists about its internal structure. (4)

   AQA

2 a) i) The diagram shows a transformer.

Primary coil
5 turns
24 V a.c.

Secondary coil
100 turns

Calculate the output voltage. Include in your answer the equation you are going to use. Show clearly how you get your final answer. (2)

(ii) Electrical cables, connected to a transformer, supply a factory with its electrical energy. Explain why it is necessary for the cables to operate at as high a voltage as possible. (3)

b) The relay circuit shown is used to switch on a car starter motor.

battery

N

1A

starter motor

Explain how this relay works when the key is turned. (2)

c) When the switch in the circuit below is closed, in which direction will the bare wire AB move? Explain why. (5)

N

A

d.c.
supply

B

S

bare wires

AQA

Answers are on pages 260–261.

ANSWERS TO CHECK YOURSELF QUESTIONS

UNIT 1: LIFE PROCESSES AND CELLS
1 Characteristics of living things (page 1)

Q1a It does not contain any chloroplasts (and therefore no chlorophyll).

> **Comment** Any green parts of a plant will contain chloroplasts.

Q1b Onions grow underground, so they will not receive any light. There is no point in them having chloroplasts as they will not be able to photosynthesise.

> **Comment** By going into detail and mentioning photosynthesis you show clearly that you understand the reason.

Q1c It has a cell wall, a large vacuole and a regular shape.

> **Comment** There are some exceptions, in that some plant cells may not have large vacuoles or a regular shape. But they all have a cell wall.

Q2a Mitochondria.

> **Comment** This is a better answer than simply saying cytoplasm.

Q2b Cell membrane.

> **Comment** Don't forget that everything that goes in or out of a cell goes through the membrane.

Q2c Nucleus or chromosomes. Both are correct.

> **Comment** Chromosomes is a more specific answer and shows more understanding.

Q2d Vacuole.

> **Comment** Don't forget that only plants have large vacuoles.

Q2e Cell wall.

> **Comment** The membrane would simply burst if the cell became too big. The cell wall is more rigid and resists this. You will find out more about this in Unit 4.

Q3a Organism.

Q3b Cell.

Q3c System.

Q3d Organ.

Q3e Tissue.

Q3f Organ.

> **Comment** Organisms are whole animals or plants. (Don't forget that there are some organisms, like bacteria, which are only one cell big.) Organs are the separate parts of a body, each of which has its own job(s). Organs are usually made of different groups of cells (tissues).

2 Transport into and out of cells (page 3)

Q1 The salt forms a very concentrated solution on the slug's surface so water leaves its body by osmosis.

> **Comment** This happens with slugs because their skin is partially permeable. It would not happen with us because our skin is not.

Q2a Diffusion.

> **Comment** There is a lower concentration of carbon dioxide inside the leaf as it is continually being used up.

Q2b Neither.

> **Comment** The food is squeezed along by muscles in the gullet.

Q2 c Neither.

> **Comment** Again, water is being forced out.

Q2 d Osmosis.

> **Comment** As the celery is dried up the cells contain very concentrated solutions.

Q3 To provide energy for the active transport of minerals like nitrates into the roots.

> **Comment** The concentration of minerals in soils is usually lower than the concentration of minerals in plant cells. Plants therefore can't rely on diffusion to get more of these minerals and must expend energy on actively 'pulling' them in.

UNIT 2: HUMAN BODY SYSTEMS
1 Respiration (page 6)

Q1 To provide energy for life processes like movement and to generate warmth.

> **Comment** Don't give vague answers like 'to stay alive'. If a question in an examination has several marks then give the correct number of points in your answer.

Q2 In every cell of the body.

> **Comment** You could be even more specific and point out that respiration occurs in the cytoplasm or in the mitochondria. Many examination candidates confuse respiration and breathing, and would have said 'lungs'.

Q3 a Aerobic respiration provides more energy (for the same amount of glucose) and does not produce lactic acid (which will have to be broken down).

> **Comment** Given sufficient oxygen, respiration will be aerobic.

Q3 b If more energy is needed and the oxygen necessary cannot be provided.

> **Comment** Anaerobic respiration is not as efficient as aerobic respiration. It is only used as a 'top up' to aerobic respiration.

2 Blood and the circulatory system (page 8)

Q1 Substances, for example oxygen, will quickly diffuse into the centre of a small organism. For larger organisms, diffusion would take too long so a transport system is needed to ensure quick movement of substances from one part of the organism to another.

> **Comment** Another way of explaining this is to say that smaller organisms have a larger surface area to volume ratio (or a larger surface relative to their size).

Q2 a In the lungs.

> **Comment** The blood arriving at the lungs contains little oxygen and is there to collect more.

Q2 b In respiring tissues around the body.

> **Comment** Every cell will need oxygen. Active cells like those in muscles will need most.

Q2 c To ensure that their bodies collect enough oxygen.

> **Comment** If the air contains less oxygen then less oxygen will enter the blood unless the body has some way of compensating.

Q3 a The ventricles pump the blood but the atria simply receive the blood before it enters the ventricles.

> **Comment** The ventricle walls contract and relax to squeeze out blood and take more in. This takes a lot of muscle. The atria, by comparison, do not need to squeeze as hard and must be easily inflated by the incoming low-pressure blood.

Q3 b The left ventricle has to pump blood around the whole body (apart from the lungs). The right ventricle 'only' sends blood to the lungs.

Comment This is why your heart sounds louder on your left side.

Q4 a Veins have valves, thinner walls and a larger lumen.

Comment The veins contain blood at a reduced pressure and are built so that they don't resist the flow of blood but rather help it on its way to the lungs.

Q4 b Capillary walls are permeable, allowing diffusion. Arteries and veins do not have permeable walls.

Comment The arteries carry blood quickly to each organ or part of the body and the veins bring it back. The capillaries form a branching network inside organs.

3 Breathing (page 13)

Q1 a Just two, the wall of the alveolus and the wall of the blood capillary.

Comment This short distance is important so gases can easily move between the alveoli and the blood. Another way of looking at it is that the short distance increases the concentration gradient.

Q1 b To ensure that oxygen rapidly diffuses from the area of high concentration, in the alveoli, to the area of low concentration, in the blood.

Comment Don't forget that there is also a concentration gradient for carbon dioxide.

Q2 The diaphragm lowers and the ribcage moves upwards and outwards.

Comment Both of these changes increase the volume of the thorax.

Q3 To keep them open to ensure that air can move freely.

Comment This is particularly important because when the air pressure drops to take in more air from the outside this could otherwise make the air passages close in on themselves.

4 Digestion (page 16)

Q1 a Proteins are too big to pass through the wall of the ileum, so they have to be broken down into the smaller amino acids.

Comment Only molecules that are already small do not need to be digested.

Q1 b Physical digestion is simply breaking food into smaller pieces. This is a physical change. Chemical digestion breaks down larger molecules into smaller ones. This is a chemical change because new substances are formed.

Comment Many candidates, if asked to describe digestion, lose marks because they do not describe the breakdown of **molecules**.

Q1 c They are denatured.

Comment This means they change their shape irreversibly, and can not work. In an examination **do not** say that they are 'killed' because they were never alive.

Q1 d To neutralise the acid from the stomach, because the enzymes in the small intestine can not work at an acidic pH.

Comment Many candidates think that stomach acid itself breaks down food. It is the fact that it allows enzymes in the stomach to work that is important.

Q2 a Ingestion is taking in food. Egestion is passing out the undigested remains. Excretion is getting rid of things we have made.

Comment Many candidates lose marks because they confuse egestion and excretion. Passing out faeces is egestion. Getting rid of urea in urine or breathing out carbon dioxide are examples of excretion because these substances are made in the body.

Q2 b Ingestion: mouth. Egestion: anus.

Comment Excretion occurs in various places. You will find out more in Unit 3.

Q3 They provide a large surface area. They have thin permeable walls. They have a good blood supply causing a concentration gradient. They are both moist.

Comment The similarities are not a coincidence. These factors are vital to ensure the efficient absorption of the different substances.

UNIT 3: BODY MAINTENANCE
1 The nervous system (page 21)

Q1 a A change, either in the surroundings or inside the body, that is detected by the body.

Comment For example, if you were crossing a road and noticed a bus approaching the stimuli would have been the sight and sound of the bus.

Q1 b Receptors detect (sense) stimuli. The sense organs are receptors. Effectors are the parts of the body that respond. Effectors are usually muscles but can also be glands.

Comment Some candidates get confused between effectors and the 'effects' that they produce.

Q2 a Brain and spinal cord.

Comment Many reflexes do not need the brain in order to function and the spinal cord is therefore not simply a nerve pathway to and from the brain but also processes some information itself.

Q2 b Neurones are nerve cells. A nerve in the body is usually a bundle of neurones wrapped in connective tissue.

Comment In exam questions you may pick up extra marks for using the correct terms.

Q2 c Membrane, cytoplasm, nucleus.

Comment Although neurones are specialised they are still cells and so share these features with other cells.

Q2 d Cell body, nerve fibres (axons or dendrons), nerve endings or dendrites. Any two.

Comment If you are asked for a certain number of answers in an exam only answer up to that number as any more will not be marked.

Q3 a A and C.

Comment The others do involve some kind of response, but reflexes happen **automatically** – without thought.

Q3 b Since they do not have to be thought about, reflexes happen very quickly. This means that if there is some kind of danger you can respond very quickly to reduce or prevent any harm.

Comment It is possible to override some reflexes by thinking about it, so you could hold on to something hot even though that is not usually a very wise thing to do.

2 The endocrine system (page 26)

Q1 In the nervous system, signals are sent very quickly as electro-chemical impulses along neurones and the effects of the signal usually last a short time. In the endocrine system signals are sent more slowly as hormones through the blood and the effects usually last longer.

Comment Both of these systems are involved in co-ordination (responding to stimuli). Both are needed because of the different nature of their effects.

Q2 a Fighting and running away both need energy. This is released by respiration, which uses oxygen to release energy from glucose. So breathing increases to take in more oxygen, and glucose is released from stores in the liver and muscles. The blood is redirected and heart rate increased to carry the oxygen and glucose quickly to the muscles that need it. Sweating starts because the body will need cooling. Hairs stand up and pupils dilate to make an animal look larger and more fierce.

Comment Although an exam question may be apparently about one particular topic, to gain full marks you might have to include ideas from other topics. In this example ideas about respiration are relevant. This is likely to happen in questions that require extended answers.

Q2 b Otherwise all the effects caused by adrenaline would persist.

Comment Where hormones are involved, constant fine adjustments need to be made – for example, in the amounts of insulin required in the blood. If hormones are not being constantly broken down and at the same time secreted this balance could not be maintained.

Q3 Glucose and glycogen are both carbohydrates, but glucose is made of small molecules that dissolve in the blood whereas glycogen is made of larger molecules (lots of glucose molecules joined together) that are insoluble and do not travel through the blood. Glucagon is a hormone that converts glycogen back into glucose (i.e. it does the opposite of insulin).

Comment It is very common for candidates to confuse these – especially glycogen and glucagon.

3 Homeostasis (page 30)

Q1 The farmer will have been sweating to stay cool and so will have lost water this way. Unless the farmer has drunk a lot, his or her kidneys will have to reduce the amount of water that is lost as urine. This is why there is less. However, there will be just as much urea, so the urine is more concentrated and darker in colour.

Comment The body has to lose extra water by sweating to maintain body temperature. Humans cannot reduce how much is lost in breathing as the lining of the alveoli in the lungs is always moist, nor can the amount lost in faeces be reduced greatly. The only way therefore to cut down on losses is to reduce urine output.

Q2 They remove carbon dioxide and water from the body.

Comment Excretion is the removal of substances that have been produced in the body. Carbon dioxide is a waste product of respiration, as is some of the water.

Q3 The veins would have a lower concentration of salt and urea than the arteries. Also, as with any other organ, the oxygen level and blood pressure would be lower.

Comment Although most other substances in the blood (e.g. glucose) are also initially filtered from the blood, most are the absorbed back before the blood leaves the kidneys. Also, don't forget that the arteries are carrying blood away from the heart into the kidneys, and the veins the reverse.

4 Good health (page 34)

Q1 a Red blood cells are needed in large quantities to carry oxygen, whereas white blood cells are fighting infection and most of the time we are not recovering from diseases.

Q1 b When there is an infection to fight off.

> **Comment** Even when we are making lots of white blood cells to fight an infection there are many times more red blood cells.

Q2 Your white blood cells remember how to make large quantities of the measles antibody quickly. If the measles virus ever entered your body again you would fight it off before it had a chance to multiply and cause the symptoms of measles.

> **Comment** You only 'have a disease' when the micro-organism has had a chance to multiply and spread.

Q3 As reaction times are slower and judgement is impaired you are much more likely to have an accident.

> **Comment** This does not just apply if you are 'drunk'. Drinking and driving is dangerous because the alcohol affects you to some extent, even after one drink. In exams a common shortcoming is to say drinking and driving is dangerous because you may have an accident, which is not wrong but might not get full marks. Always try to go beyond common-sense type answers and give a scientific reason.

UNIT 4: PLANTS
I Photosynthesis (page 38)

Q1 Carbon dioxide from the air enters the leaves through the stomata. Water moves from the soil into the roots and up the stem to the leaves.

> **Comment** As plants cannot move around, their raw materials have to be readily available. Note that sunlight is not a raw material. It is the energy source that drives the chemical reaction.

Q2 Starch is not soluble.

> **Comment** Starch is a useful storage material but needs to be broken down into smaller molecules to be able to dissolve.

Q3 Being broad allows as much light as possible to be absorbed. Being thin allows carbon dioxide to quickly reach the photosynthesising cells.

> **Comment** There are exceptions to this principle. See page 45 about cactus spines and pine needles.

2 Transport in plants (page 42)

Q1 Xylem is made of dead cells. It carries water and minerals from the roots, up the stem, to the leaves. Phloem is made of living cells. It carries dissolved food substances from the leaves to other parts of the plant.

> **Comment** Make sure you can also identify the xylem and phloem in diagrams of sections of roots, stems and leaves.

Q2 On a sunny day the guard cells will fully open the stomata, allowing water vapour to pass out more easily. When it is hot, water evaporates more quickly into the air spaces inside the leaf, which causes the water vapour to diffuse more quickly out of the leaf.

> **Comment** Don't forget that if the plant is losing more water than it is taking in it will start to wilt. In this case the stomata will start to close, so reducing transpiration.

Q3 In a turgid cell the cytoplasm presses hard against the cell wall because the cell contains as much water as it can. This gives the cell rigidity. In a plasmolysed cell so much water has been lost that the cytoplasm shrinks and comes away from the cell wall. A plasmolysed cell is flexible and can't keep a fixed shape.

> **Comment** In a healthy plant none of the cells should be plasmolysed. Remember that when cells become plasmolysed, although the cytoplasm shrinks and the membrane with it, the cell wall does not.

3 Minerals (page 46)

Q1 a Nitrogen and sulphur.

Comment Plants do not take in and use the pure elements. For example, there is a lot of nitrogen in the air (79%), but in its pure form it is very unreactive and the plants cannot use it.

Q1 b Protein is used to make new cells. For example, cell membranes contain protein.

Comment This applies to animals as well as to plants.

Q2 Magnesium is found in chlorophyll, the green pigment that gives plants their colour. Without it they cannot be green.

Comment Chlorophyll is actually chemically similar to haemoglobin in the blood, but contains magnesium instead of iron.

Q3 Minerals are absorbed by active transport. This means that energy is required, which is provided by the mitochondria.

Comment Remember that although water and minerals both enter through the roots, water enters by osmosis, which is a 'passive' process – it does not require energy.

4 Plant hormones (page 47)

Q1 Plant hormones are not made in glands. Nor are they carried in the blood.

Comment It is because of these differences that many people refer to them as growth regulators instead. Look back at Unit 3 if you need to revise about animal hormones.

Q2 A, C and D.

Comment Plant hormones affect growth and development. Pollination is simply the transfer of pollen between flowers.

Q3 Auxin is no longer concentrated more on one side than the other, so one side does not grow more than the other.

Comment Remember that growth in tropisms is by cell elongation, not the formation of new cells by cell division.

UNIT 5: ECOLOGY AND THE ENVIRONMENT
I The study of ecology (page 49)

Q1 This is because the taller trees will be taking most of the light and with their roots taking most of the water and minerals from the soil.

Comment This is an example of **competition**, in which the trees are out-competing the smaller plants for these important resources.

Q2 If the numbers of rabbits went down, foxes would just concentrate their diet on other things. For example, many foxes live in towns, scavenging rubbish. If foxes died out, other things, including humans, would still kill rabbits.

Comment There are very few other large animals in northern Canada, which is why the example of lynxes and snowshoe hares is unusual in showing so clearly the way that predators and prey affect each other.

Q3 a The greenfly numbers would go down.

Q3 b There would have to be enough food to feed them and they would have already eaten most of their prey.

Comment Numbers of most species alter a little each year, but they are usually kept more or less constant because of factors like food supply and predation.

2 Relationships between organisms in an ecosystem (page 52)

Q1 a
ladybirds
aphids
rose bushes

Q1 b
ladybirds
aphids
rose bushes

Comment In a food chain where the producers are much larger than their consumers the pyramid of numbers is inverted. However, the pyramid of biomass is always a normal pyramid shape.

Q2 It is more energy efficient to eat plant crops rather than to raise animals. This is because we are eating at a lower trophic level. At each transfer between trophic levels energy is transferred away from a food chain.

Comment **Ecologically**, therefore, it is much more efficient to be vegetarian.

Q3 Energy is lost at each stage of a food chain, so there is a limit as to how long a food chain can be.

Comment This is why pyramids of biomass are always a pyramid shape.

3 Natural recycling (page 56)

Q1 a Photosynthesis.

Comment Make sure you remember the details of photosynthesis from Unit 4.

Q1 b Respiration and combustion.

Comment Until the last few hundred years combustion played quite a small part in this. It is now playing a bigger role and this is the reason for the build up of carbon dioxide in the atmosphere.

Q2 This is the only way they can get the nitrogen they need.

Comment The nitrogen is made available by digesting the protein in the insects' bodies.

Q3 Nitrifying bacteria produce nitrates from decayed remains. Denitrifying bacteria convert nitrates and other nitrogen compounds into nitrogen gas.

Comment Denitrifying bacteria therefore have an opposite effect to nitrogen-fixing bacteria.

4 Human influences on the environment (page 59)

Q1 They do not easily break down and so remain in the bodies of organisms that have taken them in.

Comment This is the reason they accumulate in animals and are passed along food chains.

Q2 The greenhouse effect describes how some of the gases in the atmosphere restrict heat escaping from the Earth. Global warming is an increase in the Earth's temperature that may well be caused by an *increased* greenhouse effect.

Comment Remember that it is the **increased** greenhouse effect that people are concerned about. A greenhouse effect is not only normal but essential for life on Earth.

Q3 This would increase their costs, which would have to be passed on to their customers, who might not want to pay more.

Comment An added problem is that, unlike pollution into rivers, the problems caused by acid rain take place a long way from the source of the pollution.

5 Sampling techniques (page 66)

Q1 a Tullgren funnel.

Q1 b Pitfall trap.

Q1 c Beating tray and then a pooter.

Q1 d Pooter.

Comment Check with your teacher whether your science exam will ask you questions about these.

Q2 The average number of dandelions in 1 quadrat (1 m^2) was $25 \div 10 = 2.5$. The field is 200 m^2 so the total number of dandelions is $2.5 \times 200 = 500$.

Comment You might have to do some maths so don't forget your calculator in your exam.

Q3 If the pupil in the previous question had only placed her quadrat where there were dandelions and had deliberately missed out those areas without any she would have calculated a much higher estimate.

Comment It is for the same reason, to get a more reliable average and total estimate, that you also need to take a reasonably large number of measurements before you work out your average.

UNIT 6: GENETICS AND EVOLUTION
1 Variation (page 68)

Q1 a A, C and E.

Q1 b B and D.

Comment If the features fall into distinct groups they are discontinuous. If they do not, they are continuous.

Q2 a Eye colour, height, shape of face (there are other examples). These are genetic features and as they are identical twins they will have the same genes.

Q2 b Skin colour, accent, how muscular they are (there are other examples). These features are affected by the environment. They are doing different jobs in different climates, so their environments are different.

Comment Some features like eye colour are purely genetically controlled and so will be identical. Some features like accent are purely environmentally controlled and so would probably differ. Many features, like skin colour, are controlled both by genes and the environment (i.e. tanning) so they would also show differences.

Q3 Chemical base, gene, chromosome, cell nucleus, cell.

Comment Look back at the diagram on page 69 if you're not sure.

2 Inheritance (page 72)

Q1 Let R be the dominant allele for tongue rolling and r the recessive allele for not being able to roll your tongue.

parents:	Rr	Rr

gametes: R r R r

F$_1$ generation:	RR	Rr	Rr	rr
	(roller)	(roller)	(roller)	(non-roller)

Comment If not being able to roll your tongue is a recessive condition then the 'non-roller' child must be rr. This means each parent must have at least one r allele. As the parents can roll their tongues they must therefore both be Rr.

Q2 Cross the spotted leopard with a known ss leopard. If there are any black cubs then they must be ss and have received one of the s alleles from the spotted parent, which must therefore be Ss. If there are no black cubs the spotted parent is likely to be an SS. The random nature of fertilisation means that an Ss leopard may still produce no ss cubs, but this is unlikely with a large litter.

Comment *Crossing with a homozygous recessive is known as a test cross or back cross. It is used because the homozygous recessive is the only genotype that can be identified by the phenotype alone.*

Q3 As neither has the condition both must be heterozygous carriers of the recessive allele if their child has two copies of the recessive allele. The probability of a child being homozygous recessive, i.e. having cystic fibrosis, is 1 in 4.

Comment *Look back at the monohybrid cross shown on page 73. You can see that the offspring showing the recessive condition are in the ratio 1:3 to those showing the dominant condition. Another way of saying this is that there is a 1 in 4 chance of a child being homozygous recessive and showing the recessive condition. The fact that the couple have one child with the condition is not a consideration.*

3 Applications (page 76)

Q1 Pick sheep with finer wool than the others. Breed these together. From the offspring pick those with the finest wool and breed these. Continue this over many generations.

Comment *The principle of selective breeding is the same whatever the example.*

Q2 *Advantages:* many roses with identical flowers can be produced relatively quickly. This would be useful if the roses on this particular plant sold well. *Disadvantages:* there is no variation, so if one rose was attacked by a plant disease then all the rest would be susceptible too.

Comment *The key point about cloning is that the new plants are genetically identical. This may or may not be an advantage.*

Q3 New combinations of genes can be produced quickly and reliably with genetic engineering. Genetic engineering allows genes to be taken from one species and given to another, which could not be done with selective breeding as different species cannot breed together.

Comment *The second answer is probably the more important. For example, a gene for resistance to a particular disease could be taken from one species and given to another.*

4 Evolution (page 79)

Q1 a Vertebrates have hard body parts, e.g. bones and teeth, which can leave fossil remains, whereas many invertebrates have only soft body parts which rarely leave fossils.

Comment *This does not apply to all invertebrates. There are many remains of the shells of marine invertebrates. Even so, these leave little evidence of what the soft tissues were like.*

Q1 b There are many reasons, such as: the remains of the animals did not lie undisturbed in the right environmental conditions to form fossils, fossils were formed but have been destroyed – e.g. by erosion – or the fossils have not been found yet.

Comment *Although the fossil record of evolution is incomplete and may not give detailed information about how all living things evolved it is still a very important source of evidence.*

Q2 Among the shorter-necked ancestors there would have been *variation* in height. A giraffe that was only slightly taller than others would have been able to reach and feed on some leaves that others would not have been able to. They would have had a slight *advantage* in the *competition* for food and so would be slightly better fed and slightly more healthy than shorter ones. They would therefore probably on average live a little longer and be able to successfully rear slightly more offspring. If they were able to pass on the longer neck to their offspring because it was a *genetic* feature, it would mean both that there would be more of their offspring than of the shorter-necked giraffes and that the overall average height of the giraffe population would have increased. If this continued for many, many generations it would lead to the giraffes we see today.

Comment In an exam, questions about natural selection will often require extended answers and may carry four or more marks. To get full marks you will need to give a detailed response. Do not be put off if the example is unfamiliar. This is to test that you understand the **process**, which will be the same in each case. Note that natural selection favours features that give an advantage but will not always result in evolutionary change. In the example of the giraffe, being taller than they are today would pose disadvantages, e.g. the difficulty of pumping blood to the brain or problems of stability, which means that they will not just continue to get taller. Some animals alive today are known as 'living fossils' as they appear similar to ancient fossil remains. If an organism's environment has not changed significantly and it is well adapted to it, then natural selection would work to keep the animal's features the same.

UNIT 7: CHEMICAL FORMULAE AND EQUATIONS
1 How are chemical formulae calculated? (page 82)

Q1 a $NaCl$

Comment Na (group 1) combining power 1, Cl (group 7) combining power 1.

Q1 b MgF_2

Comment Mg (group 2) combining power 2, F (group 7) combining power 1. 2, 1, cross over = Mg1 F2 = MgF_2.

Q1 c AlN

Comment Al (group 3) combining power 3, N (group 5) combining power 3. 3, 3, cancel = Al1 N1 = AlN

Q1 d Li_2O

Comment Li (group 1) combining power 1, O (group 6) combining power 2.

Q1 e CO_2

Comment C (group 4) combining power 4, O (group 6) combining power 2. 4, 2, cancel = C1 O2 = CO_2.

Q2 a Fe_2O_3

Comment Fe combining power 3, O (group 6) combining power 2.

Q2 b PCl_5

Comment P combining power 5, Cl (group 7) combining power 1.

Q2 c $CrBr_3$

Comment Cr combining power 3, Br (group 7) combining power 1.

Q2d SO_3

Comment S combining power 6, O (group 6) combining power 2. 6, 2, cancel = S1 03 = SO_3.

Q2e SO_2

Comment S combining power 4, O (group 6) combining power 2. 4, 2, cancel = S1 02 = SO_2.

Q3a K_2CO_3

Comment K combining power 1, CO_3 combining power 2.

Q3b NH_4Cl

Comment NH_4 combining power 1, Cl (group 7) combining power 1.

Q3c H_2SO_4

Comment H combining power 1, SO_4 combining power 2.

Q3d $Mg(OH)_2$

Comment Mg (group 2) combining power 2, OH combining power 1. Don't forget the brackets.

Q3e $(NH_4)_2SO_4$

Comment NH_4 combining power 1, SO_4 combining power 2. Don't forget the brackets.

2 Chemical equations (page 85)

Q1a $C + O_2 \rightarrow CO_2$

Comment This doesn't need balancing!

Q1b $4Fe + 3O_2 \rightarrow 2Fe_2O_3$

Comment Remember that balancing numbers must always go in front of symbols and formulae.

Q1c $2Fe_2O_3 + 3C \rightarrow 4Fe + 3CO_2$

Comment One maths trick to use here is to realise that the number of oxygen atoms on the right-hand side must be even. Putting a '2' in front of Fe_2O_3 makes the oxygen on the left-hand side even too.

Q1d $CaCO_3 + 2HCl \rightarrow CaCl_2 + CO_2 + H_2O$

Comment Note that the carbonate radical does not appear on both sides of the equation.

Q2a $Ca^{2+} + CO_3^{2-} \rightarrow CaCO_3$
Q2b $Fe^{2+} + 2OH^- \rightarrow Fe(OH)_2$
Q2c $Ag^+ + Br^- \rightarrow AgBr$

Comment The symbols and charges must balance on each side of the equation. State symbols could be used,
e.g. $Fe^{2+}(aq) + 2OH^-(aq) \rightarrow Fe(OH)_2(s)$
$Ag^+(aq) + Br^-(aq) \rightarrow AgBr(s)$.

Q3a $Al^{3+} + 3e^- \rightarrow Al$
Q3b $Na \rightarrow Na^+ + e^-$
Q3c $2O^{2-} \rightarrow O_2 + 4e^-$
Q3d $2Br^- \rightarrow Br_2 + 2e^-$

Comment At the cathode positive ions gain electrons. At the anode negative ions lose electrons. Remember that symbols and charges must balance.

UNIT 8: STRUCTURE AND BONDING
1 How are atoms put together? (page 89)

Q1a The atomic number is the number of protons in an atom. (It is equal to the number of electrons.)

Comment Always define atomic number in terms of protons. However, as atoms are neutral there will always be equal numbers of protons and electrons.

Q1 b The mass number is the total number of protons and neutrons in an atom.

Comment Remember that electrons have very little mass and so mass number cannot refer to electrons.

Q2
Si	14	14	14	2,8,4
Mg	12	14	12	2,8,2
S	16	16	16	2,8,6
Ar	18	22	18	2,8,8

Comment The top number is the mass number and the bottom (smaller) number is the atomic number. The difference between the two numbers is the number of neutrons.

Q3 a (i) C; (ii) B; (iii) C or E or F; (iv) B; (v) C

Comment To have no overall charge the number of protons (positive charges) must equal the number of electrons (negative charges).
The atomic number (number of protons) is unique to a particular element. It is the atomic number that defines the element's position in the periodic table.

Q3 b

Comment Remember that an atomic diagram should show the number of protons and neutrons in the nucleus and the number and arrangement of electrons.

2 Chemical Bonding
(page 92)

Q1 a Covalent

Q1 b covalent

Q1 c ionic

Q1 d covalent

Q1 e ionic.

Comment Remember that ionic bonding involves a metal and a non-metal; covalent bonding involves two or more non-metals. Hydrogen, chlorine, carbon, oxygen and bromine are non-metals. Only sodium and calcium in the list are metals.

Q2 a K^+

Q2 b Al^{3+}

Q2 c S^{2-}

Q2 d F^-.

Comment These can be worked out from the position of the element in the periodic table. Look back in the unit for the rule if you have forgotten it. You will always be given a periodic table in the exam. Get used to using it: it will help you to gain marks in the exam.

Q3 a

Q3 b

O=O

Q3 c

N≡N

Q3 d

Q3 e

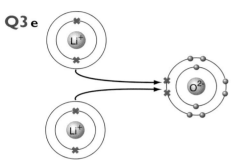

1 Remember that covalent compounds contain non-metals.

2 You can get the atomic number (needed to work out the number of electrons) from the periodic table.

3 With covalent compounds try drawing the displayed formula first. You will need to work out how many covalent bonds each atom can form. Again, the periodic table will help you. For example, oxygen is in Group 6 so it can form two covalent bonds. Once you have got the displayed formula, each bond corresponds to a shared pair of electrons. Don't forget the first electron shell can hold 2 electrons, others hold 8 electrons. So don't miss any electrons out.

4 In examples of ionic bonding don't forget to write the formulae of the ions that are formed.

3 Structures and properties (page 96)

Q1 a Potassium chloride exists as a giant ionic lattice. There are very strong electrostatic forces holding the ions together. A considerable amount of energy is needed to overcome the forces of attraction so the melting point is high.

Comment The key ideas relating to melting point are: strong forces between particles; large amounts of energy needed to overcome these forces.

Q1 b Potassium chloride is ionically bonded. When molten or dissolved in water the ions are free to move and carry an electric current.

Comment Remember that an electrolyte allows an electric current to flow through it when molten or dissolved in water – not when in the solid state.

Q2 a The carbon atoms are held by strong covalent bonds within the hexagonal layers. This can give a structure great strength.

Comment Have a look at the diagram of the structure of graphite. Remember that covalent bonds are strong bonds.

Q2 b Only three out of the four of carbon's outer shell electrons are used in forming covalent bonds. Each atom has an electron which is only loosely held to the atom. When a voltage is applied these electrons move, forming an electric current.

Comment Graphite has a structure similar to that of metals – there is a 'cloud' of electrons which are free to move. For more on metal structures see Unit 14.

Q3 The bonds within the molecule are strong (the intramolecular bonds) but the bonds holding the methane molecules together are weak (intermolecular bonds). Therefore methane molecules require very little energy to be separated from each other.

Comment This is one of the ideas candidates find very confusing. Always try to be precise. There are bonds within a molecule as well as bonds between molecules. You wouldn't be expected to use 'intramolecular' and 'intermolecular', but if you do be sure to get them the right way round!

UNIT 9: FUELS AND ENERGY
1 How do we obtain fossil fuels? (page 98)

Q1 a Small sea creatures died, their bodies settled in the mud at the bottom of the oceans and decayed. They were compressed over a period of millions of years and slowly changed into crude oil.

Comment Remember the process involves compression and takes place over millions of years. Do not confuse crude oil with coal, which is formed from plant material.

Q1 b It takes millions of years to form. Once supplies have been used up they cannot be replaced.

Comment A common mistake is to say 'it cannot be used again'. No fuel can be used again but some, such as trees (wood), can be regrown quite quickly. Wood is therefore renewable.

Q2 a Fractional distillation.

Comment There is often a mark for 'fractional' and a mark for 'distillation'.

Q2 b The boiling point of the fractions decreases.

Comment Remember the column is hotter at the bottom than at the top.

Q2 c Components that have boiling points just above the temperature of X will condense to a liquid. Components which have boiling points below the temperature of X will remain as vapour and continue up the column.

Comment If a vapour is cooled below its boiling point it will condense.

Q2 d The component would be not very runny (viscous), very dark yellow/orange in colour, very difficult to light and very smoky when burning.

Comment Again the clues are in the table. A fuel needs to ignite easily and be 'clean'.

Q2 e It would not ignite easily. It would produce a lot of soot when burning.

Comment In a question like this, the clues to the answer will be in the table. Always give as full an answer as possible. Four points can be scored using the last three columns of the table.

Q3 a A compound containing carbon and hydrogen atoms only.

Comment Don't miss out the word 'only'. A lot of compounds contain carbon and hydrogen but are not hydrocarbons (e.g. glucose, $C_6H_{12}O_6$).

Q3 b High temperature, catalyst.

Comment 'Catalytic crackers' are used at oil refineries.

Q3 c C_8H_{18}.

Comment The equation must balance so the number of carbon atoms must be $10 - 2$, the number of hydrogen atoms $22 - 4$.

2 How are hydrocarbons used? (page 102)

Q1 a petrol + oxygen $\rightarrow$ carbon dioxide + water

Comment All hydrocarbons produce carbon dioxide and water when burnt in a plentiful supply of air. It is much better to use oxygen rather than air in the equation.

Q1 b Shortage of oxygen.

Comment Remember this is incomplete combustion.

Q1 c The carbon monoxide combines with the haemoglobin in the blood, preventing oxygen from doing so. Supply of oxygen to the body is reduced. Specifically this can quickly cause the death of brain cells.

Comment A much more detailed answer is required than 'it causes suffocation'.

Q2 a (i)

hexane

Q2 a (ii)

hexene

> Comment Remember 'hex' means 6. The ending 'ane' means only single bonds whereas 'ene' means there is a carbon–carbon double bond.

Q2 b Add bromine water. It will be decolourised by hexene but not by hexane.

> Comment This is the standard test for all alkenes. You should give the test reagent and what you would observe.

Q3 a

> Comment 'Prop' means 3 carbon atoms.

Q3 b

> Comment If you had problems here look back at how ethene polymerises. Then replace one H atom by a CH_3 group.

Q3 c Poly(propene).

> Comment Just put 'poly' in front of the name of the monomer.

Q3 d Propane is saturated and doesn't have a carbon–carbon double bond to undergo addition reactions.

> Comment The carbon-carbon double bond is the reactive part of the molecule.

3 Energy transfers (page 107)

Q1 a Energy = $40 \times 4.2 \times 32 = 5376$ J.

Q1 b Energy = $5376/0.2 = 26\,880$ J/g.

> Comment Use the formula energy = mass $\times$ 4.2 $\times$ temperature change.

Q2 a The reaction is exothermic.

Q2 b More energy is released when bonds are formed than is used to break the bonds in the first place.

> Comment In an energy level diagram, if the products are lower in energy than the reactants the reaction change is exothermic. Remember that the overall energy change = energy needed to break bonds – energy released on forming bonds.

Q3 More energy is released when the H—Cl bonds are made than is needed to break the H—H and Cl—Cl bonds. The overall energy change is therefore exothermic.

> Comment Again this refers to the balance between bond breaking and bond forming. Always refer to the specific bonds involved.

UNIT 10: ROCKS AND METALS
1 Plate tectonics and geological change (page 110)

Q1 a Earthquakes (or volcanoes).

> Comment Remember that earthquakes occur when two plates rub together.

Q1 b As the two plates move apart a weakness forms in the crust. Magma from the mantle is forced up, cools and forms igneous rock.

> Comment Igneous rocks are formed when the lava from a volcano cools. Volcanoes are not always formed – sometimes the magma doesn't break through the crust.

Q1 c High temperature and high pressure.

Comment As the oceanic plate is forced into the mantle the rocks are squashed and heated.

Q2 a Convection currents in the liquid mantle.

Comment Energy from the core is transferred to the mantle, causing convection currents.

Q2 b If two continental plates collide mountains form. If a continental plate collides with an oceanic plate then an ocean trench forms.

Comment You need to distinguish between the two types of plate.

Q3 *Weathering* – water gets into cracks in the rocks and then freezes and expands. As the ice melts, fragments of rock break away. *Erosion* – running water and strong winds carrying sand can wear rocks away. Acid rain dissolves limestone. *Transportation* – rain water carries particles into streams and rivers.

Comment It is important that you are clear about these three processes. If not, look back at the diagram on page 112. The differences between weathering and erosion are slight and so you shouldn't worry if you had trouble separating them. This is a very common examination question.

2 Extraction of metals (page 114)

Q1 a Iron oxide + carbon → iron + carbon dioxide

Comment In the blast furnace much of the reduction is done by carbon monoxide.

Q1 b Reduced. Reduction is the loss of oxygen. The iron oxide has lost oxygen, forming iron.

Comment Reduction and oxidation always occur together. In this reaction the carbon is oxidised.

Q1 c The limestone reacts with impurities, forming a slag that floats to the top and is removed from the furnace.

Comment Of the three raw materials in the blast furnace (coke, iron ore, limestone) this is the easiest one to forget.

Q2 a This is the breakdown (decomposition) of a compound using electricity.

Comment If you are still puzzled by electrolysis look back at page 116.

Q2 b This is a substance which when molten or dissolved in water allows an electric current to pass through it.

Comment Electrolytes must contain ions and the ions must be free to move before a current will flow.

Q2 c This is the substance which makes the electrical contact between the battery and the electrolyte.

Comment In a circuit there will always be two electrodes.

Q2 d This is the electrode connected to the positive terminal of the battery.

Comment Ions that travel to the anode are called anions (negatively charged ions).

Q2 e This is the electrode connected to the negative terminal of the battery.

Comment Ions that travel to the cathode are called cations (positively charged ions).

Q3 a The ions must be free to move. In a solid the ions are held in a giant lattice structure.

Comment Remember that the ions in a solid can be made free to move by either melting the solid or dissolving it in water. Aluminium oxide does not dissolve in water.

Q3 b Cathode.

> **Comment** *Aluminium ions are positively charged and so will be attracted to the negative electrode.*

Q3 c Aluminium ions gain electrons and form aluminium atoms.

$$Al^{3+} + 3e^- \rightarrow Al$$

> **Comment** *The ionic equation must balance in terms of symbols and charges.*

Q3 d The oxygen that is produced at the anode oxidises the hot carbon electrodes, forming carbon dioxide.

> **Comment** *This is one of the drawbacks of the method and also adds to the expense of producing aluminium.*

UNIT 11: CHEMICAL REACTIONS
1 Chemical change (page 119)

Q1 Not all collisions provide enough energy for the reaction to take place.

> **Comment** *Energy is needed to break chemical bonds so that the atoms, molecules or ions can rearrange and form new bonds. Remember that collisions that do have sufficient energy are referred to as **effective collisions**.*

Q2 Reaction A.

> **Comment** *Reaction A has a lower activation energy than reaction B. This means that there will be more effective collisions and so the rate of reaction will be higher. If you are still not clear about this idea of an 'energy barrier', look again at the explanation of activation energy in the **collision theory** section.*

Q3 a Carbon dioxide

> **Comment** *Remember that marble has the chemical name calcium carbonate. The carbon dioxide is released from the carbonate ion.*

Q3 b (i) 20 cm³; (ii) 16 cm³; (iii) 13 cm³; (iv) 0 cm³.

> **Comment** *20 – 0 = 20; 36 – 20 = 16; 49 – 36 = 13; 70 – 70 = 0. Don't forget the units of volume.*

Q3 c The volume of gas produced in each 10 second interval decreases as the reaction proceeds. This means the rate of production of gas decreases.

> **Comment** *The rate of reaction is measured in terms of the volume of gas produced in a certain amount of time. If you wanted to calculate rates in these time intervals you would need to divide the volume of gas produced by the time taken. So between 0 and 10 seconds 20 cm³ of gas was collected giving a rate of 20/10 = 2 cm³/s. Between 20 and 30 seconds the rate was 1.3 cm³/s.*

Q3 d As the reaction proceeds there are fewer particles of hydrochloric acid and calcium carbonate to collide with each other. Therefore there will be fewer collisions and hence fewer effective collisions.

> **Comment** *Don't forget to mention the idea of 'effective collisions' (see page 119). This is a key idea in this chapter. If you want to impress the examiner use the correct names for the particles – e.g. in this reaction collisions occur between hydrogen ions (H^+ ions) and carbonate ions (CO_3^{2-} ions).*

Q3 e Measuring the change in mass as the reaction proceeds.

> **Comment** *The carbon dioxide gas will escape, causing a decrease in mass of the reaction container. The equipment you would need is shown on page 121.*

2 Controlling the rate of reaction (page 123)

Q1 As the temperature increases, the kinetic energy of the reacting particles also increases. The particles will therefore be moving faster and will collide more frequently. In addition, there will be more energy transferred in the collisions and so more are likely to be effective and lead to a reaction.

Comment Don't forget to mention the energy of the collision. Many students only mention the increased number of collisions.

Q2 a (i) Experiment 1; (ii) the reaction finishes more quickly because the curve levels out soonest.

Comment A better answer would mention the gradient of the curve – e.g. the gradient of the curve at the beginning of the reaction is the steepest.

Q2 b (i) Experiment 3; (ii) the largest chips have the smallest surface area and so the lowest rate of reaction.

Comment The curve for experiment 3 has the lowest gradient at the beginning of the reaction. If you got this wrong check the section on **surface area** again.

Q2 c (i) 7.5 minutes (approximately); (ii) the reaction finished because the marble was used up.

Comment Try to read off the graph as accurately as you can. In an examination you will be allowed a small margin of error. In this example 7.3 to 7.7 minutes would be acceptable. The question says that the hydrochloric acid was 'an excess'. This means that there was more than would be needed. Therefore the reaction must have finished because the marble was used up. Always look for the phrase 'an excess' or 'in excess'.

Q2 d The same mass of marble was used in each experiment.

Comment As the acid is in excess the amount of marble will determine how much carbon dioxide is produced.

Q2 e The curve would be steeper (have a higher gradient) at the beginning of the reaction but would reach the same plateau height.

Comment Increasing the temperature will increase the rate of the reaction but will not change the amount of carbon dioxide produced. If you are still in doubt about this read the section on **temperature** again.

Q3 a A catalyst is a substance that alters the rate of a chemical reaction but does not change itself.

Comment Remember that whilst most catalysts speed up reactions some slow them down.

Q3 b A catalyst provides another route for the reaction with a different activation energy.

Comment Think of activation energy as an energy barrier that prevents reactants changing into products.

3 Making use of enzymes (page 127)

Q1 A biological catalyst.

Comment A really good answer would include the fact that they are protein molecules.

Q2 a Yeast.

Q2 b The brewing and baking industries.

Comment Remember that the ethanol is the more important product in the brewing industry and that the carbon dioxide is more important in the baking industry.

Q2 c At higher temperatures the enzymes present in the yeast are denatured and can no longer act as catalysts.

Comment A common mistake is to say that the 'enzymes are killed' at higher temperatures. Enzymes are not alive in the first place!

Q2 d glucose → ethanol + carbon dioxide

Q2 e $C_6H_{12}O_6 \rightarrow 2C_2H_5OH + 2CO_2$

Comment Remember when balancing an equation that the balancing numbers can only be placed in front of the formulae (see Unit 7).

Q3 a An active site is the part of an enzyme molecule in which reactant molecules are trapped.

Comment You can think of it as a hole or cavity.

Q3 b The arrangement and shape of the active site in an enzyme will only 'fit' one specific type of molecule.

Comment This is sometimes referred to as a 'lock and key' model – only one key fits the lock.

4 Reversible reactions (page 129)

Q1 A reaction is in equilibrium when the number of reactant and product molecules do not change.

Comment You might remember that at equilibrium the rate of the forward reaction equals the rate of the backward reaction.

Q2 a The rate changes (usually increases).

Comment Catalysts are usually used to increase reaction rate.

Q2 b No effect.

Comment A catalyst does not change the position of equilibrium.

Q3 The higher temperature is used to increase the rate of the reaction.

Comment The choice of temperature in industrial processes often balances how much can be formed (depends on the equilibrium position) and how fast it can be formed (depends on the rate of the reaction).

UNIT 12: THE PERIODIC TABLE
1 Organising the elements (page 132)

Q1 a b

Comment Group 4 is the fourth major column from the left.

Q1 b a

Comment This is the second row.

Q1 c d

Comment The noble gas family is group 0 or 8.

Q1 d c

Comment Transition elements are in the middle block.

Q1 e b

Comment Metalloids are found near the 'staircase' on the right side of the periodic table, which separates metals from non-metals.

Q1 f d and f

Comment These are on the right of the 'staircase'. If you included b you would not be penalised.

Q1 g d

Comment Gases are non-metals and so have to be on the right side. f is a possibility but in groups 5, 6 and 7 elements near the bottom of the group are solids.

Q2 They contain the same number of electrons in the outer electron shell.

Comment Remember that how an atom reacts depends on its outermost electrons.

Q3 a B. Its pH is less than 7.

Comment Remember that the acidic oxide will also react with an alkali.

Q3 b A and B. Both react with an acid.

Comment 'A' has a pH of 7 because it doesn't dissolve in water.

Q3 c (i) Neutralisation

Comment Copper oxide is a base. The reaction of a base with an acid is neutralisation.

Q3 c (ii) Copper oxide + sulphuric acid → copper sulphate + water

Comment Remember that acid + base → salt + water.

Q3 c (iii) $CuO(s) + H_2SO_4(aq) \rightarrow CuSO_4(aq) + H_2O(l)$

Comment No extra balancing is required here.

Q3 c (iv) A.

Comment Copper(II) oxide is insoluble in water and so the mixture will have a pH of 7.

2 The metals (page 136)

Q1 a Caesium.

Comment Remember that the reactivity of metals increases down a group.

Q1 b To prevent the metal reacting with air and water.

Comment These are highly reactive metals. They oxidise rapidly without heat being needed.

Q1 c Caesium.

Comment The melting point gives a measure of hardness. Melting point decreases down the group.

Q1 d On cutting, the metal is exposed to the air and rapidly oxidises.

Comment Tarnishing is another word for oxidation.

Q1 e When added to water they react to produce an alkali.

Comment The metal hydroxides formed in the reactions are alkalis.

Q1 f Sodium is less dense than water.

Comment Density increases down the group. The more reactive metals would not float but their reaction is so violent that the metal usually flies out of the water!

Q1 g (i) rubidium + oxygen → rubidium oxide
$4Rb(s) + O_2(g) \rightarrow 2Rb_2O(s)$

Comment Rubidium behaves in the same way as sodium but more violently.

Q1 g (ii) caesium + water → caesium hydroxide + hydrogen
$2Cs(s) + 2H_2O(l) \rightarrow 2CsOH(aq) + H_2(g)$

Comment The reaction of the group 1 metals with water produces the metal hydroxide (an alkali) and hydrogen.

Q1 g (iii) potassium + chlorine → potassium chloride
$2K(s) + Cl_2(g) \rightarrow 2KCl(s)$

Comment Potassium chloride is a salt with an appearance very similar to sodium chloride, common salt.

Q2 a They are harder, have higher densities, higher melting points and are sonorous (any two).

Comment If you couldn't answer this look back at the summary on page 133.

Q2 b A catalyst is a substance that changes the speed of a chemical reaction without being changed itself.

Comment Catalysts and their effects on rates of reaction are covered in Unit 11.

Q2 c The alkali metals have only one electron in the outer electron shell. Transition metals have more than one electron in the outer electron shell.

Comment Reactivity is principally related to the number of electrons in the outer electron shell. Metals lower down a group are also more reactive than those higher up, but this is of secondary importance.

Q3 a A – sodium, B – copper, C – calcium.

Comment The sodium and calcium can be identified from the flame test information. Only one of the compounds contains a transition metal (forms a coloured compound).

Q3 b The hydroxides of the group 1 metals are soluble in water and would not form a precipitate.

Comment Calcium is in group 2. Calcium hydroxide is only sparingly soluble in water and so a precipitate forms.

Q3 c $Cu^{2+}(aq) + 2OH^-(aq) \rightarrow Cu(OH)_2(s)$

Comment The important part of the compound is the copper ion. The non-metal ion or radical does not play a part in the reaction - it is a spectator ion.

3 The non-metals (page 140)

Q1 a Fluorine

Comment Unlike groups of metals, reactivity decreases down the group.

Q1 b Bromine

Comment Bromine is the only liquid non-metal.

Q1 c Iodine

Comment Astatine would be expected to be a solid but it is radioactive with a very short half-life so it is difficult to confirm this prediction.

Q1 d They only need to gain one electron in order to have a full outer electron shell. Other non-metals need to gain more than one electron.

Comment Remember that reactivity depends on the number of electrons in the outer electron shell.

Q1 e (i) sodium + chlorine → sodium chloride
$$2Na(s) + Cl_2(g) \rightarrow 2NaCl(s)$$

Q1 e (ii) magnesium + bromine → magnesium bromide
$$Mg(s) + Br_2(l) \rightarrow MgBr_2(s)$$

Comment The halogen elements react with all metals. They form salts, called fluorides, chlorides, bromides and iodides.

Q1 e (iii) hydrogen + fluorine → hydrogen fluoride
$$H_2(g) + F_2(g) \rightarrow 2HF(g)$$

Comment Hydrogen fluoride will have very similar properties to the more familiar hydrogen chloride. Its solution in water, hydrofluoric acid, is highly corrosive.

Q2 a (i) Very pale yellow. (ii) Brown. (iii) Brown. (iv) Colourless.

Comment Bromine is more soluble in water than iodine but it is very difficult to distinguish between dilute solutions of the two. Sometimes a solvent like cyclohexane is added. The bromine is brown in the cyclohexane, the iodine is violet.

Q2 b On mixing the pale yellow solution with the colourless solution, a brown solution is formed.

Comment Observations are what you see, smell or hear. You don't see bromine; you see a brown solution.

Q2 c ✗ ✓ ✓
  ✗ ✗ ✓
  ✗ ✗ ✗

Comment The more reactive halogen will displace (take the place of) the less reactive halogen. Chlorine will displace bromine from sodium bromide because it is more reactive. Iodine cannot replace chlorine or bromine as it is less reactive than both of them.

Q2 d Bromine + sodium iodide → iodine + sodium bromide
$Br_2(aq) + 2NaI(aq) \rightarrow I_2(aq) + 2NaBr(aq)$

Comment Bromine is more reactive than iodine and so will displace it from the solution. In this reaction it would be difficult to see a change as both the bromine and iodine solutions are brown. Using cyclohexane would confirm that a reaction had taken place.

Q3 Noble gases have full outer electron shells and so do not need to gain or lose electrons in a reaction.

Comment Remember that metals want to lose electrons and form positive ions, whereas non-metals often try to gain electrons and form negative ions. Details of ionic bonding are given in Unit 8.

UNIT 13: CHEMICAL CALCULATIONS
1 Atomic masses and the mole (page 143)

Q1 a 2 moles

Comment Moles = mass/RAM = 56/28 = 2

Q1 b 0.1 mole

Comment Moles = mass/RAM = 3.1/31 = 0.1

Q1 c 0.25 mole

Comment Moles = mass/RMM = 11/44 = 0.24

Q1 d 0.5 mole

Comment Moles = mass/RFM = 50/100 = 0.5
Note: Calcium carbonate is an ionic compound so the correct term is relative formula mass.

Q2 a 48 g

Comment Mass = moles × RAM = 2 × 24 = 48 g

Q2 b 4 g

Comment Mass = moles × RMM = 2 × 2 = 4 g

Q2 c 9.8 g

Comment Mass = moles × RMM = 0.1 × 98 = 9.8 g

Q3 $TiCl_4$

Comment	Ti	Cl
mass/RAM	25/48	75/35.5
moles	0.52	2.1
ratio	0.52/0.52 = 1	2.1/0.52 = 4.04
formula is $TiCl_4$		

2 Equations and reacting masses (page 147)

Q1 4 g

Comment 2Na = 2 moles = 46 g. 2NaOH = 2 moles = 80 g. The scaling factor is ÷ 20.

Q2 a 560 tonnes

Comment Fe_2O_3 = 1 mole → 160 tonnes. 2Fe = 2 moles → 112 tonnes. The scaling factor is × 5.

Q2 b 144 litres at room temperature and pressure

Comment Fe_2O_3 = 1 mole → 160 g. $3CO_2$ = 3 × 24 = 72 litres. The scaling factor is × 2.

Q3 2.33 g

> **Comment** $BaCl_2$ = 1 mole = 1000 cm³ (1 M). $BaSO4$ =
> 1 mole = 233 g.
> First scale by ÷ 5. 1000 cm³ (0.2 M) and 46.6 g.
> Second scale by ÷ 20. 50 cm³ (0.2 M) and 2.33 g.

UNIT 14: ELECTRICITY
1 Electric circuits (page 150)

Q1 a A_1 reading 0.2 A, A_2 reading 0.2 A.

> **Comment** The current is always the same at any
> point in a series circuit.

Q1 b A_4 reading 0.30 A, A_5 reading 0.15 A.

> **Comment** The ammeter A_6 has been placed on
> one branch of the parallel circuit. Ammeter A_5 is on
> the other branch. As the lamps are identical the
> current flowing through them must be the same.
> Ammeter A_4 gives the current before it 'splits' in
> half as it flows through the two parallel branches.

Q2 Reading on V_1 = 6 V.

> **Comment** The potential difference across the
> battery is 9 V. This must equal the total p.d. in
> the circuit. Assuming there is no loss along the
> copper wiring the p.d. across the lamp must be
> 9 – 3 = 6 V.

Q3 a 0.33 A

> **Comment** Use the equation $I = Q/t$, I = 10/30 = 0.33 A.

Q3 b (i) 10 C; (ii) 36 000 C.

> **Comment** Rearranging the formula, $Q = It$, (i)
> Q = 10 × 1 = 10 C, (ii) Q = 10 × 60 × 60 = 36 000 C.

2 What affects resistance? (page 155)

Q1 a

The resistance is calculated using Ohm's law,
$R = V/I$.

> **Comment** Remember that the ammeter must be in
> series with the nichrome wire, but the voltmeter
> must be in parallel.

Q1 b (i) The resistance would double.
  (ii) The resistance would be halved.

> **Comment** Resistance is directly proportional to
> length. Resistance is inversely proportional to
> cross-sectional area. If necessary look back at
> the models on page 156.

Q2 a 24 V

> **Comment** nt $V = IR$ = 2 × 12 = 24 V

Q2 b 20 V

> **Comment** $V = IR$ = 0.1 × 200 = 20 V

Q2 c 0.12 A

> **Comment** $I = V/R$ = 12/100 = 0.12 A

Q2 d 23 A

> **Comment** $I = V/R$ = 230/10 = 23 A

Q2 e 60 Ω

> **Comment** $R = V/I$ = 6/0.1 = 60 Ω

Q2 f 23 Ω

> **Comment** $R = V/I$ = 230/10 = 23 Ω

Q3 a The resistance increases as the voltage increases.

Comment If the resistance were constant the line would be straight with a constant gradient. It curves in such a way that increasing voltage produces a smaller increase in the current, so resistance must be increasing.

Q3 b As the voltage increases the temperature of the wire must also be increasing.

Comment This is a common characteristic of non-ohmic resistors – that is, resistors that do not obey Ohm's law.

3 Power in electrical circuits (page 159)

Q1 920 W.

Comment Power = $V \times I$ = 230 × 4 = 920 W. Don't forget the unit. Power is measured in watts.

Q2 a 24p

Comment Cost = units × 8 = 1 × 3 × 8 = 24p. Remember that a unit is a kilowatt-hour so the 1000 W has to be converted into kilowatts, that is 1 kW.

Q2 b 8p.

Comment 200 W = 0.2 kW. Cost = units × 8 = 0.2 × 5 × 8 = 8p.

Q3 1800 kJ.

Comment Energy = power × time (s) = 3000 × 10 × 60 = 1 800 000 J or 1800 kJ. Remember that 1 watt is 1 joule/second.

4 Static electricity (page 162)

Q1 a Electrons are rubbed off the surface of the plastic onto the cloth.

Comment Static electricity is produced by removing electrons from one insulator to another. An excess of electrons leads to a negative charge.

Q1 b The positively charged rod induces a negative charge on the surface of the paper near to the rod. Opposite charges then attract. (A positive charge is therefore induces in the paper well away from the charged rod.)

Comment Electrostatic induction is a common phenomenon. Remember this is how you can make a balloon stick to the ceiling.

Q2 a The passenger is charged by friction as her clothes rub against the seat covers. The car is also charged by friction with the road and the air. Touching metal allows the charge to flow to earth.

Comment Remember static electricity is produced by friction.

Q2 b Touching a door handle after walking on a synthetic carpet, or removing clothing.

Comment Synthetic fibres are more likely to cause this effect than natural fibres. This must be due to the different atom arrangements.

Q3 Lightning, fuelling aircraft, in grain silos.

Comment Static electricity can cause explosions in any situations when there are fuels in the gaseous form or where there are very fine particles of solid material (dust).

UNIT 15: ELECTROMAGNETIC EFFECTS

1 Electromagnetism (page 164)

Q1 a No. Aluminium is not magnetic.

Comment *Remember that very few metals are magnetic (e.g. iron, cobalt and nickel). The electromagnet would separate steel cans as steel is an alloy containing iron.*

Q1 b Switch off the current to the electromagnet.

Comment *The magnetic field is only present when the current is flowing. An electromagnet is a temporary magnet.*

Q2 Increasing the current flowing through the coil. Increasing the number of coils. Adding a soft iron core inside the cardboard tube.

Comment *These will produce a stronger magnetic field.*

Q3 When the switch is pressed the electromagnet attracts the hammer support and the hammer hits the bell. The movement of the hammer support breaks the circuit and so the electromagnet ceases to operate. The hammer support then returns to its original position, forming the circuit again and the process is repeated.

Comment *The electromagnet is constantly activated and then deactivated. This means that the hammer will continually hit the bell and then retract.*

2 Electromagnetic induction (page 167)

Q1 If the rotation of the armature is producing electricity which is being withdrawn via A and B, then it is a generator. If, alternatively, electricity is being supplied via A and B to produce rotation then it is a motor.

Comment *The same device can be used as either a motor or a generator. A motor needs an electrical supply in order to produce movement. In a generator the movement is used to generate electricity.*

Q2 a Iron.

Comment *The core must be a magnetic material. It concentrates the magnetic effect.*

Q2 b A magnetic field is produced.

Comment *Remember that a current flowing in a wire will produce a magnetic field around it.*

Q2 c A current is induced.

Comment *The varying magnetic field in the core induces a current in the secondary coil.*

Q2 d 24 V.

Comment $V_p/V_s = N_p/N_s$; $V_p/14 = 12/7$; $V_p = 12/7 \times 14 = 24$ V.

Q3 An electric current produces a heating effect in a wire, thus transferring energy as heat. To reduce energy loss electricity is transmitted at as low a current as possible, which means transmitting at very high voltage.

Comment *The heating effect of an electric current is considered in Unit 14.*

Unit 16: Forces and Motion
1 The effects of forces (page 171)

Q1 A – the wooden block would not move; B – the car would accelerate; C – the ice skater would maintain a constant speed.

Comment A – The forces are balanced and so the stationary wooden block would not move. B – The resultant force would be 4000 N. This unbalanced force will cause the car to accelerate. (As the car moves faster the resistive force caused by air resistance will increase and eventually reach 6000 N). C – The forces are balanced. As the skier is moving she will continue to do so at the same speed.

Q2 a

Comment Friction will always oppose motion and so the arrow points in the opposite direction to the direction of motion.

Q2 b The frictional forces slow the skier down.

Comment As the skier travels downhill the friction force opposes the motion.

Q2 c Using narrower skis, or using wax on the skis.

Comment Lubricant reduces frictional forces.

Q3 a *Stage 1* – The skydiver is accelerating. The downward force of gravity is greater than the upward force caused by air resistance. *Stage 2* – The sky diver is travelling at constant speed. The forces of gravity and air resistance are balanced. *Stage 3* – The sky diver is slowing down. The force caused by the air in the parachute is greater than the force of gravity. *Stage 4* – The sky diver is travelling at a constant speed. The forces are balanced again.

Comment In questions of this sort the first thing to do is to decide which forces will be acting on the object. The next thing is to decide whether the forces are balanced or unbalanced. If they are unbalanced the skydiver will be either accelerating or decelerating. If they are balanced the skydiver will either be travelling at constant speed or not moving. In stage 2 the skydiver will have reached the terminal speed and because the forces are balanced will not accelerate or decelerate.

Q3 b The force of gravity is balanced by the upward force of the ground on the sky diver.

Comment The upward force from the ground is equal to the skydiver's weight.

2 Velocity and acceleration (page 174)

Q1 a The speed remained constant.

Comment If the line on a distance–time graph has a constant gradient then the speed is constant.

Q1 b 600 m.

Comment This can be read off the graph: after 20 s the car had travelled 200 m, after 60 s it had travelled 800 m. So the distance travelled is 800 – 200 = 600 m.

Q1 c 15 m/s.

Comment Speed = distance/time, $v = 600/40 = 15$ m/s. Don't forget the units.

Q1 d It stopped.

> **Comment** The line is horizontal during this time, indicating that the car was not moving (no distance was travelled).

Q2 a 2.0 m/s/s.

> **Comment** Acceleration = change in velocity/time, $a = (1.5 - 0)/0.75 = 2$ m/s/s.

Q2 b 2.25 m.

> **Comment** Total distance = area under the line = $(1/2 \times 0.75 \times 1.5) + (1/2 \times 2.25 \times 1.5) = 2.25$ m.
> *Note:* the tractor showed constant acceleration from A to B and then constant deceleration from B to C.

Q3 a 2.5 m/s/s.

> **Comment** Acceleration = change in speed/time, $a = (30 - 0)/12 = 2.5$ m/s/s. Don't forget the units!

Q3 b 2500 N.

> **Comment** Force = mass × acceleration, $F = 1000 \times 2.5 = 2500$ N.

UNIT 17: ENERGY
1 Where does our energy come from? (page 180)

Q1 a A source that cannot be regenerated – it takes millions of years to form.

> **Comment** A common mistake is to say that it is a source that 'cannot be used again'. Many energy sources cannot be used again but they can be regenerated (e.g. wood).

Q1 b Coal, oil and natural gas.

> **Comment** These are the fossil fuels. Substances obtained from fossil fuels such as petrol and diesel are not strictly speaking fossil fuels.

Q1 c Coal.

> **Comment** Coal is becoming increasingly more difficult to mine as more inaccessible coal seams are tackled. The 300 year estimate could be very optimistic.

Q2 a The total energy increased from 1955 to 1975 and then levelled out.

> **Comment** Always describe a graphical trend carefully. Be as precise as you can.

Q2 b The amount of coal used has significantly reduced. The amounts of oil, gas and nuclear fuel used have significantly increased.

> **Comment** It is important to refer to each of the energy sources given on the graph.

Q3 a Any two from: strength of the wind, high ground, constant supply of wind, open ground.

> **Comment** Higher ground tends to be more windy than lower ground. However, the wind farm cannot be built too far away from the centres of population otherwise costs will be incurred in connecting to the National Grid.

Q3 b *Advantage:* renewable energy source, no air pollution. *Disadvantage:* unsightly, takes up too much space.

> **Comment** Wind turbines can be very efficient. However, they need to be reasonably small and so a large number are needed to generate significant amounts of electricity. Environmentally, although they produce no air pollution they do take up a lot of land.

2 Transferring energy (page 182)

Q1 The thin layers will trap air between them. Air is an insulator and so will reduce thermal transfer from the body.

Comment Remember that air is a very good insulator. Trapping it between layers of clothing means that convection is inhibited as well as conduction.

Q2 The molecules that are able to leave the surface of the liquid are those that are moving the fastest, that is, the molecules with the most energy. The average energy of the remaining molecules is therefore reduced and so the liquid is cooler.

Comment The temperature of a liquid is related to the average speed of its molecules. If the temperature is reduced, on average, the molecules will move more slowly.

Q3 Energy from the hot water is transferred from the inner to the outer surface of the metal by conduction. Energy is transferred through the still air by radiation.

Comment In a question like this it is important to take the energy transfer stage by stage. Thermal transfer through a solid involves conduction. Thermal transfer through still air must involve radiation. In fact, convection would be occurring and it is very likely that the air behind the radiator would be moving (convention currents).

3 Work, power and energy (page 186)

Q1 12.5 m.

Comment Work done = $F s$
$F = 400 \times 10 = 4000$ N
$s = W/F = 50\,000/4000 = 12.5$ m

Q2 a 6000 J.

Comment Energy transferred = $30 \times 200 = 6000$ J

Q2 b 33.3 W.

Comment Power = work done/time taken = $6000/180 = 33.3$ W. Remember that a watt is 1 joule/s so the time must be in seconds.

Q3 a 10 500 J.

Comment P.E. = $m g h = 35 \times 10 \times 30 = 10\,5000$ J

Q3 b 24.5 m/s.

Comment Assuming all the potential energy is transferred to kinetic energy:
K.E. = $1/2\ mv^2$, so $v^2 = 2$ K.E./m
$= 2 \times 10\,500/35 = 600$, and $v = 24.5$ m/s

Q3 c Some of the gravitational potential energy will have been transferred to thermal energy due to the friction between the sledge and the snow.

Comment Energy must be conserved but friction is a very common cause of energy being wasted, that is, being transferred into less useful forms.

UNIT 18: WAVES
1 The properties of waves (page 189)

Q1 a D.

Comment The crest is the top of the wave.

Q1 b A and E.

Comment The wavelength is the length of the repeating pattern.

Q1 c B.

Comment The amplitude is half the distance between the crest and the trough. If you had difficulty with parts a to c look back at the diagram on page 190.

Q1 **d** 512.

Comment Frequency is measured in hertz and 1Hz = 1 cycle (or wave) per second.

Q2 0.33 m.

Comment $v = f \times \lambda$ or $\lambda = v/f$
$$\lambda = 3 \times 10^8 / 9 \times 10^8 = 0.33 \text{ m}$$

Q3 1.33 m

Comment $v = f \times \lambda$ or $\lambda = v/f$
$$\lambda = 340/256 = 1.33 \text{ m}$$

2 The electromagnetic spectrum (page 193)

Q1 **a** Light.

Comment The sensitive cells form a part of the eye called the retina.

Q1 **b** Ultraviolet.

Comment Suntan lotions contain chemicals that absorb some of the UV radiation from the Sun before it can act on the skin.

Q1 **c** Microwaves.

Comment The key word here was 'rapid'. Electric cookers make use of infrared radiation for cooking but microwaves produce much more rapid cooking.

Q1 **d** X-rays.

Comment A gamma camera would not be as good for this purpose as the gamma rays penetrate the bone as well as the flesh.

Q1 **e** Infrared.

Comment Remote car locking sometimes uses infrared beams.

Q2 **a** They can pass through soft tissue and kill cancer cells.

Comment Gamma rays are useful because of their great penetrating power. This is also their disadvantage. Consequently they have to be used extremely carefully. They are the highest energy waves in the electromagnetic spectrum.

Q2 **b** They can damage healthy cells and cause cancer because of their very high energy.

Comment All waves in the electromagnetic spectrum have different frequencies and wavelengths.

Q2 **c** They have different frequencies and wavelengths.

Comment All waves in the electromagnetic spectrum travel at the same speed in a vacuum – the speed of light.

Q2 **d** 300 000 000 m/s.

Comment As you might have guessed this is an important point and one that is often tested in exams!

3 Light reflection and refraction (page 195)

Q1 **a** In reflection light changes direction when it bounces off a surface. In refraction the light changes direction when it passes from one medium to another.

Comment In reflection the angle of incidence and the angle of reflection are the same. In refraction the angle of incidence does not equal the angle of refraction, as the ray of light bends towards or away from the normal.

QI b (i)

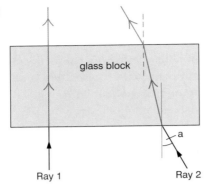

glass block

Ray 1 Ray 2 a

QI b (ii) The angle of incidence.

QI b (iii) The normal line.

Comment The ray of light will only be bent if it hits the block at an angle. In both cases the speed of the light in the block will be slower than in air.

Q2 a

E

Comment Remember that with a plane mirror the image is the same size as the object and will be the same distance behind the mirror as the object is in front. When drawing the ray diagram check that the angles of incidence and reflection are the same.

Q2 b Light will be reflected off the hair onto the first mirror. If the angle is correct the reflected ray will then travel to the second mirror. If the angle is correct it will then be reflected into the eye.

Comment Don't forget that the light travels from the object to the eye! In an examination you might find it easier to draw a diagram showing the passage of the ray of light. In this way you can show the correct angles on the mirrors.

Q3 a

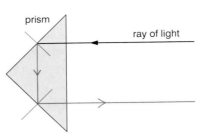

prism ray of light

Comment You should draw a normal line to ensure that for each reflection the angles of incidence and reflection are the same.

Q3 b Binoculars, bicycle reflector, cat's eyes.

Comment Periscopes are also often made using prisms rather than mirrors.

Q3 c R, T, T.

Comment Total internal reflection occurs only when the angle of incidence is equal to or greater than the critical angle.

4 Sound waves (page 198)

QI a (i) Vibrations. (ii) Compressions and rarefactions travel through the air.

Comment These are both common questions, so don't forget. Sound is a longitudinal wave. The compressions and rarefactions are small differences in air pressure.

QI b Sound waves cannot travel through a vacuum. Radio waves don't require a medium.

Comment This is a big difference between sound waves and electromagnetic waves.

QI c Particles in water are closer together so the vibrations are passed on more quickly.

Comment The denser the material the greater the speed of sound. In concrete, for example, the speed of sound is 5000 m/s.

Q2 a Above the limit of audible sound.

Comment *The frequency of ultrasonic waves is too high for the human ear to hear.*

Q2 b The motion of the medium is parallel to the direction of movement of the wave.

Comment *This contrasts with transverse waves where the medium moves at right angles to the movement of the wave.*

Q2 c The wavelength decreases, the frequency remains the same.

Comment *You should remember that $v = f \times \lambda$; v decreases, f stays the same so λ must decrease.*

Q3 375 m.

Comment *$s = v \times t \times 1/2 = 1500 \times 0.5 \times 0.5 = 375$ m*

UNIT 19: THE EARTH AND BEYOND
1 The Solar System (page 200)

Q1 Hydrogen nuclei join together to make helium nuclei in a process known as nuclear fusion.

Comment *Don't get confused with nuclear fission, which is the process used to obtain energy in nuclear power stations. Very high temperatures are required before nuclear fusion will take place.*

Q2 Clouds of hydrogen gas → blue star → red supergiant → supernova.

Comment *The sequence is given in the table on page 202. A supernova is only produced from a very large star. A star such as our Sun will eventually form a white dwarf.*

Q3 a (i) The force due to gravity, its weight, which (ii) acts towards the centre of the Earth.

Comment *Gravity always pulls towards the centre of the Earth. The satellite's weight is providing the centripetal force required for it to move in a circle.*

Q3 b The satellite is always at the same position above the surface of the Earth.

Comment *The ring directly above the equator at the height of geostationary orbits is full of communication satellites.*

2 How did the Universe begin? (page 203)

Q1 Light waves from a star near the Earth with a lower frequency than that emitted by the star.

Comment *If the emitter is moving away from the observer the frequency is reduced. In the case of light waves, a reduction in frequency results in a shift to the lower frequency (red) end of the visible spectrum.*

Q2 Red shift evidence shows that all galaxies are moving apart from each other. Reversing the direction of movement of the galaxies shows that they could all have come from the same starting point.

Comment *It was the famous astronomer Edwin Hubble who first observed the red shift and then proposed the Big Bang theory.*

UNIT 20: RADIOACTIVITY
1 Unstable atoms (page 204)

Q1 a Alpha particles.

Comment *Gamma particles would not have deflected at all as they are uncharged. Beta particles might work, but they deflect very easily because they have such a small mass.*

Q1 b Most of the atom is empty space.

Comment *The neutron wasn't discovered until 1932.*

Q1 c The atom must have a very high concentration of mass and positive charge. Rutherford called this the nucleus.

Q2 a 11 protons, 13 neutrons.

Comment The atomic number gives the number of protons. The difference between the mass number and the atomic number equals the number of neutrons.

Q2 b 15 hours.

Comment The count falls from 100 Bq to 50 Bq in 15 hours. It also falls from 50 Bq to 25 Bq in 15 hours.

Q3 a Beta particle.

Comment A beta particle is an electron. The 'beta' symbol can also be written as an electron, 'e'. The electron is shown with an atomic number of −1 and a mass number of 0.

Q3 b $x = 24; y = 12$.

Comment The mass numbers must balance on the left-hand and right-hand sides of the equation (24 = 24 + 0). The atomic numbers must balance on the left-hand and right-hand sides of the equation (11 = 12 − 1).

2 Uses and dangers of radioactivity (page 208)

Q1 a Alpha particles.

Q1 b Beta particles.

Q1 c Gamma rays.

Comment Details of these uses are given on page 208. Alpha particles are the most ionising, gamma rays are the most penetrating.

Q2 a A tracer is a radioactive isotope used in detection.

Comment Tracers are widely used to detect leaks and blockages.

Q2 b Sodium-24. The lawrencium-257 has too short a half-life; the sulphur-35 and carbon-14 have half-lives which are too long.

Comment The tracer must be radioactive for long enough for it to be detected after injection into the body but must not remain radioactive in the body for longer than necessary.

Q3 a Lead.

Comment In fact the uranium-238 decays through a chain of short-lived intermediate elements before forming lead.

Q3 b The ratio of uranium-238 to lead-207 enables the age of the rock to be determined.

Comment In a similar way the carbon-14: carbon-12 ratio is important in finding out the age of previously living material.

UNIT 21: EXAM PRACTICE
Biology (page 214)

Q1 a X (1).

Examiner's comments
Smaller molecules are absorbed more easily. **Even if you are not sure of the answer, make sure you do attempt the question, especially when you have answers to choose from.**

Q1 b Diffusion (1).

Examiner's comments
Active transport would also be a correct answer.

Q1 c To be carried round the body/to all body cells (1).

Examiner's comments
Although you may have studied science by studying different topics at different times, in exam questions you can expect to refer to different topics in the same question. This question is really about the job of the blood. **Do not be afraid of using information from other topic areas in your answer.**

Q1 d (i) Enzymes (1).
(ii) Converts large molecules to small molecules (1).

Examiner's comments
Common mistakes would be to give acid or bile. These help enzymes to work but it is the enzymes that digest the food. Part (ii) is really just asking what is meant by digestion.

Q2 a (i) **Three** from: water logged soil contains no air / spaces filled with water; therefore bacteria are active / favoured; nitrates broken down / nitrogen lost; less nitrate in soil; nitrate shortage limits photosynthesis. (3)
(ii) Plants need nitrogen / nitrates (1). Shortage limits photosynthesis / growth (1).

Examiner's comments
Make sure you look carefully at all the information you are given in the question. The diagram reminds you that denitrifying bacteria convert nitrates in the soil into nitrogen gas in the air. You should know that 'anaerobic' means that the bacteria do not need oxygen (see Unit 2). You are expected to make the link that waterlogged soil will contain little oxygen so only the denitrifying bacteria will survive in it and these will be removing the nitrates that would otherwise be available to the plants. **Three marks indicates that a detailed explanation is needed for part (i).**

Q2 b **Two** from: cereal crops / wheat need lots of nitrate; would soon exhaust natural supply; extra N_2 promotes photosynthesis / growth. (2). Plus **two** from: clover has nitrogen-fixing bacteria; returns nitrates to soil; therefore doesn't need extra supply. (2)

Examiner's comments
You should know that clover is a leguminous plant and contains nitrogen-fixing bacteria but here you are given a big help in the diagram which shows clover taking nitrogen from the air. **Spell out all the steps in your line of reasoning to make sure you get full marks.**

Q2 c Nitrates needed for growth in spring (1); artificial nitrate available immediately (1); manure breaks down slowly (1); therefore must be added well in advance (1).

Examiner's comments
You may not have learned this point but you should know that manure decays and releases nitrates slowly (remember this is why it causes less water pollution than artificial fertilisers). Follow that line of reasoning and you are on your way to the answer.

Chemistry (page 219)

Q1 a A reversible reaction (1).

Examiner's comments
This is a very common question.

Q1 b **Two** from: add a catalyst (iron); increase temperature; increase the concentration of the reactants; increase pressure. (2)

Examiner's comments
In this reaction all the common ways of controlling a reaction can be used. In fact, the catalyst is finely ground to increase its surface area as well.

Q1 c **Four** from: (*economic*) provides income for local industry, community; provides income for the nation; increases the yield of food crops / provides more food; (*social*) provides employment; (*environmental*) factory could be an eyesore; increased transport close to factory; possible pollution risks. (Maximum of 4)

Examiner's comments
The question asks for economic, social and environmental effects. You should try to give at least one example in each category. **Always read the question carefully and look for the key words.**

Q1 d (i) 32% ± 1% (1). (ii) Decreases (1).
(iii) Increases (1).

Examiner's comments
Always take care to understand the scale on a graph. It is a common mistake to assume that each 'square' is one unit. **Always look carefully at the scale of a graph.**

Q2 a (i) Group 1 / alkali metals (1).
(ii) Rubidium hydroxide (1). Hydrogen (1).
(iii) **Two** from: metal melts; flames; fizzing; metal floats; metal dissolves. (2)

Examiner's comments
(i) The question stated that the periodic table could be used. The question is much harder if you don't use it. **Always read the question carefully.**
(ii) As the question states you are not required to know the chemistry of rubidium but you are expected to know that it will behave in a similar way to sodium. Therefore, as sodium forms sodium hydroxide and hydrogen the products from the rubidium reaction can be predicted.
(iii) The question asks for observations. Candidates very often write about the products formed and not what they would see. **Always look for the key word in the question – here it is 'observations'.**

Q2 b (i) Any named acid (hydrochloric acid, nitric acid, sulphuric acid) (1).
(ii) Magnesium iodide (1) and hydrogen (1).
(iii) Magnesium dissolves (1) bubbles of gas / colourless gas formed (1).

Examiner's comments
(i) Once again you are not expected to know the chemistry of iodine but you should know that iodine behaves in a similar way to chlorine. Hydrogen iodide solution will resemble hydrogen chloride solution which is commonly called hydrochloric acid.
(ii) Magnesium and hydrogen *chloride* would form magnesium chloride and hydrogen, therefore hydrogen *iodide* would form magnesium *iodide* and hydrogen.

(iii) The question is still asking whether you can recall the reaction of magnesium and hydrochloric acid.

Q2 c (i) Acid effect / red / pH < 7 (1).
(ii) Sodium carbonate dissolves (1) fizzing / bubbles of gas (1).
(iii) Sodium selenate / water / carbon dioxide (1).

Examiner's comments
(i) H_2SeO_4 will behave in exactly the same way as H_2SO_4, sulphuric acid, as selenium and sulphur are both in Group 6 of the periodic table. H_2SeO_4 must be acidic.
(ii) A carbonate reacts with an acid to produce carbon dioxide and the carbonate will dissolve.
(iii) The word equation for this type of reaction is: carbonate + acid → salt + carbon dioxide + water. In this case the salt is sodium selenate (like sodium sulphate).

Physics (page 224)

Q1 a (i) C (1), (ii) B (1).

Examiner's comments
The wave with the loudest sound has the greatest amplitude. The wave with the highest pitch has the highest frequency.

Q1 b $v = f \times \lambda$ or $\lambda = v / f$ (1 mark).
$\lambda = 340/500$ (1 mark), $= 0.68m$ (1)

Examiner's comments
Always write down the equation you are going to use and don't forget the units.

Q1 c (i) At 3000 km the solid rock mantle (1) changes to the liquid rock (1) outer core.
(ii) The velocity increases quickly – the Earth has a thin crust (1). The velocity increases within the mantle – the density (viscosity) of the mantle increases with depth. (1) The velocity drops appreciably at the beginning of the outer core – the outer core is liquid (1). The velocity increases from the outer core to the inner core – the inner core is solid (1).

(i) Always refer back to the graph. **Always look carefully at graphs.** The clues given are the labels 'mantle' and 'outer core'.

(ii) This question requires an extended prose answer. You must look for at least 4 scoring points. You can see that the scoring points refer to the four key areas of the graph. **Always look at the number of marks available for the question.**

Q2a (i) $V_p/V_s = N_p/N_s$ (1 mark), $24/V_s = 5/100$, $V_s = 480$ V (1 mark).

(ii) To reduce energy loss (1).
Higher voltage results in lower current (1).
The lower the current the less the heating effect (1).

Examiner's comments

(i) **Don't forget to write down the equation.** You will notice that 1 mark has been given for this. **The information needed for the calculation is on the diagram. Always look at diagrams carefully.**

(ii) The use of high voltages for transmitting electricity is a common question on higher tier papers.

Q2b **Two** from: key connects circuit; causing the electromagnet to pull contacts; thus completing the circuit to the starter motor. (2)

Examiner's comments

Always try to follow the sequence logically. In questions about relays remember that there will be two circuits. The one with the electromagnet in will be used to switch on the other one.

Q2c The wires have a magnetic field around them (1), they are in the magnetic field produced by the permanent magnet (1), the two magnetic fields interact (1), Fleming's Left Hand rule (1) predicts the movement will be to the right (1).

Examiner's comments

A very detailed answer is required to obtain 5 marks. **Always look at the number of marks available. The key command word here is 'explain'.** Again it is very important to think the situation through logically. You will notice only one mark is given for the movement of the wire. Fleming's left hand rule: **f**irst finger = **f**ield, se**c**ond finger = **c**urrent, thu**m**b = **m**ovement.

Published by HarperCollinsPublishers Ltd
77-85 Fulham Palace Road
London W6 8JB

www.**Collins**Education.com
On-line support for schools and colleges

© HarperCollins*Publishers* Ltd 2003

First published 2001
This new edition published 2003

ISBN 0 00 713619 6

Chris Sunley and Mike Smith assert the moral right to be identified as the authors of this work.

British Library Cataloguing in Publication Data
A catalogue record for this book is available from the British Library.

Edited by Jane Bryant
Production by Jack Murphy
Series design by Sally Boothroyd
Book design by Ken Vail Graphic Design, Cambridge
Index compiled by Julie Rimington
Printed and bound in China by Imago

Acknowledgements
The Author and Publishers are grateful to the following for permission to reproduce copyright material:

AQA: pp. 222, 224, 225
Edexcel: pp. 215, 220,
OCR: pp. 211, 212, 214, 217, 219, 221
All answers to questions taken from past examination papers are entirely the responsibility of the authors.

Photographs
(T = Top, B = Bottom, C = Centre, L = Left, R = Right):
John Birdsall Photography 160T; Peter Gould 86; Holt Studios International 51, 61; Andrew Lambert 70T, 77T, 85B, 129L,C&R, 138, 158, 160B; Natural History Museum 97 T&B; Natural History Photographic Agency 76L,T,B&R, 81; Science Photo Library 9, 68, 70B, 77B, 85T, 193, 199; Taxi/Getty Images 80.

Illustrations
Roger Bastow, Harvey Collins, Richard Deverell, Jerry Fowler, Gecko Ltd, Ian Law, Mike Parsons, Dave Poole, Chris Rothero and Tony Warne

Every effort has been made to contact the holders of copyright material, but if any have been inadvertently overlooked, the Publishers will be pleased to make the necessary arrangements at the first opportunity.

You might also like to visit:

www.**fire**and**water**.com
The book lover's website

The Secrets of
Great
Botanists

RHS The Secrets of Great Botanists
Author: Matthew Biggs
First published in Great Britain in 2018 by Mitchell Beazley, an imprint of
Octopus Publishing Group Ltd, Carmelite House, 50 Victoria Embankment,
London EC4Y 0DZ
www.octopusbooks.co.uk

An Hachette UK Company
www.hachette.co.uk

Published in association with the Royal Horticultural Society

ISBN: 978 1 78472 497 9

A CIP record of this book is available from the British Library
Set in Gentium Basic and Gill Sans
Printed and bound in China

Mitchell Beazley Publisher: Alison Starling
RHS Publisher: Rae Spencer-Jones
RHS Consultant Editor: Simon Maughan

Conceived, designed and produced by
The Bright Press
Part of the Quarto Group
Ovest House
58 West Street
Brighton
BN1 2RA
England
Publisher: Mark Searle
Associate Publisher: Emma Bastow
Creative Director: James Evans
Senior Editor: Lucy York
Managing Editor: Isheeta Mustafi
Project Editor: Katriona Feinstein
Design and image research: Lindsey Johns

The Royal Horticultural Society is the UK's leading gardening charity dedicated to advancing
horticulture and promoting good gardening. Its charitable work includes providing expert advice and
information, training the next generation of gardeners, creating hands-on opportunities for children to
grow plants and conducting research into plants, pests and environmental issues affecting gardeners.

For more information visit www.rhs.org.uk or call 0845 130 4646.

**This book is dedicated to two great plantsmen, Roy Lancaster CBE, VMH, FCIHort, FLS and
the late Mark Flanagan DHE (Hons.), M. Hort. (RHS), MVO, VMH, for so generously sharing
their knowledge and inspiring everyone who loves plants.**

RHS

The Secrets of

Great
Botanists

and What They
Teach Us About
Gardening

Matthew Biggs

MITCHELL
BEAZLEY

Contents

Colchicum autumnale
(meadow saffron, see p22)

Meconopsis betonicifolia
(blue poppy, see p166)

Introduction

Welcome to the lives of thirty-five great botanists, past and present, whose study of plants revolutionised the scientific world and increased our understanding of the importance of plants for our survival. All of the botanists included in this book were passionate about their particular specialism within this vast subject. Whether they were searching for plants in wild places, prescribing herbal medicines or forming new structures of plant classification, they were driven by an insatiable desire to learn and discover, so that humans might benefit from improved crops, medicines or gardens. When eminent naturalist Sir David Attenborough reopened the restored Temperate House at the Royal Botanic Gardens, Kew, on 3 May 2018, he remarked, 'the best gardener is a good botanist and the best botanist is a good gardener'. It is necessary to have an understanding of both disciplines, if we are to have a full understanding of plants.

BOTANY FOR CHANGE

Much is written about gardening and the aesthetic use of plants, but less is said about the scientific study of botany or those botanists who changed the world of gardening and beyond. Botanists are not just white-coated scientists who

spend their lives in laboratories, squinting down microscopes at the cells of plants – they are the explorers, the trailblazers and the inventors, advancing a range of fields through their studies of the natural world.

Among the huge number of iconic botanists that have shaped the way we live today are those who studied plant-based medicines; cytologists, who researched cells and chromosomes; plant breeders and geneticists, who developed economic crops; field botanists, who endured extreme hardship while collecting species that were new to science; palaeobotanists, who studied fossils, and ethnobotanists, who lived and learned among indigenous peoples and their plants.

Dr Richard Evans Schultes (see pp194–199), a pioneering ethnobotanist, lived and worked among the plants and people of the Amazon rainforest.

A HISTORY OF BOTANY

For the majority of our history as a species, we lived as hunter-gatherers. Selecting useful plants would have been a process of trial and error; they would have eaten then rejected some plants that were unpalatable, even deadly, and continued to acquire other plants that were tasty or provided other benefits. In time, people settled where food was plentiful and discovered that seeds of the best plants could be collected, cultivated and selected to safeguard supplies and ensure their survival. It was only once civilisations and empires were established that widespread scientific research began. Early plant studies began with medical botany. Physicians needed to identify and record the characteristics and doses of plants as treatments; when the results were documented, the first 'herbal' books appeared, describing the medicinal properties of herbs. The Greeks began the tradition of questioning and deduction that led to scientific ways of thinking. Theophrastus (c. 372–c. 287BC), a great philosopher, wrote over 200 works, including two on botany. His *Enquiry into Plants* dealt with the description and classification of about 550 plant species and his *On the Causes of Plant Phenomena* discussed the physiology and reproduction of plants. Both books were influential from the time of Dioscorides (c. AD 40–90, see pp8–13) to the Renaissance.

De Materia Medica (c. AD 30) by Dioscorides (see pp8–13), was translated into many languages, including Arabic. It became the basis of many medieval books on botany.

THE FINAL CUT

So, which botanists were chosen for this book? It was inevitably a personal selection, made from hundreds of iconic botanists from around the world, from ancient times to the present day. Although the choices were subjective, it was important to represent a wide range of disciplines and contributions to botany. Instead of providing 'hands-on' lessons for gardeners, this book aims to teach readers about the observations and ideas of groundbreaking botanists, and show how influential they have been on gardening and the wider world. The 'Inspiration for Gardeners' pages at the end of each botanist's section detail plants and discoveries related to the botanist, to inspire readers to try these plants and tips at home.

Pedanius Dioscorides

DATE C. AD 40–90	
ORIGIN PRESENT-DAY TURKEY	
MAJOR ACHIEVEMENT *DE MATERIA MEDICA*	

Dioscorides, the 'Father of Pharmacology', was a herbalist with the Roman Army, and one of the first to observe and record plants in detail and to recognise the uses of medicines from all three kingdoms of the natural world – animal, vegetable and mineral. His *De Materia Medica* ('On Medical Materials') was laid out by category and then by the physiological effects they had on the body, a format that he believed would make it easy to learn and retain the information. This was proven in practice and it became the basis of medicine for sixteen centuries.

Euphorbia characias,
Mediterranean spurge

Pedanius Dioscorides was born in Anazarbus, a small city northeast of Tarsus in the Roman province of Cilicia (now Turkey), at the time of Nero and Vespasian. His travels as a surgeon with the Roman Army into Italy, Greece, northern Africa, Gaul, Persia, Egypt and Armenia provided him with a wealth of opportunities to study the features, distribution and medicinal properties of plants, animals and minerals.

Dioscorides started *De Materia Medica*, a list of known medicinal plants of the Roman Empire and new introductions, around AD 50, finishing it roughly 20 years later. He would collect samples of local medicinal or useful herbs as he travelled, many of them previously unknown to Greek and Roman physicians, describing their restorative effects and botany, including roots, foliage and sometimes flowers. Dioscorides was also one of the first writers to observe and identify plants at all stages of their growth, and in all seasons, noting variations due to climate, altitude and precipitation. In addition, he offered practical advice on collecting and storing drugs, as well their preparation and dosage; he even trialled drugs clinically, and thoroughly researched traditional usage of herbs in the locations where he found them. His writings included information gleaned from oral traditions and drawn from earlier texts, including 130 plants from the Hippocratic Collection, and others from the work of the ancient Greek physician Crataeus.

Dioscorides' original non-illustrated manuscripts, which no longer exist, contained medical information on around 600 plants, 90 minerals and 35 animal products (including two using viper's flesh; one being pickled in wine, oil, dill and salt for calming nerves and sharpening eyesight). These were divided into five volumes. Book One covered aromatics, oils, salves, trees and shrubs; Book Two dealt with animals, animal parts and products, cereals and herbs; Book Three discussed roots, juices, herbs and seeds; Book Four addressed additional roots and herbs; and Book Five housed information about wines and minerals.

BODILY AILMENTS

As you would expect, painkillers feature prominently in this work. For example, Dioscorides wrote of the willow (the *Salix* species, a natural remedy for pain and fever, and the basis of aspirin): 'a decoction of them is an excellent fomentation for gout'. He also alerted readers to the difference between a therapeutic and toxic dose of that powerful painkiller and dangerous narcotic, opium: 'a little of it, taken as much as a grain of ervum [probably the seed of *Vicia ervilia*, known as ervil or bitter vetch, an ancient legume found in the Mediterranean region], is a pain-easer, and a sleep-causer, and a digester ... but being drank too much it hurts, making men lethargicall, and it kills.'

There are also several remedies for toothache, including the resin of *Commiphora* (myrrh); the bark of *Platanus* (plane trees) soaked in vinegar; a decoction of tamarisk leaves mixed with wine; oak galls; the resin of *Rhus* (sumac); a decoction of mulberry leaves and bark; latex taken from the fig tree and *Euphorbia characias*

(Mediterranean spurge, pictured on p8) mixed with oil; and a decoction of asparagus roots and *Plantago* (plantain). If the problem could only be solved by extraction, olive oil sediment mixed with the juice from unripe grapes and cooked to the consistency of honey was to be smeared on decayed teeth to loosen them.

Dioscorides' manuscript reveals much about other uses of plants in the Roman Empire, too – for example, young *Pistacia lentiscus* twigs used for dental hygiene, shampoo made by pounding henna leaves soaked in the juice of soapwort (which acted as a foaming agent) and soot from the burnt resin of conifers used to darken eyebrows and eyelashes. And he often warns against adulteration, mentioning methods and the means of detection: frankincense, which was frequently adulterated with pine resin and gum, and valerian root, which when adulterated with butcher's broom became hard, difficult to break and lost its pleasant aroma.

A LASTING HERITAGE

Remarkably, *De Materia Medica* remained the leading herbal text for sixteen centuries, proving the accuracy of its author's observations and instructions through many generations. During the Middle Ages it was copied by hand, illustrated and translated into Arabic, Greek and Latin. From the sixteenth century, translations extended to Italian, German, Spanish and French, and an English version by the botanist John Goodyer appeared in 1655. Goodyer, together with his assistant John Heath, worked on his translation from 1652 to 1655, consulting at least 18 editions of *De Materia Medica* along the way. The pair worked quickly, beginning the first volume (728 pages) on 27 April 1652, and moving on to the second by 28 March 1653. *De Materia Medica* also formed the basis for later herbals written by the likes of Leonhart Fuchs, Matthaeus Lobelius, Carolus Clusius, John Gerard and William Turner, though these authors' own thoughts and observations gradually displaced Dioscorides' original text.

Salix alba (white willow). Dioscorides recommended the use of willow to treat gout.

However, in 1934 Sir Arthur Hill, Director of the Royal Botanic Gardens at Kew, found the original work still in use on Mount Athos: 'The official botanist monk ... a remarkable old man with an extensive knowledge of plants and their properties ... travelled very quickly, usually on foot, and sometimes on a mule, carrying his Flora with him in a large black bulky bag ... his Flora was nothing less than four manuscript volumes of Dioscorides, which apparently, he himself had copied out. This Flora he invariably used for determining any plant which he could not name at sight, and he could find his way in his books – and identify his plants to his own satisfaction – with remarkable rapidity.'

The oldest surviving and most famous copy is the so-called 'Vienna Dioscorides', created for Princess Juliana Anicia, daughter of the Western Roman Emperor Olybrius and now held in the Austrian National Library. This richly illustrated Byzantine version was completed in Constantinople in 512, and contains 383 paintings of Mediterranean plants, many of which can still be recognised today.

Pedanius Dioscorides:
INSPIRATION FOR GARDENERS

❧ Dioscorides recorded the use of euphorbia latex in dentistry but this sap can be harmful, causing inflammation of the skin, so it would have to be applied with care to avoid any soft tissue. The difference between a therapeutic and toxic dose can be minimal, when ingested, too, so always treat plants with respect. Do not self-medicate if you are uncertain about the dosage, or take expert advice before doing so. Familiar plants with common uses – such as mint and parsley for garnishes – are not eaten in large enough quantities to be dangerous.

BELOW Dioscorides prescribed the stem of *Physalis alkekengi* (Chinese lantern) as a sedative, and its berries as a diuretic.

❧ The sap of several plants can cause problems. Wear goggles when pruning euphorbia to protect your eyes. Rue causes blistering in the presence of sunlight, so prune or harvest on a dull day and cover your hands and arms as a precaution. When pruning ivy, wear gloves, goggles and a face mask; old plants contain dust, and the hairs on the leaves can trigger asthma attacks.

❧ Although Dioscorides prescribed the berries of *Physalis alkekengi* as a diuretic, fruiting plants should be sited with care. If you have young children, or young visitors to your garden, position plants with tempting berries away from places where

they can be reached by tiny hands. If you suspect poisoning, seek medical help immediately, taking a sample of the plant to the doctor or hospital for identification.

✤ According to Dioscorides, a poultice of fresh bay laurel leaves relieved the sting of wasps and bees, and could be drunk in wine to treat a scorpion sting. The juice of the leaves mixed with old wine and rose oil was also recommended as eardrops to improve hearing, while the bark would shatter kidney and bladder stones and heal an unhealthy liver. Modern drugs have replaced such remedies, though, and today the bay is used mostly as garden ornamentation and an ingredient in a bouquet garni.

✤ Dioscorides mentioned several Mediterranean herbs in his text, including lavender, rosemary and dill. Harvest these herbs early in the morning before the essential oils start to evaporate in the heat of the day, and put your clippings straight into a polythene bag. Mediterranean herbs should be grown 'hard', in poor, free-draining soil in an open sunny site, encouraging compact growth and a greater concentration of oils.

TOP RIGHT Widely used today, Dioscorides is believed to have been the first person to record the healing properties of *Lavandula* (lavender).

RIGHT *Laurus nobilis* (bay tree) can be medicinal, edible and ornamental. Dioscorides would also have known of its use in a victor's wreath.

Leonhart Fuchs

DATE	1501–1566
ORIGIN	BAVARIA
MAJOR ACHIEVEMENT	*DE HISTORIA STIRPIUM*

Fuchs made his name in botany with the publication of his 1542
De Historia Stirpium ('Notable Commentaries on the History of Plants').
First published in Basel, this masterpiece of Renaissance botany is widely
recognised as one of the most beautiful books ever printed, due to its
exquisite hand-coloured illustrations. It was also the first time that
many new species from the New World – including now-familiar and
widespread plants like tomatoes, corn and chillies – were described
and illustrated in a book. Despite its beauty, only around 100 copies
are known to have survived.

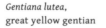

Gentiana lutea,
great yellow gentian

L eonhart Fuchs, a childhood genius, was born in Bavaria in 1501 at the height of the German Renaissance. He gained a BA at the age of 14, opened his own school, then at 18 attended Ingolstadt University in Bavaria, studying classics, philosophy and medicine. He became a physician in Munich in 1524 and was later summoned to Ansbach to become the personal physician of the Margrave of Brandenburg. It was during this time that he also became established as a writer.

Fuchs first found fame by creating a cure for the fatal and fast-acting English sweating sickness, using a number of plants, including rosemary, butterbur and various types of gentian (such as *Gentiana lutea*, pictured on p14). In 1535 he became Professor of Medicine at the University of Tübingen, a post he held for the rest of his life. Teaching was Fuchs's priority: he brought many innovations to the curriculum, including botanical field trips for medical students.

Fuchs was passionate about his subject: 'there is nothing in this life pleasanter and more delightful than to wander over woods, mountains, plains, garlanded and adorned with flowerlets and plants of various sorts, and most elegant to boot, and to gaze intently on them. But it increases that pleasure and delight not a little, if there be added an acquaintance with the virtues and powers of these same plants.'

A PICTURE TELLS A THOUSAND WORDS

In the preface of *De Historia Stirpium* Fuchs explained that he was writing for the benefit of his fellow physicians, lamenting the difficulty of finding one physician in a hundred with accurate knowledge of even a few plants: 'I have compiled these commentaries on the nature of plants with the utmost care as well as expense, emulating the devotion of the eminent scholars mentioned above. In the first place, we have included whatever relates to the whole history of every plant, with all the superfluities cut out, briefly and, we hope, in the best order, one we shall follow regularly. Then, to the description of each plant we have added an illustration. These are lifelike and modelled after nature and rendered more skillfully, if I may say so, than ever before. This we have done for no other reason than "a picture expresses things more surely and fixes them more deeply in the mind than the bare words of the text".'

His book was one of the first to include images drawn from nature, presenting plants at several stages during their life cycle, showing seeds, roots, flowers and fruits. Plants were listed alphabetically according to the Greek alphabet. The illustrations were to be used for identifying plants, and the medicinal uses were taken from ancient herbalists, primarily Dioscorides, then Galen and Pliny (always in that order), sometimes with Fuchs's own observations added. He notes, for example: 'a drachma in weight' of the thistle root taken in wine, is of benefit against the contagion of pestilence or sweating sickness. Furthermore, the same 'steeped in vinegar, is helpful against scabies, impetigo, and all blemishes of the skin difficult to cure, if they are washed with the decoction. The same also helps toothache.'

The illustration of *Capsicum annuum*
(ornamental pepper) in *De Historia
Stirpium* includes its root system. Fuchs
wanted to understand the whole plant.

A NEW WORLD OF PLANTS

Fuchs grew many of the plants featured in his
herbal in his Tübingen garden, including the
new and exotic. Of around 500 species, 100
were illustrated for the first time, including
several from the New World, such as cacti,
pumpkins, marigolds, potatoes, squashes,
kidney beans, tobacco, corn and chillies, the
specimens probably coming from Fuchs's
garden. Fuchs also broke with tradition by
being interested in illustrating plants exactly
as they looked in nature, hand-painted with
a watercolour wash under his supervision
for the greatest possible accuracy. Sadly, his
original set of drawings was lost.

Unusually, there are portraits of the
three artists at the conclusion of the book:
Albrecht Meyer, who drew the plants from
living specimens; Heinrich Füllmaurer, who
transferred the drawings into woodblocks;
and Vitus Rudolph Speckle, 'by far the best
engraver in Strasbourg', who cut them into
wood for printing.

The book is also believed to be the first
herbal to include a botanical glossary in the
form of its introductory chapter, referred to as
an 'Explanation of Difficult Terms' – 132 in all
– but this helpful addition was only included
in the Latin versions. The glossary also sheds
light on many horticultural ideas of the time,
like *Toparium*: 'topiary work which arranges
trees, shrubs or herbs, into arches or vaults

Unusually, Fuchs's book depicts
the artist-craftsmen who
illustrated the work.

for decoration. Hence those trees and herbs should be called topiariae which are particularly adapted to this work owing to their natural flexibility and pliancy.' Or propagation, or *Propago*: 'an old vine bent down and buried in the earth in the form of arches, so that from one, many vines grow...'. And *Tomentum*: 'By tomentum the Latins meant anything with which mattresses could be stuffed to make them softer and warmer, whether this be wool or feathers, or anything else one wishes, suitable for making them softer and the body warm. So the leaves of *Dictamnus* which seem to be soft are called *tomentitia* and *lanea* by Dioscorides.'

Fuchs's herbal was very popular. It was abridged from Latin into a German folio edition (though still weighing about 5kg), then into field guides; in 1545 an edition containing only plates was published for the illiterate. During Fuchs's lifetime there were 39 imprints in various formats in Latin, German, French, Spanish and Dutch, and it was translated into English 20 years after his death. English artist and designer William Morris owned a copy and is said to have taken inspiration from its prints for some of his designs – 'I have a poor copy of it which I have found very useful: it is a rare book; but for refinement of drawing it is the best of all as one would expect from the date.'

Corn was illustrated and labelled with the name *Turcicum frumentum* in *De Historia Stirpium*.

Leonhart Fuchs:
INSPIRATION FOR GARDENERS

❧ Fuchs never saw a fuchsia; the plant was named in his honour more than a century after his death. The first species to be found was *Fuchsia triphylla*, on the Caribbean island of Hispaniola in around 1696, by the French Franciscan monk and botanist Charles Plumier, during his third expedition to the Greater Antilles. Plumier made detailed drawings of the flowering plants and ferns he saw and also revived the ancient practice of naming genera after people. The genus *Plumeria*, commonly known as frangipani, was in turn named after him.

❧ Fuchs often commented on where he saw plants. He said that clove pink was 'widely grown in pots' and 'you seldom find a house that does not have one displayed in front', for example. Basil was grown 'in clay pots on the windowsill' and the hart's tongue fern was 'prized in most gardens'. Fuchs also recorded the popularity of the chilli pepper – 'found almost everywhere in Germany now, planted in clay pots and earthen vessels. A few years ago it was unknown'.

TOP LEFT *Fuchsia triphylla* was the first fuchsia species discovered by the botanist Charles Plumier. Plumier named the genus after Leonhart Fuchs.

LEFT Fuchs recorded that *Asplenium scolopendrium* (hart's tongue fern) was 'prized in most gardens'. It is still a reliable choice today, in damp or dry shade.

✤ Fuchs included a description of corn, or maize, as one of the new introductions to Europe at the time. Elsewhere in the world it was a plant with a long history of cultivation as a staple crop. As Nikolai Vavilov writes in his *Origin and Geography of Cultivated Plants*, 'Maize (*Zea mays*) plays the same role [in Southern Mexico] as wheat in the Old World: without it there would not have been any Mayan civilization'. It is included among plants of south Mexican and Central American origins, alongside kidney beans and runner beans. Corn was first domesticated in Mexico as many as 10,000 years ago, and cobs have been found in cave excavations in Tehuacán. Older varieties are smaller and multicoloured, as opposed to the more familiar yellow, and are more often dried and used as ornaments.

TOP *Plumeria* sp. (frangipani). Charles Plumier, who commemorated Fuchs in the naming of *Fuchsia*, was himself honoured with the genus *Plumeria*, a choice plant for Mediterranean and tropical gardens.

ABOVE Fuchs recorded the everyday use of *Ocimum basilicum* (sweet basil) in Germany, noting its regular appearance on windowsills.

William Turner

DATE C. 1508–1568	
ORIGIN ENGLAND	
MAJOR ACHIEVEMENT *A NEW HERBALL*	

William Turner is famous for producing the first scientific herbal
in English rather than Latin and thereby introducing medical and plant
knowledge to English speakers. When not studying or writing on
ornithology or botany, his life was spent in religious controversy. During
the English Reformation, his religious beliefs led to an exile in Europe,
where he travelled extensively and continued his studies. Turner described
himself as 'a physician delighting in the study of sacred literature';
today he is better known as the 'Father of English Botany'.

Acanthus mollis,
bear's breeches

Turner was born in Morpeth, Northumberland, in around 1508, and went up to Pembroke Hall, Cambridge University, in 1526, where he was awarded an MA in 1533. The second part of his famous work *A New Herball* is dedicated to his sponsor, Sir Thomas Wentworth: 'who hath deserved better to have my book of herbs to be given to him than he whose father with his yearly exhibition did help me, being student in Cambridge of physic and philosophy?'

Despite his achievements, Turner's life was one of turmoil, due to his passionate non-conformist beliefs. During the reign of Henry VII, his writings were banned, and he was imprisoned for preaching without a licence. He was also twice exiled to Europe, and banned by the Church for non-conformity after returning home to Britain.

EARLY WORKS

During his first exile, Turner travelled throughout the Continent visiting France, then Italy, where he obtained a degree in medicine and studied under Luca Ghini, Professor of Botany at Bologna (and credited with creating the first herbarium). Turner then travelled to Switzerland and to Germany, where he met Leonhart Fuchs (see pp14–19). In Holland, Turner wrote that he became personal physician to 'the Erle of Emden for four full years' and in East Friesland, 'bought two whole Porpesses and dissected them'.

Despite his interest in plants, Turner's first printed book was on ornithology – *The Principal Birds of Aristotle and Pliny*, published in 1544 and including his own observations alongside those of his chosen authors. Turner notes, for example, that the blue tit is 'very fond of suet' and that in towns and cities, red kites are known for 'snatching food from children's hands'. Such is the importance of this work that Turner is often described as the 'Father of English Ornithology'.

On the subject of plants, Turner wrote *Libellus de re Herbaria Nova* in 1538, listing 144 plants with synonyms in Latin, Greek and English. He gave a forthright explanation of his reasons for writing the book in its preface: 'you will wonder, perhaps to the verge of astonishment, what has driven me, still a beardless youth, and but slightly infected with knowledge of medicine, to publish a book on herbary … [I would rather] try something difficult of this sort rather than let young students who hardly know the names of their plants correctly to go on in their blindness.' Among the plants he mentions in the text are *Acorus calamus* (sweet flag) and *Acanthus mollis* (bear's breeches, pictured on p20).

This was followed ten years later by an extended version of the same work, entitled *The Names of Herbes*, which includes three times as many plants, and provides foreign terms alongside the English: 'Acanthus is called in greke acantha, in English Branke vrsin, in duche welshe bearenklawe, in frenche branke vrsine…. In the greatest plentie I euer sawe it, I did see it in my Lorde Protectour's graces gardine in Syon'. Syon Park is believed to have been the first botanical garden created in England, and the laying out of the formal gardens within the wall around Syon House is traditionally attributed to Turner. He is also said to have planted the mulberry trees by the east front, which remain today. Remarkably, only one original copy of the *Libellus* and fewer than ten of *The Names of Herbes* survive.

Turner's great work, *A New Herball*, arranged alphabetically and published in three parts between 1551 and 1568, broke with tradition, becoming the first important herbal to be written in English and the first scientific record of some 238 native species. Most of the illustrations came from his friend Leonhart Fuchs but they were poor copies. Turner attempted to analyse plants

Colchicum autumnale (meadow saffron) was observed and noted by Turner near Bath.

scientifically, describing their appearance and giving details of where they grew, together with medicinal and other uses. The text was written in English to enable ordinary people who could read, and apothecaries whose Latin was poor, to identify and use plants safely.

Turner's publications include references to plants seen by him on various research trips. There are descriptions of plants from his childhood: 'I never saw any plaine tree in Englande saving one in Northumberlande beside Morpeth and another at Barnwel Abbey beside Cambrydge'. In Somerset he saw meadow saffron 'growe in the west cuntre besyde Bathe'. He also provides an early description of the famous Glastonbury thorn: 'about six myles from Welles, in ye parke of G[l]assenberry there is an hawthorne which is grene all the wynter, as all they that dwell there about do stedfastly holde.' Further afield, he sighted several plants on 'Mount Appenine besyde Bonony', among them cyclamens and sumac, which the Italians used to tan leather, and in Chiavenna he found 'Monkshood growing in great plenty upon the alps'.

NEW NAMES FOR OLD

Where there were no common names, Turner created his own, often translated directly from the Latin. Some have religious overtones. Wood sorrel is called 'Alleluya, because it appereth about Easter when Alleluya is song agayn'; Solomon's seal 'is called in English scala celi' (stairway to heaven) because of its leaf formation. He experimented, too: bog myrtle 'is tried by experience that it is good to be put in beare [beer], both [by] me and by diverse other in Summersetshyre.' One event, however, illustrates the the dangers associated with experimentation: 'I washed an aching tooth with a little opio mixed with water; and a little of the same unawares went down, within an hour after my handes began to swell about the wrestes, and to itch, and my breth was so stopped, that if I hand not taken in a pece of th roote of masterwurt ... with wyne I thynck that it would have kylled me.'

Turner created several gardens in his lifetime in addition to the one at Syon – including one near Tower Hill in London. A memorial to him can be seen close by, on the southeast wall of St Olav's church.

A hand-coloured woodcut featuring an illustration of a rose, taken from a 1568 publication of Turner's great work, *A New Herball*.

William Turner:
INSPIRATION FOR GARDENERS

✤ William Turner mentions that the hawthorn known as *Crataegus monogyna* 'Biflora' is unusual in that it flowers not only in May but in in mid-winter, too. Tradition says that it flowers on Christmas Day, but depending on the weather, it blooms in milder periods any time from November until April. Legend tells that after the crucifixion of Christ, Joseph of Arimathea preached Christianity in England. Tired of travelling and being ignored, he rested on 'Weary-all Hill', at Glastonbury, where he prayed for a miracle to convince the doubters. The staff he leaned on, 'being thrust into the ground', simultaneously burst into leaf and flower. It was Christmas Day, and the miracle is said to be repeated every

Christmas. Sprays are sent to the royal family as decoration for Christmas Day; the late Queen Mother placed hers on a writing desk and Queen Elizabeth II is said to have hers on her breakfast table. This small, spreading, spiny deciduous tree or shrub likes moisture-retentive, free-draining soil, in sunshine or partial shade.

✤ When William Turner was Dean of Wells, in Somerset, he created a garden at what is now known as the Old Deanery, off Cathedral Green. The garden was restored to a Tudor layout and replanted by volunteers in 2003 using plants mentioned in *A New Herball*. The garden is open to the public (www.olddeanerygarden.org.uk).

✤ One of the plants Turner mentions is 'perfoliata', a 'herbe wyth a leafe lyke pease & lytle blacke seedes in the top ... it may be called in England Thorowwax because the stalke waxeth thorowe the leaues'. *Bupleurum rotundifolium*, a cornfield annual, retains the same common name of thorow-wax. It looks like a spurge but is actually a member of the carrot family. Seed companies sell several selected forms, which are attractive in a contemporary cottage garden and excellent for flower arranging.

LEFT *Bupleurum rotundifolium* (thorow-wax) was given its common name by Turner, who first noted it growing in Germany.

RIGHT *Crataegus monogyna* 'Biflora' (Glastonbury thorn) was another plant observed by Turner in the wild and later described in his work.

John Ray

DATE	1627–1705
ORIGIN	ENGLAND
MAJOR ACHIEVEMENT	*HISTORIA PLANTARUM*

A naturalist, theologian and prolific writer, John Ray published around
20 works, including a 1669 paper, 'Experiments concerning the Motion
of Sap in Trees', containing an early description of dendrochronology
– explaining how an ash tree could be aged by its rings. Ray's works were
based on his journeys, observing plants in their native habitats; Carl Linnaeus
would later draw on them for inspiration in creating his famous binomial
system. Known as the 'Father of Natural History', Ray published systematic
works on plants, birds, mammals, fish and insects, bringing order to the
chaotic mass of names and systems used by naturalists at the time.

Anethum graveolens,
dill

J ohn Ray, son of an Essex blacksmith, proved that social class was no barrier to intellect by attending the local grammar school, and gaining a scholarship to Cambridge University aged 16. While there he studied at three colleges; lectured in Greek, Latin, mathematics and humanities; preached in the college chapel and became friends with John Nidd, Francis Willughby and Peter Courthope before leaving Cambridge in 1662, casting himself, he said, 'upon Providence and good friends' to fulfil his wish to travel, observing nature – particularly plants. His inspiration came in part from his mother, who during his childhood had shared her good knowledge on the uses of plants (such as dill, pictured on p26).

While at university, Ray had packed a small garden with plants he had collected or received as gifts from friends, analysing the differences between each one and developing his own system of classification. In doing so, he had discovered the limitations of existing botanical literature and became certain it could be improved. In the early 1650s he began to catalogue the plants he found during long horse rides through the Cambridgeshire countryside. His *Catalogus plantarum circa Cantabrigiam nascentium* (1660) described 558 wild species and crops growing in the county. Arranged alphabetically, it included the uses of the plants, alongside their English names and locations. Ray also identified several new plants and grouped similar plants together, rather than dividing them up (taxonomists are still divided into 'splitters' and 'lumpers'). His catalogue contained a brief outline of the structure and classification of plants, according to the principles of Swiss botanist Jean Bauhin, and revealed Ray's own meticulous approach to science.

A LIFE OF TRAVEL AND OBSERVATION

On 9 August 1658, Ray embarked on the first of seven extensive botanising trips throughout Great Britain, riding to Northampton, Warwick, the Peak District, Worcester and Gloucester, observing and documenting plants, nature and landscapes along the way. Inspired by what he saw, Ray decided to compile a work cataloguing every English plant, writing to friends across the country to ask for their help. As a result, he made seven extensive tours of Britain, accompanied by his university friends, making meticulous observations of flora, fauna and sea creatures (on one occasion dissecting a porpoise). He also made a mammoth three-year trip around Europe, at Willughby's instigation, which allowed Ray to collect and catalogue non-native plants along the way.

After his extensive travels through Britain, Wray published his *Catalogus Plantarum Angliae* in 1670, dedicated to Willughby. A second edition was published in 1677, with an appendix of newly observed plants by 'John Ray and his friends'. The preface proclaimed Ray's conviction that the divine creation of plants indicated there was a reason for their existence, which could only be discovered by putting them to practical use. Continuing his work on the classification and nature of plants in *Methodus Plantarum Nova* (1682), 'a catalogue of Species not native to England', Ray classified plants using the whole plant: 'There was leisure

to contemplate by the way what lay constantly before the eyes and were so often trodden thoughtlessly under foot ... the shape, colour and structure of particular plants fascinated and absorbed me: Interest in botany became a passion.' Ray also believed that local species were likely to be preserved by providence somewhere else in the world – that the Creator would ensure the survival of a species by placing it in different locations around the world – and was first to make a distinction between monocotyledons and dicotyledons.

Ray's greatest work was his *Historia Plantarum*. The two volumes, published in 1686 and 1688, described approximately 6,100 species of plants. The second volume also contained 15 rare North American plants from bishop and botanist Henry Compton's garden (see pp38–43). A third volume, detailing a further 10,000 species, was based on research rather than Ray's own observations, old age and infirmity preventing him from visiting Oxford University and the Chelsea Physic Garden, where he could have observed new and exotic plants first hand. The classification used in the *Historia Plantarum* was an important step towards modern taxonomy, and volume one included the first usage of the term 'species'.

Salvia officinalis (common sage) was widely grown in the 1600s for its culinary and medicinal uses.

In 1690 Ray published *Synopsis Methodica Stirpium Britannicarum*, following the classificatory system of his *Methodus Plantarum*. With Sloane's encouragement, he drew up all but one of the county lists of plants for Edmund Gibson's edition of Camden's *Britannia* (1695), and he issued a further catalogue of European plants (*Stirpium Europaearum Extra Britannias Nascentium Sylloge*) in 1694. This included a stout defence of his method of classification against that of German botanist Augustus Rivinus (also known as A. Q. Bachmann), based on differences in the shape of flowers. An exchange of letters appeared in the second edition of his *Synopsis*, where Ray referred to the writings of French taxonomist Joseph Pitton de Tournefort, and he took the work of both Rivinus and Tournefort into account in *Methodus Plantarum Emendata et Aucta* (1703), when he revised his classifications, introducing divisions between flowering and non-flowering plants. This time of turmoil for plant classification was only resolved once Linnaeus's binomial system became established.

In 1691 Ray published *The Wisdom of God Manifested in the Works of the Creation*. Based on his sermons at Trinity College, this was a statement of his faith. He believed in 'natural theology', in which the heavens, geology, botany, zoology and human anatomy were evidence of a providential, benevolent god. Ray believed 'Divinity is my Profession', stating, 'I know of no occupation which is more worthy or more delightful for a free man than to contemplate the beauteous works of Nature and to honour the infinite wisdom and goodness of God the Creator'.

On 15 March 1679 , upon the death of his mother, Ray and his wife moved back to Black Notley, his birthplace, and settled in the family home. Suffering from chronic ill health during his later years, he died at home on 17 January 1705, having laid the foundations for modern taxonomy.

John Ray:
INSPIRATION FOR GARDENERS

✤ John Ray was the first to formally recognise the distinction between monocotyledons and dicotyledons, noting differences in their leaves, stems, roots and flowers. Monocots have one seed leaf; dicots have two. Monocots tend to have fibrous roots, which are found near the soil surface, while dicots have one main root, the taproot, with smaller roots branching from it. As monocots grow, the sap system carrying nutrients to each portion of the plant are scattered; in dicots the system is structured. Their leaves look different, too; monocot leaves have parallel veins, but dicots form branching veins. The flowers of monocots are grouped in threes, but dicotyledon flowers are in groups of four or five. Monocot pollen has one furrow; in dicots there are three.

✤ Ray learned about culinary and medicinal uses of plants from his mother, Elizabeth, and some of these are still familiar today. Examples include the use of *Salvia officinalis* (sage) and *Thymus serpyllum* var. *albus* (white-flowered creeping thyme) to flavour stuffings, and *Anethum graveolens* (dill) as an accompaniment to fish.

BELOW *Thymus serpyllum* var. *albus* (white-flowered creeping thyme). Ray was introduced to thyme by his mother, who passed on her knowledge of plants.

BELOW A medicinal plant in Ray's era, *Campanula persicifolia* (fairy bellflower) is now used as an ornamental herbaceous plant.

❧ *Campanula persicifolia* (fairy bellflower) was known to Ray as a remedy for mouth ulcers and sore throats. Now an ornamental, it thrives in fertile, moist, well-drained, neutral to alkaline soil, in sun or part shade. Used as a dressing for wounds in Ray's era, the late-spring flowering *Polygonatum multiflorum* (common Solomon's seal) is now used as a garden plant, in moist, free-draining, organic rich soil, in part shade.

❧ *Rosa* 'John Ray' was bred by Heather Horner and named in 2000 at the request of the John Ray Trust, in Braintree, Essex, to mark the millennium. It is a deep yellow, semi-double, cluster-flowering rose, with a mild to strong fragrance, producing flushes of blooms throughout the season. This rarely found rose grows at Middleton Hall near Tamworth in Staffordshire, home to Francis Willughby and where John Ray lived between 1660 and 1673. As with all roses, 'John Ray' is a surface-rooting plant, so avoid hoeing and control weeds by mulching around it in spring with a thick layer of well-rotted organic matter.

TOP Ray mentions *Cerinthe major* 'Purpurascens' (honeywort) in his *Historia Plantarum*. It is still popular as a garden plant, for cut flowers.

ABOVE The spring-flowering *Polygonatum multiflorum* (common Solomon's seal) was known to Ray as a good dressing for wounds.

Mary Somerset

DATE	1630–1715
ORIGIN	ENGLAND
MAJOR ACHIEVEMENT	12-VOLUME HERBARIUM OF PRESSED PLANTS

Mary Somerset, Duchess of Beaufort, was a passionate botanical collector, cataloguer and cultivator of exotic plants in her gardens and greenhouses in London and Badminton, which were among the finest of their day. She kept detailed lists and records of her plants and her collections, and expanded her botanical knowledge by reading and corresponding with the great botanists and gardeners of the day, including John Ray and Sir Hans Sloane. Her greatest legacy is a 12-volume herbarium of pressed plants that she bequeathed to Sloane after her death.

Bombax ceiba,
South American
silk cotton tree

Mary Somerset, first Duchess of Beaufort, was well placed to garden and botanise. Not only did she have an estate in Gloucestershire but her neighbours in Chelsea were physician and collector Sir Hans Sloane and the Chelsea Physic Garden. The Duchess's skill as a gardener, combined with her wealth and personal connections, enabled her to accumulate a diverse collection of botanical curiosities. Plant collector James Petiver wrote: 'in her grace the Duchess of Beaufort's most Noble Garden as the Matchless Stoves at Badminton in Gloucestershire, I the last summer met with many new rare and very curious plants, most of them raised to that perfection I never saw before.' Like many of the great estates of the time, it included 'an extensive orchard of many different fruits [including oranges under glass] as well as gardens containing fashionable flowers of the time: tulips, narcissus, ranunculus, anemones, etc.' There were also collections of 'curios' at her London home, Beaufort House. During the last decade of the seventeenth century, the Duchess amassed a collection of variegated plants in pots, including 'Strip't Phillerea, (*Phillyrea latifolia* 'Variegata'), Strip't thyme (*Thymus serpyllum* 'Aureus') ... Silver Strip't Myrtle (*Myrtus communis* 'Variegata') and Silver Strip't honeysuckle (*Lonicera periclymenum* 'Variegata')', which were placed in prominent places in the knot garden or wilderness. Her lists from 1692 to 1699 feature an increasing range of 'striped plants'. The first contains 28 varieties, mainly evergreens and herbs; by 1697 these numbered 69, including deciduous woody plants, such as beech (*Fagus sylvatica* 'Luteovariegata') and netted elder (*Sambucus nigra* 'Marginata'), and a greater variety of herbs and ornamentals like sweet williams and sage. A third list contains around 91 varieties, including several *Amaranthus*: 'A.tricolor ye common', the cultivar 'Splendens' ('from ye East Indiis, much better'), and another that had 'a deep red spot in ye middle of ye leav's a very good kind'.

A GLOBAL COLLECTION

The Duchess's hot houses were renowned for botanical curiosities that had come from all parts of the world, notably India, Sri Lanka, Japan, China, South Africa and the West Indies. George London, of the Brompton Park Nursery, and William III's gardener at Hampton Court, was a major source of seeds and plants. In 1695 and 1696 the Duchess received a number of letters from him containing seeds from the West Indies, notably the Barbardos lily (*Hippeastrum puniceum*); he also sent seeds from Guinea, the Cape of Good Hope, Portugal, the Canary Islands, and from the East Indies – the 'Java bean tree', black datura and tamarind. A letter accompanying a 'Cheste of silke cotton trees' (*Bombax ceiba*, pictured on p32) included a list of the merchant ships (and their captains) on which these plants were travelling. These are later recorded in the Duchess's census of 1 June 1697 as growing in her garden, along with a 'Benjamin tree', or spice bush (*Lindera benzoin*), bamboo and a date tree.

The Duchess compiled detailed inventories of her plants, particularly during the last decade of the seventeenth and the first of the eighteenth century. These were

cross-referenced to the botanical authorities of the time, arranged alphabetically according to the country of origin, and often accompanied by practical details, such as cultivation and propagation. ('Mark't in my booke', she writes on a list of plants from Portugal and Guinea in 1695.) From around 1700, the botanist William Sherard was employed at Badminton as tutor to Mary's grandson. While there, through his correspondence and contacts, the Duchess added over 1,500 plants to her collection.

STUDENT AND PATRON

The Duchess exchanged plants and knowledge with all of the great gardeners and botanists of her day; Sloane also gave her the transactions of the Royal Society to read, indicating the depth of her understanding of botany and horticulture. It is evident from the cross-references on her inventories that she also read the works of luminaries of the time, including John Gerard, John Parkinson and John Ray (see pp26–31). However, she was not averse to criticising the work of established botanists, based on what she considered more accurate information, gleaned from the plants she was growing herself, stating, 'none of the Lyrium in Parkisons H[erbal] are like those plants of mine', and declaring others 'not well described by any of them the plants I have being more beautifull than any of these prints'. She corrected another work, writing, 'Wild Callabash and Wild Cashe trees, should have been with the trees', and in another note – 'These plants I grow which I can find no figures of in any of my books, they are therefore to be described as they grow now at Badminton in 1693' – indicated that some of her plants were yet to be recorded and may have been new species to cultivation.

Several cultivars of *Amaranthus tricolor* (tampala) were grown and recorded by Mary Somerset. She enjoyed growing unusual tropical plants.

Although her vast plant collections and great stoves have long disappeared, her legacy, a 12-volume large-folio herbarium, containing dried specimens of 'plants, most rare and some common gathered in the field and gardens at Badminton, Chelsea, etc. dryed by order of Mary Duchess of Beaufort', and entitled 'the Duchess of Beaufort's plants', was left to Sir Hans Sloane on her death and is now in the Natural History Museum. The Duchess also oversaw a two-volume *Florilegium* of botanical illustrations of some of the more interesting plants in her collection. The first volume was painted by Everhardus Kickius, and the second volume by Daniel Francome, both of which are held in the library at Badminton House. We know that Sloane loaned the Duchess's herbarium to botanist John Ray, who made various annotations on its pages and a few revisions to her descriptions, indicating that he respected the Duchess's work and its careful preservation. Sloane also obviously shared these views. The Duchess of Beaufort died on 7 January 1715. She was suitably commemorated a century later with the naming of *Beaufortia*.

Mary Somerset:
INSPIRATION FOR GARDENERS

❧ Among the plants painted in the Duchess's *Florilegium* is *Melianthus major* (honey flower), an evergreen sub-shrub introduced from the Cape of Good Hope to Britain in 1688. Its grey-green leaves with serrated edges are very architectural but they have an unpleasant smell. Flowers, produced during long, hot summers, are dark red in colour, with copious black nectar that can be shaken from the flower onto the palm of the hand. It is then that you discover why it was given its common name. Honey flower needs moderately fertile soil in a sheltered, sunny position, away from cold or drying winds, and a dry mulch in winter to protect the roots. In colder areas, grow it in a pot and overwinter under protection.

BELOW *Melianthus major* (honey flower), illustrated in the Duchess's *Florilegium*. It has spectacular spikes of flowers in hot summers.

❧ In volume two of the *Florilegium*, Francome painted *Hibiscus rosa-sinensis* (Chinese hibiscus), now a widespread garden shrub throughout the tropics, grown for its large, brightly coloured flowers. It can be grown under glass or as a houseplant in cooler climates in a warm bright position, with moderate to high humidity; mist around the plant with tepid water or stand it on a tray of pebbles filled with water to the bottom of the pot. You should water this plant when the compost surface starts to dry out, but reduce watering in winter. The double-flowered 'Chiffon' range of hardy hibiscus come in lavender, pink and blue. These hardy plants are covered with flowers from mid-summer to autumn.

❧ The Duchess grew pelargoniums that had arrived from South Africa. Among them were those with scented leaves. *Pelargonium papilonaceum* has a lemon fragrance, 'Prince of Orange' smells of orange, 'Lady Plymouth' of rose, and the large furry leaves of *Pelargonium tomentosum* smell of peppermint. Pelargoniums are not frost hardy, so are better grown in containers and brought indoors over winter before the first frosts. Reduce watering from early autumn. Feed during the growing season with high-potash fertiliser for compact, flower-covered plants, and grow in fibrous, free-draining compost.

TOP RIGHT *Hibiscus rosa-sinensis* (tropical hibiscus) appeared in volume two of Somerset's *Florilegium*. It is a garden plant in warmer climates and a house plant in cooler conditions.

RIGHT The Duchess loved pelargoniums and maintained a large collection. Among this was *Pelargonium tomentosum* (peppermint geranium).

Henry Compton

DATE	1632–1713
ORIGIN	ENGLAND
MAJOR ACHIEVEMENT	BOTANIST AND BISHOP

After a short career as an officer in the Life Guards, Compton turned
to religion and, as Bishop of London, was responsible for the Church of
England overseas, including the colonies in America, the Caribbean, Africa
and India. When he appointed clergymen, those with a botanical interest
were always favoured. After being suspended by King James II for his
overly Protestant beliefs, Compton focused on bringing glory to his
garden by planting rare and unusual plants. In doing so, the 'Botanising
Bishop' became one of the great ecclesiastical botanists of all time.

Magnolia virginiana,
swamp bay

T he garden at Fulham Palace was already well established in 1675, when Henry Compton arrived to plant and garden the 36 acres of land, but it had yet to reach the peak of its fame. A biography published after his death recorded that he 'had a great genius for Botanism, and ... he apply'd himself to the improvement of his Garden at Fulham, with new variety of Domestik and Exotick plants'; contemporary botanist Richard Pulteney also noted Compton combined 'his taste for gardening' with 'a real and scientific knowledge of plants'. According to an 1813 book on the progress of English botany, Compton's aim was 'to collect a greater variety of Greenhouse rarities and to plant a greater variety of hardy Exotic trees and Shrubs than had been seen in any garden before in England', and in many ways he succeeded.

Compton appointed George London (subsequent founder of the Brompton Park Nursery) as his advisor and gardener, and by 1686, William Penn's gardener was hoping for an arrangement with the 'Bishop of London's gardener' to supply him with garden plants in exchange for products from Pennsylvania.

SOURCING THE NEW WORLD

Compton sent Reverend John Banister, one of the first university-trained naturalists in North America and the first notable Virginian botanist, to North America via the West Indies in 1678, where, botanist Richard Pulteney noted, Banister 'industriously sought for plants, described them and drew the figures of the rarer species'. Banister sent trees, shrubs and seeds back to Fulham Palace and other gardens, including the University of Oxford Botanic Garden and the Temple Coffee House Botany Club (both Compton and London were members), where the most eminent botanists of the day met to compare notes once a week. In the second volume of his 1688 *Historia Plantarum*, John Ray (see pp26–31) attempted to describe all known plants, including those from Virginia growing in the Bishop's garden, making it the first publication dealing with North American flora. Compton was a friend and supporter of Ray.

Banister's first consignment (1683) included *Liquidamber styraciflua* (sweet gum) and *Lindera benzoin* (spice bush). The second (1687) included *Acer negundo* (box elder) and *Magnolia virginiana* (the first magnolia to be grown in Britain – pictured on p38). He also sent *Gillenia trifoliata* (Bowman's root), which was successfully grown by Head Gardener William Milward. It was named after Arnold Gille (Gillenius), a seventeenth-century German botanist, and by 1713 was already found in several gardens in London. Banister's life was cut short when he was accidentally shot dead (or fell from a rock – it remains a mystery) while on expedition. Compton also received plants from others. Reverend John Clayton, a rector in Jamestown, and Sir William Berkeley, Govenor of Virginia, sent regular shipments of trees to England, including at least one recorded shipment to Fulham Palace. Mark Catesby, an English naturalist who had moved to Virginia and become a professional plant collector, also sent seeds and rare plants to Compton shortly before the Bishop's death.

Plants arrived from other parts of the world, too. Scottish surgeon and botanist James Cunningham brought a large *Rhus chinensis* (Chinese gall), which contemporary botanist E. H. M. Cox said had 'ripe berries on it from China, which James Petiver [plant collector and "compulsive natural historian"] gave to the Right Reverend, my Lord Bishop of London'. Compton's garden was so esteemed that when new plants arrived, some were always sent to Fulham Palace. In 1687 the collector Hans Sloane sailed to Jamaica as physician for the Duke of Albermarle, describing every plant he saw in detail. On his return, he brought with him around 800 plants, which were sent to Compton and Mary Somerset, the Duchess of Beaufort (see pp32–37).

Bishop Compton dispersed his clergy worldwide to preach and collect plants, such as *Crotalaria juncea* (bengal hemp).

PLANT COLLECTOR EXTRAORDINAIRE

Hortus Kewensis credits Compton with over 40 new introductions, two-thirds of them hardy trees and shrubs. He had a great passion for trees; in the 38 years that he presided as Bishop, the grounds became densely planted with *Liquidambar*, *Liriodendron*, scarlet oak, black walnut, pines, juniper, cedars, maples, hollies, hickories, hawthorns, dogwoods, robinias and more. Professor John Hope, Professor of Botany at Edinburgh University, visited in 1766, and was the first to note a 20-metre-high *Juglans nigra* (black walnut), a *Quercus suber* (cork oak) of 12 metres, and an *Acer rubrum* (red maple) of around 9 metres. The garden also included *Lycium barbarum* (bearing goji berry fruits), *Adiantum pedatum* (five-fingered maidenhair fern), *Arisaema triphyllum* (bloody arum), *Dodecatheon meadia* (shooting star), *Mertensia virginica* (Virginian bluebells) and several pelargoniums, including *P. capitatum*, *P. myrrhifolium* and *P. cucullatum*, all introduced in 1690 by Hans William Bentinck, Head Steward of William of Orange (who Compton supported). *P. inquinans*, one of the parents of the modern bedding geranium, also featured in the garden; the other parent, *P. zonale*, was grown by the Duchess of Beaufort.

Arisaema triphyllum (bloody arum), a native of the eastern North American woodlands, was recorded as growing in Compton's garden.

There was space for edibles, too. Compton was interested in vegetables and grew kidney beans to eat at a time when they were seen as purely ornamental. Many of the names of his plants have now changed – the *Clematis hederacea* listed in the *Sloane Herbarium*, for example, is actually *Campsis radicans*. It is not known whether Compton grew the 'Fearne tree of Virginia' (later named *Comptonia asplenifolia* in his honour), but it was already in cultivation in his day, being grown by the Duchess of Beaufort and in the Chelsea Physic Garden before 1700.

According to William Watson's *Philosophical Transactions*, most of Compton's plants were dispersed to other collections after his death by 'ignorant persons ... to make way for the more ordinary productions of the kitchen garden'. Some plants went to the University of Oxford Botanic Garden, others to the Chelsea Physic Garden, and the Head Gardener sold yet others to nurserymen, which were then dispersed into general cultivation. Fulham Palace garden is currently being restored.

Henry Compton:
INSPIRATION FOR GARDENERS

✤ Bishop Compton grew *Rhododendron viscosum* (swamp azalea), the first azalea to be grown in Britain. It makes an excellent garden shrub due to it being late flowering, and producing exquisitely fragrant white to pink-flushed flowers from late spring into summer. It also has excellent autumn colour. It is said to be a parent of a great number of azalea hybrids; Loddiges' nursery catalogue of 1836 lists 107 varieties. Grow this plant in pots of ericaceous compost, and water it with rainwater, or plant it in acidic soil in a sheltered position, in dappled shade or sunshine (but not scorching sunshine). As a native of swampy lowlands, it is best grown in acidic, woodland soil. It tolerates moist to wet soils, but will not grow in soils where the roots are permanently underwater. Deadhead and feed after flowering, and mulch with well-rotted compost in spring.

✤ *Liquidambar styraciflua* (sweet gum) is a native of the eastern United States, and also often found in swampy ground. It has long been valued for its stately form and handsome foliage. There are several good selections, including 'Lane Roberts', which produces outstanding black-red, ember-like autumn colour. It was named after eminent London gynaecologist, rugby player and keen gardener Cedric Sydney Lane-Roberts, who purchased several seedlings from Hillier Nurseries. When Sir Harold Hillier visited one day, he was impressed with one of the seedlings, asked for some scionwood and named the new cultivar after his friend.

BELOW Compton grew *Rhododendron viscosum* (swamp azalea). This was the first azalea species to be grown anywhere in Britain.

✤ *Lycium barbarum* (Chinese box thorn), grown by Compton, produces goji berries – now considered a 'super food'. It is a fast-growing deciduous shrub with long, lax stems. It has long been grown in gardens and has naturalised in many parts of the world, including Britain. Its white and purple, trumpet-shaped flowers appear from early spring to midsummer, and are followed by the shiny red berries. These can either be picked and eaten straight from the bush, or dried. It takes two to three years for the shrub to produce its first crop.

TOP RIGHT *Lycium barbarum* (Chinese box thorn), which produces goji berries, grew in Compton's garden. Native to south-eastern Europe and Asia, the plant has now been naturalised throughout Britain.

RIGHT Compton filled his grounds with trees, including *Liquidambar styraciflua* (sweet gum). This can be mistaken for a maple, due to the shape of its leaves and its vivid colours in autumn.

William Dampier

DATE 1651–1715

ORIGIN ENGLAND

MAJOR ACHIEVEMENT *A NEW VOYAGE ROUND THE WORLD*

William Dampier, a maritime maverick, combined the unlikely disciplines of exploration, piracy and natural history. He circumnavigated the world three times, collected plants from Australia 71 years before Banks arrived and published detailed records bringing these experiences to life. Dampier was the first to describe the breadfruit in English, described the Galápagos turtles before Darwin, and even produced the first recipe in English for guacamole. His reports on breadfruit also led to the voyage of HMS *Bounty*, which infamously ended in mutiny in 1789.

Abrus precatorius,
coral bead plant

On leaving school, Dampier became apprenticed to a seaman in Weymouth, fought briefly during the Third Anglo-Dutch War, was employed on a Jamaican sugar plantation, then traded in dye in Mexico. His pay was so poor, that Dampier became a 'privateer', raiding Spanish towns along the coast of southeast Mexico. By 1678, he had made enough money to return to England and marry. However, he returned to Jamaica, and piracy, a year later, becoming infamous for his attacks on the Spanish along the east and west coasts of Central America. From March to May 1686, Dampier navigated from Mexico across the Pacific to Guam, exploring the South China Sea, the coasts of Southeast Asia, Western Australia, Sumatra and India, arriving back in England in September 1691, the first seventeenth-century Englishman to circumnavigate the globe. Dampier capitalised on his notoriety and success by publishing *A New Voyage Round the World* (1697), giving a detailed description of the flora, fauna and people he encountered on his travels. In 1699, the Admiralty gave him command of HMS *Roebuck* to circumnavigate Terra Australis (Australia) to assess its potential; once again he published an account of his voyage – *A Voyage to New Holland* (1703). From 1703 to 1707 he returned to harry the Spanish in the Pacific, this time unsuccessfully. Dampier left on his third circumnavigation in 1708, with two ships, the *Duke* and the *Duchess*, returning to England in 1711. This time in triumph and wealthy enough to retire.

DAMPIER THE NATURAL HISTORIAN

On his second circumnavigation, on 22 February 1699, Dampier left the Cape Verde islands in HMS *Roebuck* for Brazil, arriving off the coast of Bahia, which he described as 'checker'd with Woods and Savannahs'. After anchoring at Salvador, the historic capital of colonial Brazil, he began botanising around the city, noting that it was 'well watered with Rivers, Brooks and Springs.... The Soil in general is good, naturally producing very latge [sic] Trees of divers sorts, and fit for any uses. The Savannahs also are loaden with Grass, Herbs, and many sorts of smaller Vegetables', but noting, too, that gardens were 'order'd with no great Care nor Art'.

The specimens Dampier collected were usually just fragments of larger plants; the largest of his Brazilian specimens could be laid on a single sheet of paper. At least two specimens from his Brazilian collections appear to be missing from the herbarium at Oxford University, where 66 that are attributed to Dampier remain (27 from the Americas, 27 from Australia, 9 from Southeast Asia and 3 unknown). Two sterile shoots, 'from the new Island in the East Indies discovered by Dampier', (Australia) are in the Sloane Herbarium at London's Natural History Museum. Dampier also recorded the names and detailed information on the uses of 73 plants encountered in Brazil. He used English names where possible, but if unavailable, he informed his readers, they were recorded 'as they were pronounc'd to me'. In five cases, the details of the plants and their names were reported to him by 'an Irish Inhabitant of Bahia', rather than from his own observations.

AN ENGLISHMAN IN AUSTRALIA

In August and September 1699, William Dampier became the first Englishman to collect plants in Australia. He passed Dirk Hartog Island to enter Shark Bay, on the coast of what is now Western Australia. He then visited an island in the Dampier Archipelago that he called 'Rosemary Island' – because a plant there, *Olearia axillaris*, reminded him of rosemary back home (the shape of the leaves was similar, although it was not fragrant and turned out to belong to a different family). He then visited Lagrange Bay. Dampier collected and pressed 26 species, mostly from Dirk Hartog Island, including *Solanum orbiculatum*, endemics including *Beaufortia sprengeliodes* (originally *Beaufortia dampieri*) and reflexed panic grass (*Paractaenum novaehollandiae*). All are now found in the Oxford University Herbaria, but were unknown to scientists before they were collected by Dampier. According to him, in Shark Bay 'the blossoms of the different sorts of trees were of several colours, as red, white, yellow etc. but mostly blue'. So it is appropriate that the plant commemorating him, *Dampiera incana*, has blue flowers; it was named by Robert Brown, first Keeper of Botany at the British Museum in London.

Dampier also pressed the flowers of a spectacular plant from East Lewis Island in the Dampier Archipelago, known as desert pea or the Dampier pea, neglecting the leaves. It was first named *Clianthus formosus*, then *Swainsona formosa*, but was recently proposed as *Willdampia formosa*.

Dampier reported that 'many of my Books and Papers [were] lost' on the journey home, when his ship sprang a leak and sank off Ascension Island. However, he managed to save his specimens (possibly the only herbarium specimens to survive a shipwreck), which were then exposed to the elements for several weeks before the crew were rescued. We also still have Dampier's recordings of many newly-discovered plants in his journals, such as *Crotalaria cunninghamii*, *Canavalia rosea* and *Abrus precatorius* (pictured on p44).

Dampier collected the first specimens of *Swainsona formosa* (desert pea); these can be found today at an Oxford University herbarium.

On his return, Dampier passed all of his specimens to Dr John Woodward, Professor of Physic at Gresham College, London, and Fellow of the Royal Society of London, who lent specimens to John Ray (see pp26–31). Ray named 18 of them in the appendix to the third volume of his *Historiae Plantarum* (1704). He also lent some to Leonard Plukenet, botanist to Queen Mary II, who described and illustrated them in the appendix of his *Amaltheum Botanicum* (1705). Dampier also described some of his plants in his own publication *A Voyage to New Holland*, with line drawings of 18 plants, including 2 seaweeds, of which 9 were Australian plants.

After a life of plants, travel and adventure, Dampier retired to the parish of St Stephen's, Coleman Street, London, where he lived modestly on his pension and earnings from privateering and died in 1715.

William Dampier:
INSPIRATION FOR GARDENERS

✤ Among the species Dampier collected
was *Scaevola crassifolia* from Dirk Hartog Island,
a drought-tolerant coastal shrub with blue
fan-shaped flowers. The plant, with tiny seeds,
is available commercially and although not
frost hardy, can be grown in a container and
overwintered indoors, or grown as a border
specimen or hedging in warmer climates.
Replicate its natural habitat by growing it in
sandy or free-draining soil, in full sunshine, and
deadhead to prolong the flowering season. In
Australia there is a low-growing selection called
'Flat Fred'. A close relative, the *Scaevola aemula*
'Blue Wonder' (fairy fan-flower) and similar
cultivars are also good subjects for pots and
hanging baskets in cooler climates.

✤ Dampier discovered *Swainsona formosa*,
(desert pea, formerly Sturt's desert pea). It
was named after English explorer Charles Sturt,
who, in his *Narrative of an Expedition into Central
Australia* (1849), refers to the flowers several
times, and to the harsh habitat where he found
the plant. Sturt saw it in large numbers while
exploring central Australia in 1844 and wrote
that, beyond the Darling River, 'we saw that
beautiful flower the *Clianthus formosa* [sic] in
splendid blossom on the plains. It was growing
amid barrenness and decay, but its long runners

BELOW Dampier was the first to bring *Scaevola
crassifolia* to Britain, from Dirk Hartog Island.
Its relative, *Scaevola aemula* (pictured), is now
a popular choice for containers.

ABOVE Among the species collected and pressed by Dampier was the shrub *Solanum orbiculatum*, a native of Western Australia.

were covered with flowers that gave a crimson tint to the ground'. The flowers are usually blood red or scarlet, sometimes with a glossy black swelling or 'boss' at the base of the upper petal, but they can be white to deep pink. A bicoloured form is occasionally found in scarlet and white. Seeds remain viable for years: abrade the seed gently with sandpaper, carefully 'nick' the seed coat opposite the 'eye' with a sharp knife, or soak in warm water overnight. Plants grow happily in free-draining soil and sunshine, tolerating slight frosts once established. Sow seeds in pots of gritty compost and transplant them before the long tap root develops, or grow them in tall pots.

ABOVE *Beaufortia sprengeliodes* was originally named *Beaufortia dampieri* to honour the botanising buccaneer. The plant thrives in poor, free-draining soils.

John Bartram

DATE	1699–1777
ORIGIN	UNITED STATES OF AMERICA
MAJOR ACHIEVEMENT	PLANT SUPPLIER

Bartram, a farmer turned botanical collector, travelled widely, enduring arduous conditions to supply his friend, agent and fellow Quaker, Peter Collinson, with new plants – the first to arrive in Europe from North America. Collections of seeds arrived regularly in containers as aristocratic gardeners competed with each other to be the first to grow the new species and planting the landscape with American trees became fashionable. Linnaeus described Bartram as the 'greatest natural botanist in the world', and he was appointed Royal Botanist for North America by George III.

Quercus x *heterophylla*,
Bartram's oak

J ohn Bartram was born on 23 March 1699 on a farm at Marple, Pennsylvania, the eldest son of William Bartram, who emigrated as a child from Compton, Derbyshire, the first of the family to be born in the New World. A letter he wrote in 1764, reveals: 'I had always since ten years old, a great inclination to plants, and knew all that I once observed by sight, though not their proper names, having no person nor books to instruct me.' He focused on medical botany and later in life, between his duties as a farmer, developed America's first botanical garden on 8 acres of his own land, using plants he collected while on extensive trips throughout the eastern North American colonies. His travels, by boat, on horseback and on foot, took him north to New England, south to Florida and west to Lake Ontario. Sometimes he would collect for a few days, at other times for weeks or months, either alone or with his son William, who also became a notable naturalist, ornithologist and author.

SUPPLYING THE ENGLISH COLLECTORS

Throughout his life, Bartram's Quaker connections were influential. Merchant Joseph Breintnell and physician Samuel Chew both recommended Bartram as 'a very proper person' to assist fellow Quaker Peter Collinson, a London-based cloth merchant and keen collector of plants and seeds, in his quest to supply flora, fauna and exotic specimens of natural history from North America. The two began corresponding in 1732, exchanging several letters a year until Collinson's death in 1768, becoming best friends, even though they never met. Bartram agreed to send Collinson plants for a fee of five guineas a box, but Collinson, who expected to receive only a few boxes, had not anticipated his diligence and skill. Box after box of rare and fascinating plants arrived in London and Collinson was delighted. In return, Bartram received advice, encouragement, money and a constant supply of natural history books, which he enjoyed. Most of Bartram's longer trips were made in the autumn, after harvest, when he would gather ripe seeds and nuts, roots and bulbs.

Word of his collecting soon spread and Collinson became Bartram's chief agent in London. The containers he sent, generally containing 100 or more varieties of seeds, and occasionally herbarium specimens and natural history curiosities, became known as 'Bartram's Boxes'. Collinson selected his patrons shrewdly, to secure regular funding that could support future expeditions. It came from three main sources: Lord Petre agreed ten guineas per annum and became the foremost collector of North American trees and shrubs in Europe; a further ten guineas were supplied equally by the Duke of Richmond at Goodwood House, and Philip Miller of the Chelsea Physic Garden, where many of Bartram's early plants were grown (he later became advisor on American plants to the aristocracy). Bartram ultimately filled orders for 21 nursery gardeners and 124 individual customers, and he exchanged plants with at least 33 friends and correspondents. Competition became fierce. The Duke of Richmond urged Collinson to act quickly on his behalf or

'the dukes of Norfolk and Bedford will sweep them all away'. Others contributed occasionally, including Charles Hamilton at Painshill Park in Surrey, which now holds the John Bartram Heritage Collection of North American trees and shrubs in Britain. All painted their landscaped grounds with North American trees. Bartram both fuelled and benefited from the enthusiasm for landscape gardening that was sweeping England at the time; the nobility wanted exotic plants and trees for these gardens, and Bartram was the collector who supplied them.

Through his letters, Collinson introduced Bartram to many important naturalists of the day, both in England and in the colonies, including Dr John Fothergill, a distinguished English physician, authority on herbs and a Quaker. Carl Linnaeus also wrote to Bartram, requesting botanical information; Peter Kalm, one of Linnaeus's favourite students, travelled to America specifically to talk with Bartram, who became a sought-after and respected contact.

In 1765, Bartram's son William discovered *Franklinia alatamaha* (Franklin tree). It was last found outside of conservation in 1803.

In spring 1765, after Collinson's persistent lobbying efforts through the Duke of Northumberland, Bartram was appointed botanist to George III, with an annual stipend of £50. Bartram's seeds and plants now went to the Royal Botanic Gardens at Edinburgh and Kew.

This new and abundant influx of plants was of keen interest to both scientists and artists. Philip Miller was also able to clarify uncertainties in his *Gardener's Dictionary* using specimens he received from Bartram, as did Linnaeus, while respected botanical illustrators Mark Catesby and G. D. Ehret produced eagerly awaited illustrations of the American plants that thrived in Collinson's and Miller's gardens.

COLLECTORS

Most of Bartram's plant discoveries were named by botanists in Europe. He is best known today for the discovery and introduction into cultivation of a wide range of North American flowering trees and shrubs, including kalmia, rhododendron and magnolia species; for introducing *Dionaea muscipula* (Venus fly trap) to cultivation; and for the discovery of *Franklinia alatamaha* (the Franklin tree) in southeastern Georgia in 1765; it was later named by his son William. Bartram is remembered in a genus of mosses, *Bartramia*, and in plants like *Amelanchier bartramiana* (shadbush), *Commersonia bartramia* and *Quercus × heterophylla* (Bartram's oak).

In 1769 Bartram was elected to the Royal Swedish Academy of Sciences, having assisted Swedish naturalist Peter Kalm on a visit to North America. In 1772 he received a gold medal from the Society of Gentlemen in Edinburgh, and artefacts he sent to the Royal Society can still be seen at the British Museum. Bartram remained alert and productive until his death on 22 September 1777, allegedly precipitated by his concern for the safety of his beloved personal garden in the face of advancing British troops.

John Bartram:
INSPIRATION FOR GARDENERS

❧ Bartram's oak (*Quercus* × *heterophylla*) — a hybrid of *Quercus phellos* (willow oak) and *Quercus rubra* (red oak) — was described in 1812 from a tree growing in Bartram's garden that had first been discovered on an estate nearby; its parentage was first remarked on by Asa Gray (see pp104–109). This hybrid, occurring elsewhere in the United States and probably also in cultivation, is a medium to large tree with leaf margins varying from smooth to strongly toothed.

❧ In 1765, the same year that John Bartram was appointed Royal Botanist for North America by King George III, he and his son William discovered *Franklinia alatamaha* growing in 'two or three acres of ground where it grows plentifully', according to William, along the banks of the Altamaha River in southeastern Georgia. On a return trip in 1773, William collected seed and brought it back to John Bartram's garden where the tree was successfully grown. Last seen in the wild in 1803, all the plants in botanic gardens and arboreta around the world are offspring of that seed. It is a small, multi-stemmed deciduous tree and a relative of the camellia, producing fragrant, single, white waxy flowers with a central boss of golden stamens. It flowers from midsummer to autumn, when the leaves turn crimson. It prefers acidic, well-drained soil and needs high summer temperatures to grow well. Grow it up against a sheltered sunny wall in cooler climates.

❧ *Kalmia* was named for Peter Kalm, who arrived in Pennsylvania in 1748 and was befriended by John Bartram. *Kalmia latifolia* (mountain laurel) looks much like a rhododendron, apart from the flowers. It likes acidic conditions and flowers in midsummer. Clusters of flowers burst from buds that look like icing sugar. In 'Alba', pale pink buds open to white, pink-flushed flowers; 'Clementine Churchill' has deep pink buds opening to bright pink; 'Freckles' has pink buds and is cream with purple spots and 'Ostbo Red' is red in bud, opening to soft pale pink.

LEFT *Amelanchier bartramiana* (shadbush), named for Bartram, grows in cold bogs in eastern Canada and northeastern USA; it is a challenging garden plant.

TOP RIGHT After Bartram helped Peter Kalm on his trip to North America, Kalm was commemorated in a North American genus that includes *Kalmia latifolia* (mountain laurel), noted for its pretty flowers.

RIGHT *Dionaea muscipula* (Venus fly trap), an endangered species from North and South Carolina, USA, was introduced into cultivation by Bartram.

Carl Linnaeus

DATE	1707–1778
ORIGIN	SWEDEN
MAJOR ACHIEVEMENT	LINNAEAN BINOMIAL SYSTEM

Linnaeus revolutionised natural history by introducing a system of classification based on the sexual organs of plants, simplifying their names into a concise binomial (two-word) description. Prior to this, plant descriptions had been long and complicated. French botanist Antoine de Jussieu, for example, had described coffee as *Jasminum, arabicum, lori folio, cujus semen apud nos coffee cicitur* – under Linnaeus's classification it was simply *Coffea arabica*. No wonder he said 'God created; Linnaeus organised' to describe his own contribution to science. Linnaeus named over 7,700 plants and 4,400 animals, and was the first to describe whales as mammals and to place humans with other primates.

Aloe succotrina,
fynbos aloe

C arl Linnaeus was born on 23 May 1707 in a turf-roofed homestead in Råsult, southern Sweden. He was the eldest of five children and the son of Rector Nils Linnaeus, a keen gardener and amateur botanist.

As soon as Carl became aware of his surroundings, his father decorated his cradle with flowers. Later, his father often carried the young boy to the garden or a meadow and set him on the ground with a flower to play with; even as a child Linnaeus wanted to learn plant names, and later played truant from school, preferring to search the nearby fields for plants.

At the age of 20, Linnaeus studied medicine, first at Lund University and later at Uppsala University, where Professor of Medicine Olof Rudbeck the Younger appointed him Demonstrator at the Botanic Garden. Employing a knowledgeable, enthusiastic second-year student instead of the usual jaded old lecturer caused a sensation, and classes of 70 to 80 suddenly became 400.

Around the same time, Linnaeus became aware of the limitations of existing systems of plant classification and decided to devise his own. Using the number and arrangements of the sexual organs, he grouped plants into class, order, genera and species, and introduced a binomial system for the genus and species. After revising an earlier thesis to incorporate this new system, he had this work presented to the Royal Society of Science by Rudbeck the Younger. Linnaeus wrote afterwards that the audience 'at first thought I was mad; but when I explained my intention they stopped laughing and promised their full support.'

A GROWING REPUTATION

In 1735, while on a trip to Holland, Linnaeus met a director of the Dutch East India Company, George Clifford, who kept a grand garden and zoo on his country estate. Linnaeus wrote that these were 'masterpieces of Nature aided by Art ... with shady walks ... artificial mounds and mazes', but it was the hothouses that excited him most of all: 'The first contained plants from southern Europe, the second treasures from Asia, like cloves, mangosteens and coconut palms ... the third plants from Africa including succulents like Aloes and *Stapelia* and the fourth, plants from the New World – cacti, passion flowers, calabash trees, bananas and camphor trees.'

Clifford was impressed by Linnaeus's ability to classify plants by opening a flower and examining its floral parts. When Clifford, a hypochondriac, suggested Linnaeus work as his physician and superintendent of his garden, Linnaeus accepted, receiving a salary of 1,000 florins a year, plus free board and lodging. In return, he supervised the hothouses, classified and catalogued Clifford's herbarium and garden plants, recorded every plant (such as *Aloe succotrina*, pictured on p56) in his *Hortus Cliffortianus* and monitored the health of his employer.

While in Clifford's employment, Linnaeus spent around three weeks in England, where he met Sir Hans Sloane, president of the Royal Society. Biographer John Lauris Blake noted in 1840 that Sloane 'did not pay [Linnaeus] that respect and attention that his merits deserved'; however, during these

weeks in England, Linnaeus did win over Philip Miller, superintendent of the Society of Apothecaries' garden at Chelsea, whose *Gardener's Dictionary* Linnaeus declared enthusiastically was 'not a dictionary for gardeners but for Botanists'.

Miller used current names, such as *Symphytum consolida major, flore luteo*, Linnaeus later recalled. 'I remained silent, with the result that he said the next day: "This botanist of Clifford's doesn't know a single plant." When he again began using them I said "Don't use such names, we have shorter and surer ones" then gave him examples.' Linnaeus also travelled to Oxford to meet Sherardian Professor of Botany, Johann Jacob Dillenius, who disagreed with him, too. However, after discussing what Dillenius had marked as errors in the soon-to-be published *Genera Plantarum*, Linnaeus dissected some of the flowers, showed him the individual parts and proved that his system was correct.

Coffea arabica: Linnaeus reduced de Jussieu's Latin description from ten words to just two.

Soon, Linnaeus was fêted everywhere except Sweden, where his work was ridiculed. 'I was the laughing stock of everyone on account of my botany', he wrote later. However, his fortunes gradually changed and on 27 October 1741 he became Professor of Botany at Uppsala University, inheriting its run-down botanical garden. In 1685, it had contained 1,800 plants; by 1739, there were only 300. The Senate financed the construction of a glasshouse and extended the garden, the Prince Regent sent him a racoon to add to the menagerie and demanded he examine it, and goldfish were sent from England. Linnaeus wrote: 'Do send the goldfish tomorrow, so that I can see what I have wanted all my life but never dared to hope for.' There was also a talking parrot. If Linnaeus was late for his lunch it would squawk 'Twelve o'clock, Mr Carl!' until he appeared.

LINNAEUS'S LEGACY

Linnaeus wrote papers on lemmings and ants, a phosphorescent Chinese grasshopper, Siberian buckwheat, rhubarb, fossils and crystals, and he investigated leprosy and epilepsy – amounting to 170 papers and dissertations in all. His rules for plant classification were elucidated in *Fundamenta Botanica* (1736), expanded in his *Classes Plantarum* (1738) and reached their zenith in his two volumes of *Species Plantarum* (1753) – a work he called 'the greatest in botany'. The 1,200 pages cover 5,900 species in 1,098 genera and are the basis of modern taxonomy. He also wrote *Systema Naturae*, its zoological equivalent.

Linnaeus's British contacts were among the earliest to endorse his work. Among them were naturalist and apothecary John Hill, and Philip Miller, who incorporated Linnaeus's names and taxonomy into the eighth edition of his *Gardener's Dictionary*. Sir Joseph Banks took Daniel Solander, Linnaeus's pupil, on James Cook's first voyage then employed him as curator, and James Edward Smith (see pp74–79) bought Linnaeus's collections after his death and established the Linnean Society of London – thereby securing the future of Linnaeus's binomial system. This system was a work of powerful simplicity, and we depend on its genius today.

Carl Linnaeus:
INSPIRATION FOR GARDENERS

❧ Like many of his predecessors, Linnaeus stuck to Latin for his binomial system. Being a historical language, Latin wasn't likely to evolve, and it has now become a global lingua franca for botanists.

❧ In Linnaeus's system of plant names, genus comes first, followed by any individual or specific names. Genus: *Magnolia*; species: *grandiflora*. These can then be divided further, into subspecies (subsp.), variety (var.) and form (f.).

BELOW *Magnolia grandiflora* (southern magnolia) from the USA; Linnaeus's system tells us that this is the *grandiflora* species within the *Magnolia* genus.

❧ Cultivars (cultivated varieties of plants) were a twentieth-century addition to Linnaeus's system, and can be found in single quote marks in plant names, as in *Camellia japonica* 'Apollo'. To create a cultivar, a plant with a particular combination of features is selected and then vegetatively propagated (a form of asexual reproduction, requiring only one parent) to produce an identical version of the parent plant. There can also be groups of cultivars with similar features; the *Acer palmatum* Dissectum Group all have the fern-like leaves of the *Acer palmatum* 'Dissectum' cultivar.

❧ There are usually nuggets of interesting or useful information in a plant's Latin name. For example, *Paulownia tomentosa* took its name from the nineteenth-century Russian princess Anna Paulowna and the Latin for

BELOW *Camellia japonica* (Japanese camellia), one parent of the famous *Camellia* × *williamsii* hybrids. The '×' in a plant name always denotes a hybrid.

'woolly with matted hair' – the latter being a description of its leaves. Linnaeus loved the honeysuckle he named *Linnaea borealis*, describing it as 'a plant from Lapland, lowly, insignificant, disregarded, flowering but for a brief space, from Linnaeus who resembles it'; *borealis* means 'northern'.

❧ The 'x' in a plant's name means it is a hybrid. A group of hybrids from the same parentage are often given a collective name, such as *Camellia* x *williamsii* (a cross of *Camellia japonica* and *Camellia saluenensis*). Hybrids bred from two different genera are written like x *Mahoberberis* (a cross of *Mahonia* and *Berberis*). However, there are very few intergeneric hybrids in cultivation.

❧ A new variety of plant may also be sold under its trade name, which protects the breeder's rights over its propagation – for instance, Magnolia 'Shirazz'™ ('Vulden').

TOP *Paulownia tomentosa* (empress tree) was named for Russian princess Anna Paulowna and *tomentosus*, the Latin for woolly and matted, on account of its hairy leaves.

ABOVE The names of intergeneric hybrids – crosses from two different genera – start with an 'x', such as this x *Mahoberberis*.

Jeanne Baret

DATE	1740–1807
ORIGIN	FRANCE
MAJOR ACHIEVEMENT	BOTANIST AND PLANT COLLECTOR

When Philibert Commerçon joined Louis-Antoine de Bougainville's 1766 expedition to circumnavigate the world, he took Jeanne Baret with him as his valet and botanical assistant – disguised as a boy. An expert botanist due to her knowledge of medicinal plants, Baret thereby became the first woman to circumnavigate the globe, and proved herself a resilient plant collector. Among her discoveries were the first specimens of the famous *Bougainvillea spectabilis* from the forests of Brazil. As expedition naturalist, Commerçon received considerable recognition for his work; Baret has only recently been commemorated through the name of a plant.

Ixora coccinea,
burning love

Sometime between 1760 and 1764, Jeanne Baret, a country girl as well as a knowledgeable botanist, became the housekeeper and lover of naturalist and botanist Philibert Commerçon, friend of Voltaire and correspondent of Linnaeus (pp56–61). Several years later, in 1766, Louis-Antoine de Bougainville was selected to command an expedition to discover flora and fauna of commercial value that would flourish in France or her colonies, and Commerçon was invited to join it. It was the first expedition to include a professional naturalist paid for by a sovereign, and aimed to be the first French circumnavigation of the world. The two ships, *Boudeuse* and *Étoile*, were to sail from France to Montevideo, Rio de Janeiro, Buenos Aires, the Falkland Islands, Tierra del Fuego, the coasts of Magellan and the South Pacific Islands, returning via Australia, the Molluccas, Java and Réunion; Commerçon helped to plan the itinerary.

Commerçon's senior role permitted him a servant, but the French Navy did not allow women on board ships, so in a daring plan, for which she became famous, Jeanne bound her breasts in tight strips of linen, wore baggy clothes, changed her name to Jean, and joined Commerçon as his botanical assistant and personal valet. Although there were mutterings among the crew, her plan succeeded until 1767 when the ships reached Tahiti and the indigenous people saw through her disguise. Nothing is reported of their relationship after her discovery, other than that she continued to be dedicated to him and to botanising in search of new plants.

AN INTREPID PLANT HUNTER

In *A Voyage Around the World*, his published account of the trip, Bougainville recalled: 'For some time there was a report in both ships, that the servant of M. de Commerçon, named Baré, was a woman. His shape, voice, beardless chin, and scrupulous attention of not changing his linen, or making the natural discharges in the presence of any one, besides several other signs, had given rise to, and kept up this suspicion. But how was it possible to discover the woman in the indefatigable Baré, who was already an expert botanist, had followed his master in all his botanical walks, amidst the snows and frozen mountains of the straits of Magalhaens, and had even on such troublesome excursions carried provisions, arms, and herbals, with so much courage and strength, that the naturalist had called him his "beast of burden"?' Commerçon was equally complimentary, writing that she traversed the highest mountains with agility and the deepest forests without complaint: 'Armed with a bow like Diana ... armed with intelligence and seriousness like Minerva ... she eluded the snare of animals and men, not without many times risking her life and her honor.' Commerçon praised her for the numerous plants she collected, the herbaria she constructed and the collections of insects and shells she curated.

Most populist literature focuses on Jeanne Baret's story of deception, rarely mentioning her botanical skills. Yet she and Commerçon worked together, and when he suffered from ill health, as he often did on the voyage, she collected alone. Such a collaborative partnership in the discovery of botanical and

zoological wonders is unique in the history of science. Every time the ship docked, the pair disembarked to collect samples. They recorded their observations and were amazed at the wealth of diversity they encountered. Commerçon wrote of Madagascar: 'I can announce to naturalists that this is the true Promised Land. Here nature created a special sanctuary where she seems to have withdrawn to experiment with designs different from those used anywhere else. At every step one finds more remarkable and marvellous forms of life.'

Bougainvillea spectabilis, a plant believed to have been discovered by Jeanne Baret in Rio de Janeiro in 1767.

One of the expedition's most notable collections is thought to have been made by Jean Baret (if not, she was certainly with Commerçon when the collection was made). On the basis of notes made by François Vivez, the *Étoile*'s surgeon, the hypothesis has been put forward that because of the varicose ulcers and gangrene that constantly afflicted him, Commerçon was possibly too ill to collect plants during his stay in Rio de Janeiro between 13 and 15 June 1767. All of the plants from that location were therefore gathered by Baret – one of many times she might have assumed the role of chief botanist. It was here that a flamboyant scrambling plant was collected and later named *Bougainvillea spectabilis* in honour of the expedition's commander. Five herbarium specimens exist from the voyage, three with the 'Buginvillaea' written on them, in what appears to be Commerçon's handwriting; the plant was officially named by Antoine Laurent de Jussieu in 1789, based on these specimens and notes.

A WELL-DESERVED TRIBUTE

Commerçon and Baret (though uncredited) amassed 1,735 specimens for the French National Herbarium at the National Museum of Natural History in Paris. Of these, 234 were from Madagascar, 144 from Mauritius, 84 from Brazil and 50 from Java; many formed the basis of new species. They also documented unknown plants introduced to new habitats by human populations, such as *Ixora coccinea* (pictured on p62), which was brought to Tahiti by early Polynesian settlers.

When the ship stopped in Mauritius, Commerçon and Baret disembarked, leaving the rest of the expedition to visit Madagascar and Reunion. When Commerçon died, aged 46, after years of ill health, Baret married French officer Jean Dubernat on Mauritius, returning to France several years later in 1774, and becoming the first woman to sail across the Pacific and to circumnavigate the world.

Over 70 different types of flora and fauna were named after Commerçon, yet despite her vital role in the expedition, not a single species was named after Baret. Commerçon had proposed *Baretia* for a Madagascan tree but that name had already been taken. It was not until 2012 that a new species of *Solanum* from the Andean cloud forest of Ecuador and Peru was named *Solanum baretiae*. A distinguishing feature of the plant is its numerous different leaf shapes – simple or divided, with varying numbers of leaflets, the perfect plant to commemorate Jeanne Baret, botanist and master of disguise!

Jeanne Baret:
INSPIRATION FOR GARDENERS

✤ Bougainvillea, along with hibiscus, are quintessential exotic garden plants. A plant in full bloom against a bright blue sky is a sight never to be forgotten. The colour does not come from the flowers, which are small and white, but the brightly coloured bracts (modified leaves) surrounding them. They can be planted in a conservatory in cooler climates, but as pot plants, can be put outside on hot summer days. They need bright light, blooming prolifically after a cool winter rest,

but when temperatures are too low they take a long time to recover in spring. Keep the compost just moist in winter, reducing watering further if the leaves fall, then increase watering as growth increases in spring.

✤ For an eyecatching display, allow as many main stems to grow as possible, as cutting them back to the chosen height encourages flowering side shoots. Cut side shoots back to two buds in late winter to keep plants under control and encourage flowering. Feeding with high-potash fertiliser also encourages flowering in cooler climates. In tropical or Mediterranean climates, these plants are

BELOW Baret made important botanical discoveries; bougainvilleas are popular ornamental plants today, with tiny white flowers, surrounded by vivid bracts.

excellent on large pergolas or draped over boundary walls where their thick growth and spiny stems provide a natural deterrent to intruders.

❖ Mauritius, where Commerçon and Baret disembarked, is home to some extraordinary native plants and pollinators, many now endangered. As one of the few places in the world where there were no honeybees and few common tropical pollinators, many native plants were pollinated by geckos, attracted to the flowers' coloured nectar. *Nesocodon mauritianus*, found on Mauritius and nowhere else in the world, has pale blue flowers and its blood red nectar is produced in such volumes that it drips from the flowers. *Roussea simplex,* native to the mountain forests, with its orange-yellow nectar is a botanical oddity. It is pollinated and seeds are dispersed by the Mauritian blue-tailed day gecko (*Phelsuma cepediana*), the only known plant in the world to have the same pollinator and seed dispersal agent.

TOP *Geum magellanicum* was collected by Commerçon in 1767; one of the original specimens can be found at the University of Montpellier's herbarium in France.

ABOVE New species are still being discovered on Mauritius, centuries after Baret's voyage. The endangered *Nesocodon mauritianus* was found in 1976, growing in a single location, on a near-vertical cliff.

Joseph Banks

DATE	1743–1820
ORIGIN	ENGLAND
MAJOR ACHIEVEMENT	JAMES COOK'S BOTANIST ON THE *ENDEAVOUR*

Joseph Banks gained fame as a naturalist and botanist after James Cook's first voyage. He also promoted other people's research, while his own work developing the collections at the Royal Botanic Gardens at Kew transformed it into the great garden it is today. Banks's knowledge was respected by contemporaries such as Johann Reinhold Forster, naturalist on Cook's second voyage, who stated upon the death of Carl Linnaeus (see pp56–61): 'great as the loss of Linnaeus must certainly be to science, it will not be severely felt while we have so enlightened botanists as Mr Banks and Dr Solander.'

Fuchsia coccinea,
scarlet fuchsia

A s a boy, Banks explored the Lincolnshire countryside and developed a keen interest in natural history. He was educated at Harrow and Eton, botanised in England and Wales, created his own herbarium, and studied Linnaean taxonomy. When he went to Christchurch College, Oxford, the Professor of Botany Humphry Sibthorpe, who had not published a scientific paper and delivered just one public lecture during his 35-year tenure, did not object when Banks hired a lecturer of his own. Banks left Oxford without a degree, however, and immersed himself in London society. He then secured a position onboard the HMS *Niger* heading to Newfoundland on fishery protection duties; while he was there, Banks collected birds, insects and rocks, and observed the habitats of Eskimos. His botanical collections and notes confirmed his proficiency in botany and he was elected Fellow of the Royal Society, aged 23. The success of this voyage whetted Banks's appetite to see the world. When the Government and Royal Society decided to send a ship to observe the transit of Venus in Tahiti in 1766, the captain, James Cook, also had secret instructions to discover Terra Australis. The Royal Society asked if Banks could join HMS *Endeavour* for 'the advancement of useful knowledge'; Banks, a man of considerable means after the death of his father in 1761, paid his own passage plus that of his entourage of eight, including the Swedish botanist Daniel Solander, and Sydney Parkinson, a scientific artist.

COOK'S FIRST VOYAGE

The *Endeavour* left Plymouth on 25 August 1768, bound for South America, with Banks and his staff collecting plants in Madeira, Rio de Janeiro and Tierra del Fuego. On leaving Tahiti, the *Endeavour* explored the coasts of New Zealand and Australia before returning home in July 1771. Before his death at sea from malaria and dysentery, Parkinson produced 280 paintings and 900 sketches and drawings. On his return to England, Banks commissioned over 700 copper engravings, ready for publication, but his *Florilegium* was not published until two centuries later. Overall, Banks collected 3,600 species of dried plants, of which 1,400 were new to science, plus seeds, plants and drawings. He was fêted by society, had an audience with George III at St James's Palace, and instantly became a highly respected botanist and naturalist.

Within a few months, a second voyage was planned. Banks automatically assumed he would be included, and this time his party was to include botanist Solander, four artists, two secretaries, six servants and two horn players. When Cook complained, Banks petulantly withdrew and went to Iceland, giving some of the ship's ballast of lava to the Chelsea Physic Garden for their rock garden and to Kew, where it provided the structure for the Moss Garden, on his return.

KEW GARDENS

Banks was well aware of Princess Augusta's exotic or physic garden at Kew; the *Westminster Journal* for the 24–31 August 1771 reported, 'Dr Solander and Mr Banks had the honour of frequently waiting on his Majesty in Richmond, who is in a

course of examining their whole collection of drawings of plants and views of the country'. Banks became a considerable horticultural and botanical influence on George III, with William Townsend Aiton, who had been responsible for the small physic garden since 1759, admitting, 'this establishment is placed under the direction of Sir Joseph Banks'. They regularly met on Saturdays, one equerry noting: 'the King continued his walk with Sir Joseph Banks about 3 hours, they first visited the exotic garden, then walked through the Richmond gardens.'

Gradually, Banks transformed Kew into a centre for global transfer of plants, insisting that 'as many new plants as possible should make their first appearance at the Royal Gardens'. Banks revealed: 'I have long ago given up the collection of plants in order that I might be better able to promote the King's wishes to make the Royal Botanic Gardens at Kew as respectable as possible, so that everything that comes to me from whatever quarter it may be, is instantly sent to Kew.' Banks was ably supported in these ambitions by William Aiton, and the swift, seamless conversion of Kew from royal pleasure grounds to botanic garden, owed much to their amicable working relationship.

In 1773 nearly 800 species were planted, most from North America, and Banks began to send out plant hunters. In 1774, Francis Masson, Kew's first collector, returned with 80 different species from the Cape of Good Hope, including *Protea*, *Crassula*, *Mesembryanthemum*, *Erica*, *Pelargonium*, *Ixia* and *Gladiolus*, and a special 'Cape House' was built to house his introductions. Masson believed that he added 400 species to the garden. Banks was delighted, believing these collections enhanced Kew's 'superiority which it now holds over every similar Establishment in Europe'.

This plate depicting *Banksia serrata* (saw banksia), from Banks's *Florilegium*, illustrates the level of artistic skill needed to complete this project.

Banks also reminded government officials, military officers, merchants and missionaries to remember Kew's needs during their travels. Sir John Murray, on active service in India with the British Army, despatched several packages of seed; the Governor of St Helena sent plants; and the Receiver General made large donations. When a precious specimen of *Fuchsia coccinea* (scarlet fuchsia, pictured on p68) from South Africa was presented to Kew in 1778, Sir Joseph Banks carried it into the garden on his head, not trusting anyone else to transport it. Sir George Staunton sent Banks a nutmeg tree, some mangosteens and six pots of plants. Bulbs arrived from Adam Afzelius, Swedish botanist to the Sierra Leone Company, and Governor Philip returned from Australia with over 82 tubs and boxes of plants. William Kerr introduced many plants, too, including *Rosa banksiae*. A delivery in 1793 of nearly 800 pots, the largest single despatch ever made to Kew, filled HMS *Providence* when it docked at Deptford after Bligh's second voyage to source breadfruit. During the reign of George III some 7,000 new species were introduced from abroad, and the botanical mastermind behind it all was Sir Joseph Banks.

Joseph Banks:
INSPIRATION FOR GARDENERS

❧ *Rosa banksiae* (Banksian rose) is a slender climber with few spines on the stems. It likes warmth and sunshine and needs a position against a sheltered sunny wall in cooler climates. There are several desirable cultivars: 'Alba Plena' the white, double-flowered, violet-scented form from which the species was described, was introduced by Kew collector William Kerr from Canton in 1807. 'Lutea', the most familiar form in gardens due to it being the most hardy and floriferous, has dainty double yellow flowers and little scent; it was introduced through the RHS from China in 1824. 'Lutescens' has yellow, fragrant flowers, while var. *normalis* has white, fragrant flowers. The flowers are not borne on laterals from the previous year's growths, as in most ramblers, but on twigs produced by the

laterals, so stems will be two or three years old before it flowers. Don't prune annually, just remove older stems periodically, once flowering is over.

❧ *Banksia* was first collected by Joseph Banks and Daniel Solander, at what was later named Botany Bay, due to the sheer quantity of plants Banks and Solander found there. There were four species in this first collection: *B. serrata* (saw banksia), *B. integrifolia* (coast banksia), *B. ericifolia* (heath-leaved banksia) and *B. robur* (swamp banksia). *Banksia* plants must have well-drained soil to survive. Fork finely chopped forest bark or gravel into heavier soils, or plant on a mound and mulch with gravel. They rarely need feeding but if you do use fertiliser, make sure it is phosphate-free; phosphates can kill the plants.

❧ Francis Masson, sent out on expedition by Banks and Kew, introduced various new pelargoniums in 1774, including *P. cordifolium*. This has pale pink flowers with dark veins, and large, grey-green tri-lobed leaves, with the underside covered with silvery hairs. It is also lemon-scented. *P. grandiflorum* has petite white flowers with red veins, matt blue-green leaves, and was introduced by Masson after his second expedition to South Africa in 1797.

LEFT Banks sent Francis Masson to South Africa to search for plants; one of the treasures he returned with was *Pelargonium grandiflorum*.

RIGHT *Rosa banksiae* 'Lutea' (yellow Banksian rose, formerly Lady Banks rose), named for Banks's wife. It needs a sheltered, sunny spot in a mild climate or conservatory, protected from winds and the cold.

James Edward Smith

DATE	1759–1828
ORIGIN	ENGLAND
MAJOR ACHIEVEMENT	FOUNDER OF THE LINNEAN SOCIETY

Passionate about plants and botany from childhood, James Edward Smith's enlightenment came on 10 January 1778, the day Carl Linnaeus died (see pp56–61). Despite it being midwinter, the 18-year-old was deep in the ditches of Norwich Castle collecting his first plants, having bought his first botanical book the previous day – John Berkenhout's *Outlines of the Natural History of Great Britain and Ireland*, arranged according to the new Linnaean principles. Later in life, Smith would purchase the Linnaean Collections and establish the Linnean Society of London, elevating the status of British science and popularising botany.

Linaria vulgaris,
yellow toad-flax

J ames Edward Smith was born on 2 December 1759 at 37 Gentleman's Way, Norwich, the eldest of eight children of a wealthy textile merchant. A delicate, indulged favourite, he was home-schooled – one of his earliest memories was 'tugging ineffectually with all my infant strength at the tough stalks of the wild zuchery [chicory] on the chalky hillocks about Norwich'.

Destined for the silk trade, Smith was determined to study botany instead, but as there were no professional positions available in this field, he chose to train as a physic, where a knowledge of plants would be essential. In 1781 he began studying medicine at the University of Edinburgh, where his botany lecturer was Dr John Hope, one of the earliest teachers of the Linnaean system. Here Smith gained a reputation for both fastidious attention to botanical detail, and social skills, forming a natural history society for the students of the university. Two years later, Smith moved to London and St Bartholomew's Hospital Anatomy School (where he was famously squeamish), carrying an introduction from Hope to Sir Joseph Banks, then President of the Royal Society.

THE LINNEAN SOCIETY

On 23 December 1873, the 24-year-old Smith attended a breakfast party, at which Joseph Banks was also present. Banks had received a letter from Sweden offering him the entire collection of Linnaeus's books and specimens for the sum of 1,000 guineas. Banks was forced to turn down the offer due to his financial situation, but he suggested that Smith purchase it instead. Smith responded quickly; aided by a loan from his father, he secured a deal before the rest of the world had caught on – including the king of Sweden (who was in Italy at the time) – and outwitting potential bidders Catherine the Great of Russia and John Sibthorp, Sherardian Professor of Botany at Oxford.

The vast collection arrived in London on 10 October 1784 and Smith, who was most interested in the 14,000 plant specimens, suddenly became a patron of learning and supporter of British advancement. As one friend wrote, 'the nobel purchase of the Linnaean cabinet, most decidedly sets Britain above all other nations in the botanical empire'. The following winter, Smith catalogued the collections with the help of Banks and his librarian, Jonas Dryander, and a friend, John Pitchford, urged Smith to prepare 'a Flora Britannica, the most correct that can appear in the Linnaean dress'. Smith was soon elected a Fellow of the Royal Society, and in June 1786, he set out on his Grand Tour, visiting herbaria and botanical libraries en route. At Versailles, he even encountered Louix XVI, noting in a letter home that the monarch had 'grown fat and had an agreeable countenance, his ears are remarkably large and ugly, he had some very fine diamonds in his hat'.

In 1788 Smith moved to Great Marlborough Street in London, and on 18 March he founded the Linnean Society of London with the botanist and Bishop of Carlisle, Samuel Goodenough, and the entomologist Thomas Marsham. At the first meeting, on 8 April 1788, Smith was elected president, and delivered an

introductory talk on the rise and progress of natural history. Marsham became secretary, Goodenough was made treasurer, and Dryander librarian. Banks joined as an honorary member. Smith's house quickly became a hub of scientific activity.

Smith soon came to the attention of Queen Charlotte, wife of George III of England and a keen amateur botanist, and in October 1792 Smith was invited to teach botany and zoology to the Queen and Princesses at the royal residence, Frogmore House. However, the account of his recent journey, *Sketch of a Tour on the Continent*, contained passages praising Rousseau and referring to Marie Antoinette as Messalina (the ruthlessly ambitious, promiscuous third wife of the Roman emperor Claudius), which outraged the Queen, and the offer was subsequently withdrawn.

LORD TREASURER OF BOTANY

On 1 March 1796 Smith married Pleasance Reeve, daughter of a Lowestoft attorney and merchant, whom he described as a 'very fine person, with an angelic countenance and a very pretty fortune' (she was also great aunt of Alice Pleasance Liddell, immortalised in *Alice in Wonderland*). Soon after, Smith retired to Norwich, visiting London for two or three months each year to deliver a series of lectures at the Royal Institution – spending the rest of his time in his museum, with his old-fashioned cabinets from Uppsala looking very out of place (it is said in an 1829 issue of *The Philosophical Magazine* that 'the relics of Mohammed are not enshrined with more devotion'). Every day, he wrote from 9am until 3pm, then from 7 to 9pm, also replying to numerous correspondents. He was re-elected president of the Linnean Society annually until his death.

Cichorium intybus (chicory) was one of the plants that Smith later recalled learning about as a young child.

After completing his three-volume *Flora Britannica* (cataloguing British plants, such as *Linaria vulgaris*, pictured on p74), Smith was chosen by John Sibthorp's executors to edit *Flora Graeca*. In 1807 he published his most successful work, *The Introduction to Physiological and Systematic Botany*. Five editions were produced during his lifetime, and two posthumously. He also contributed 3,348 botanical articles and 57 biographies of botanists to Rees's *Cyclopaedia* – including one on William Curtis. In 1814, the Prince Regent became Patron of the Linnean Society, and Smith was knighted for his services to science.

In the last seven years of his life, Smith worked on *The English Flora*, often described as his 'last and best work', with descriptions drawn from years of critical study. The first two volumes appeared in 1824, a third in 1825, the fourth in 1828, days before his death; the fifth, with a contribution on mosses by Sir W. J. Hooker, appeared between 1833 and 1836. Smith died in Norwich, on 17 March 1828, and was buried at St Margaret's Church, Lowestoft, in the Reeve family vault. Josef August Schultes, Professor of Natural History at the University of Landshut in Bavaria, perhaps best summarised Smith's achievements, hailing him during his lifetime as 'the only orthodox Botanist in Europe' and 'Lord Treasurer of Botany'.

James Edward Smith:
INSPIRATION FOR GARDENERS

✤ In the 36-volume *English Botany* — published between 1791 and 1814 by James Edward Smith and the publisher and illustrator James Sowerby — Smith remarked that the best place to find *Vinca minor* (lesser periwinkle) growing wild was at Honingham Church, Norfolk. *Vinca minor* is useful groundcover in most soils, thriving in shade or light, dry shade under trees. If the foliage becomes untidy, cut it hard back at the end of winter. There are several garden-worthy varieties: *Vinca minor* 'La Grave', an evergreen with glossy oval leaves and bright blue, rounded flowers, was found by the horticulturalist E. A. Bowles in a churchyard in La Grave, France; *Vinca minor* f. *alba* 'Gertrude

BELOW Boldly coloured *Dryandra formosa* (showy dryandra), also known as *Banksia formosa*, was named for Banks by botanist Carl Linnaeus's son.

BELOW Smith deemed a local churchyard the best spot for *Vinca minor* (lesser periwinkle). Try *Vinca minor* 'Atropurpurea' (dark purple-flowered periwinkle) in shady spots.

Jekyll' has white flowers and small, shiny green leaves; and *Vinca minor* 'Atropurpurea' bears small plum-coloured flowers. They can become a weedy species in borders unless carefully controlled, and are better naturalised in a wild area where they will happily spread.

✤ Chicory, which Smith found 'in the chalky hillocks about Norwich', is grown in the vegetable garden as 'Whitloof' or 'Belgian' chicory; the leaves are eaten after blanching to remove their bitterness. Chicory can be forced – lifting the roots prematurely and moving them to a dark place to encourage premature growth. It needs an open sunny site. Sow in spring, keeping the plants watered and weed-free for lifting from late autumn until midwinter. The ideal size for forcing is between 3.5 to 5cm diameter across the top. Trim the leaves to 2.5cm above the neck, then cover with straw outside or indoors, in flat trays of sand. Force a few at a time in 23cm pots containing moist compost, cutting the roots to length if needed. Exclude light by covering with a similar-sized pot with the drainage holes covered, or a large box to discourage humidity. Maintain temperatures of 10 to 18°C. Blanching takes at least three weeks.

TOP Smith used *Ilex aquifolium* (common holly) to comment on the natural classification of plants in his notes, which were published posthumously in 1832.

ABOVE *Carex riparia* (greater pond sedge), one of many plants illustrated in Sowerby's and Smith's *English Botany*. It is an ideal plant for a bog garden.

Philipp von Siebold

DATE 1796–1866	
ORIGIN GERMANY	
MAJOR ACHIEVEMENT *FLORA JAPONICA*	

Philipp von Siebold, a German physician, worked for the Dutch
government and introduced Western medicine into Japan. At a time
when the country was closed to the rest of the world, he practised
medicine and collected plants and Japanese artefacts. He was expelled
from the country twice, the first time after being accused as a Russian
spy. His daughter Kusumoto Ine became the first female doctor in Japan
and Siebold introduced over 800 species of plants into Europe, including
hostas, hydrangeas, *Cercidiphyllum japonicum*, *Chaenomeles japonica*
(pictured below) and *Rosa rugosa* 'Alba'.

Chaenomeles japonica,
Japanese quince

P hilipp von Siebold was born into a well-connected family of physicians in Würzburg, Germany. After university, he followed into the family profession, specialising in ophthalmology. After the death of his father, relatives wrote to one of the many influential family friends, Franz Joseph Harbaur, Inspector-General of the Dutch Army and Navy medical corps, to enquire about a position for him; around about the same time, Siebold developed a love of natural history.

In 1822 Siebold was appointed 'Surgeon First Class' in the Dutch East-Indies Army for the Dutch Government Service and headed to their colonies (in what is now Indonesia), leaving Rotterdam on 23 September 1822. On the long journey at sea, Siebold learned to speak basic Dutch and Malay. Arriving in Jakarta, a further post was added when he was appointed 'Surgeon First Class in charge of research into natural science in the Japanese Empire' at the Dutch trading settlement of Dejima in Japan, and told to study not just local natural history but the land and its peoples, to increase opportunities for trade with that country.

LIFE IN JAPAN

Siebold arrived in Dejima on 12 August 1823, having survived a raging storm. He remained there for six years, collecting wild plants in the hilly, densely wooded countryside around Nagasaki and gaining respect, friends and admirers for his use of belladonna (*Atropa belladonna*) in treating cataracts, and introducing Western medicine to Japan. Siebold collected plants at every opportunity, particularly while visiting the local medical school that he established. He also began a small botanic garden behind his home and many of the plants were planted there, then shipped to the Netherlands. Siebold also bought plants from local growers outside the city, and encouraged colleagues and assistants to send him plants, too. By 1825 he had assembled more than 1,000 plants in his garden, adding to his collections by creating another garden around his medical school.

During the seventeenth and eighteenth centuries, Dutch merchants made an annual pilgrimage to pay homage to the ruling shogun in the city of Edo (now Tokyo). On one such occasion Siebold was introduced to several important Japanese natural scientists, including the artist Katsuragawa Hoken, known as Wilhelm Botanicus, a physician to the shogun and later one of Siebold's most talented botanical artists, and the botanist Keisuke Ito, who presented Siebold with a herbarium and collected with him in the hills around Nagasaki.

In 1827, the Dutch government recalled Siebold to the Netherlands, to devote himself to processing his collections, but as his ship was preparing to sail with his plants, artefacts and hand-drawn maps, a huge storm struck Nagasaki, rendering the ship unseaworthy. An undercover agent had already reported that Siebold was leaving with forbidden maps and a kimono jacket bearing the shogun's emblem – three golden leaves of *Asarum nipponicum*; the former was strictly forbidden, and the latter was seen as a grave insult. Siebold was placed under house arrest, tried,

revealed to be German not Dutch, accused of spying for the Russians, then ignominiously banished from the country. (While under house arrest, however, he managed to grow seeds taken from the fodder for his goat and made herbarium specimens of the plants.)

RETURN TO EUROPE

Siebold's arrival in Europe coincided with Belgium's battle for independence from the Netherlands so he rushed to remove the manuscripts, specimens and collections he had sent to Antwerp, Brussels and Ghent to the safety of Leiden. The collection of 80 of his most precious Japanese plants remained in Ghent Botanical Garden and inaccessible to him for several years. However, following a string of angry complaints about the loss of his plants and the fact that they had been made available to Ghent nurserymen who were, in turn, selling them for profit, Siebold was donated one plant of each by the director of the gardens as a gesture of goodwill.

Siebold settled in Leiden, curated his collections and began writing. His three works revealed Japan to the West: *Nippon* (1832–58), *Fauna Japonica* (1833–50) and *Flora Japonica* (1835–42), with the German botanist Joseph Gerhard Zuccarini, who provided botanical descriptions for the first section. Siebold and his assistant contributed plant specimens, information on localities, Japanese and Chinese vernacular and scientific names, and French plant descriptions.

Siebold was particularly interested in economic plants, growing tea from Japan, China and Assam; trialling the edible root *gobo*, or burdock (*Arctium lappa*); and the Chinese weeping white mulberry (*Morus alba*). However, his most significant crop was sweet potato (*Ipomoea batatas*), which had been introduced to Japan in the early eighteenth century. He grew this for four years in his 'Jardin d'Acclimatation' in Leiden, listing four different cultivars in the catalogue of his nursery, Von Siebold & Comp., in 1856.

Siebold gained fame for treating cataracts with *Atropa belladonna* (deadly nightshade) and bringing Western medicine to Japan.

In 1859, when he was officially pardoned by the Japanese and the country had opened up to the West, Siebold returned to Japan, where he wrote a catalogue of 263 plant species that he had collected. He collected large numbers of ornamental plants for his nursery, dispatching crates to Leiden on 7 January 1861, and again three months later. He also made several botanical trips into the hills above Yokohama in April and his assistant copied various documents for him, again landing him in trouble; he was asked to leave for a second time on 31 October 1861.

Back in Europe, Siebold oversaw the cultivation of 280 new introductions in his garden and held plant sales in 1865 and 1866, alongside an exhibition of 10,000 new plants from Japan, of 800 species and varieties. Even in his later years, Siebold continued working energetically until he contracted typhoid from contaminated water and died in Munich on 18 October 1866. Twelve of his plants are still growing in the University of Leiden Botanic Garden – among them, *Clethra barbinervis* (Japanese clethra), *Parthenocissus tricuspidata* (boston ivy) and *Zelkova serrata* (keaki).

Philipp von Siebold:
INSPIRATION FOR GARDENERS

❖ *Fallopia japonica* (Japanese knotweed), introduced to Europe by Philipp von Siebold around 1829, illustrates the dangers that can be posed by the introduction of garden plants. The original plant was propagated in Holland and marketed around Europe by Siebold's Leiden nursery. It was sold primarily as a ornamental plant. Siebold brought back just one female plant and all Japanese knotweed in Europe is a clone of that original plant. If you have this on your property, ensure it is removed immediately by specialist contractors.

BELOW One of Siebold's introductions to Europe, *Fallopia japonica* (Japanese knotweed), is hugely invasive and has wreaked widespread havoc.

BELOW RIGHT *Wisteria brachybotrys* f. *albiflora* 'Shiro-kapitan' (silky wisteria); this species was first described in 1839 by Siebold and Joseph Zuccarini, based on a Siebold collection.

❖ One of the plants first described in 1839 in *Flora Japonica* was from a collection made by Siebold in the village of Kosedo, on Kyushu Island, near Nagasaki. This was *Wisteria brachybotrys* (silky wisteria). It had been grown for centuries in Japan for its sumptuous scent. It has large individual flowers, and stems and leaves are covered in sillky golden hairs when they first emerge.

This plant was listed in Siebold's catalogue of Japanese plants offered by his nursery. The first record in England appears to have been in the 1881–82 catalogue of the Veitch & Sons nursery in London's Chelsea. There are several commonly available cultivars: *Wisteria brachybotrys* f. *albiflora* 'Shiro Kapitan', with white tassels of flowers up to 15cm long; 'Okayama', a pale lilac-flowered cultivar; 'Shiro-beni', with grey-pink young buds and bracts, and white flowers; and 'Showa-beni', which has pink flowers.

✤ Siebold introduced over 20 hosta species and forms, in those days classified in the genus *Funkia*. Two species were named for him, *Hosta sieboldiana* and *Hosta sieboldii*. *Hosta sieboldiana*, with large, grey-green leaves, with a blue-green edge, has been described as the 'archetypal hosta'; this and *Hosta sieboldiana* var. *elegans* are said to have good resistance to slugs. *H. sieboldii*, with white-margined or plain green leaves, makes good ground cover.

✤ Other garden plants Siebold collected include *Clematis florida* 'Sieboldii' (passion flower clematis), *Aucuba japonica* 'Variegata', and several hydrangeas, including *Hydrangea macrophylla* 'Maculata' and *Hydrangea paniculata* 'Grandiflora'.

TOP RIGHT *Hosta sieboldiana* was one of many hostas introduced to cultivation in Europe by Siebold. This clump-forming herbaceous perennial has white bell-shaped flowers in summer.

RIGHT *Clematis florida* 'Sieboldiana', introduced to England by Siebold in 1836, is notable for having stamens that have become petaloid. It is best kept in a sheltered spot.

John Lindley

DATE	1799–1865
ORIGIN	ENGLAND
MAJOR ACHIEVEMENT	*THE VEGETABLE KINGDOM*

Lindley, whose supreme talent as a botanist, horticulturist and organiser manifested itself in myriad administrative and academic roles, possessed formidable stamina and an appetite for incessant hard work. He published prolifically in the scientific and popular press, lectured constantly, giving the 1833 Royal Institution Christmas Lecture, and identified and named many plants, including Georgiana Molloy's specimens from Australia and William Lobb's giant redwood from North America. As consultant and campaigner, he saved the Royal Botanic Gardens, Kew, from threatened closure, and he campaigned against the glass tax that inhibited conservatory building.

Aeranthes grandiflora,
air flower

As a boy, Lindley collected wild plants as a hobby, and in his teens he became friends with William Jackson Hooker, another alumnus of Norwich grammar school. Lindley completed his first publication, *Observations on the Structure of Fruits and Seeds* (1819), a translation of Louis-Claude Richard's *Demonstrations botaniques, ou, L'analyse du fruit* at Hooker's home, working almost continuously on it for three days without going to bed. Hooker introduced Lindley to Robert Brown, botanist and librarian to Joseph Banks (see pp68–73), who in turn introduced him to Banks himself. Banks promised to send Lindley overseas as a naturalist, but later decided to employ him in his library and herbarium at Soho Square. By Banks's death, Lindley had completed important works on *Rosa*, aged 22, which he illustrated himself, describing 13 species for the first time, plus a monograph on *Digitalis* and a survey on *Pomoideae*. Lindley dedicated his monograph on roses to the botanist Charles Lyell, who presented him with £100 in return; Lindley used the money to purchase a microscope and a herbarium, which, by his death, contained around 58,000 specimens.

Lindley worked relentlessly, driven by financial circumstances – his father's nursery business had failed and Lindley had taken responsibility for his debts. His days began at dawn and continued into the evening, and he gave up to 19 different lectures a week. In order to keep up appearances, he was forced to borrow funds, too, living in debt to the banks and friends like Sir Joseph Paxton, with whom he shared a passion for orchids.

A PROLIFIC OUTPUT

Unable to refuse work, Lindley's output as an author and editor for the amateur gardener and botanist was significant, and he became one of the most important public figures in Victorian horticulture. He was an enthusiastic supporter of Antoine de Jussieu's 'natural system' rather than that of Linnaeus (see pp56–61), an early lecture proposing that botany should encompass 'the vegetable system in all its forms and bearings' to place plants in their natural families. These ideas were transcribed in *Synopsis of the British Flora* (1829) and *Introduction to the Natural System of Botany* (1830). Asa Gray, who reviewed the American edition, rejoiced, 'No book, since printed bibles were sold in Paris by Dr Faustus, ever excited so much surprise and wonder'. It was later revised and expanded, becoming *A Natural System of Botany* (1836). Among his arguments was the suggestion that names of families should end with '-acae', and orders with '-ales'. Lindley also published *The Vegetable Kingdom* in 1846.

Lindley was particularly passionate about orchids, writing *The Genera and Species of Orchidaceous Plants* (1830–40), *Sertum Orchidaceum* (1838), *Orchidacae Lindenianae* (1846) and *Folia Orchidacea* (1852–59). At a time when orchid imports from the tropics were in full flow and new, exotic plants, such as *Aeranthes grandiflora* (pictured on p86), needed names, Lindley established some 120 genera, becoming to many the 'Father of Orchidology'. Sarah Drake, a brilliant

botanical artist and one of the greatest orchid painters of all time, lived with the family from around 1830 to 1847, illustrating Lindley's work. Another collaborator was the geologist William Hutton; aware that transport and heating greenhouses depended on coal, Lindley's interest in fossil finds in coal seams encouraging him to compile *The Fossil Flora of Great Britain* (1831–37) with Hutton.

Although several of his works were accessible only to the wealthy, Lindley also wrote extensively for general readership, contributing 16,712 plant descriptions to John Loudon's *Encyclopaedia of Plants* (1829), alongside entries for the *Penny Cyclopaedia*, the *Dictionary of Science, Literature and Art* (1837) and Paxton's *Pocket Botanical Dictionary* (1840). Among his other works, *Ladies' Botany* (two volumes, 1837–38) sold well, but most successful of all was *Elements of Botany* (1841), a textbook that ran to numerous editions and translations. Lindley also edited *The Botanical Register* (1826–47), devoted to portraying new plants in colour, *The Journal of the Horticultural Society* (1846–55) and *The Gardeners' Chronicle*.

A LIFE OF ACHIEVEMENTS

In 1822 Lindley had overseen the construction of the Horticultural Society's garden at Chiswick, and by 1841 was its vice secretary. He and botanist George Bentham planned the first annual flower show for the organisation, and Lindley's collection of books became the basis of the RHS's Lindley Library.

As a consultant, Lindley advised the Board of Ordnance (on vegetable sources of carbon for gunpowder), the Admiralty (on the cultivation and reforestation of Ascension Island) and the Inland Revenue (on coffee and its adulterants). He also took part in a commission to investigate the Irish Potato Famine, having witnessed its effects first hand. In 1838 Lindley wrote an influential report on the Royal Botanic Gardens at Kew – at the time in a state of disrepair – recommending it become a national centre for botany, and thereby helping preserve it for future generations.

Rosa fraxinifolia (Newfoundland rose), collected by Sir Joseph Banks and painted by Lindley, who was not only a scientist but also a talented artist.

Lindley was elected to the Linnean and the Geological societies in 1820, to the Imperial Academy of Natural History in Bonn in 1821, and to the Royal Society in 1828 (and awarded its royal medal in 1857). His work was honoured with the naming of the genus *Lindleya* (1824). In 1829 Lindley became the first Professor of Botany at the University of London, a post he held until 1860. By retirement he had authored over 200 publications.

In his rare moments of leisure, Lindley gardened and enjoyed archery and rifle shooting, having a 100-yard range in his garden. Although reputed to be a good shot, he once missed and hit his servant in the thigh. (He later returned the compliment, accidentally striking Lindley on the head with an axe handle.)

Lindley died of apoplexy on 1 November 1865, shattered by ill health and exhaustion – just outlasting his friends Sir Joseph Paxton (8 June 1865) and Sir William Hooker (12 August 1865). He was buried in Acton cemetery five days later.

John Lindley:
INSPIRATION FOR GARDENERS

❖ One genus established by Lindley was *Chaenomeles* (Japanese quince), excellent free-standing or wall-trained deciduous plants, flowering in early spring before leaves appear. *Chaenomeles speciosa* has red flowers, followed by small green, fragrant fruits; *C. speciosa* 'Nivalis' has pure white flowers with pink tints; *C. speciosa* 'Moerloosei' has white flowers tinged with deep pink.

❖ Lindley also named the genus *Eriobotrya* and the species, *Eriobotria japonica* (loquat), a large shrub or medium-sized evergreen tree with large glossy leaves and clusters of small fragrant flowers, followed by small edible fruit that rarely ripen in Britain, but do in

BELOW Lindley established the genus *Chaenomeles*, which includes *Chaenomeles speciosa* (Japanese quince), a colourful shrub that is easy to grow.

Mediterranean climates. Since it is not reliably hardy, grow it in a warm, sheltered position or by a hot sunny wall. This plant was introduced into cultivation in Britain through Kew in 1787, at the time of Sir Joseph Banks.

✤ Lindley named two *Phalaenopsis* species in the *Gardeners' Chronicle* of 1848 – *Phalaenopsis rosea* (pink butterfly plant), introduced by collector Thomas Lobb from Manila through the Veitch Nurseries, and *Phalaenopsis grandiflorum* (now *P. amabilis*), which Lobb sent from Java. Both men would have been delighted at how selections of this genus have become widely grown as houseplants. They need good light in winter; a bright windowsill is ideal. Remove them from the windowsill overnight before closing the curtains, and provide shade from scorching sunshine in summer. Temperatures at night should range from 16 to 19°C and day temperatures should be between 19 and 30°C, avoiding fluctuations and draughts. When flowers fade, cut off the spike to the joint below on the flowering stem and a new shoot will develop. If this does not happen, reduce temperatures by 5°C to initiate flowering. Water regularly through the growing season, and reduce watering in winter. Do not wet the leaves, but mist them occasionally with tepid water in summer. The roots should not remain constantly wet, but neither should they dry out completely. Feed the plant when you water it apart from every fourth time, when the pure water will prevent the build-up of excess salts in the compost. Feed occasionally in winter and repot in spring.

ABOVE RIGHT Lindley named a new genus and species when he described *Eriobotrya japonica* (loquat), which will fruit after long hot summers.

RIGHT *Phalaenopsis amabilis* (East Indian butterfly plant), named by Lindley, has become a 'must have' orchid for the home.

91

Anna Atkins

DATE	1799–1871
ORIGIN	ENGLAND
MAJOR ACHIEVEMENT	*PHOTOGRAPHS OF BRITISH ALGAE*

The botanist Anna Atkins became famous for perfecting the art of
the cyanotype, an early photographic printing process, and producing
the first book in the world to be illustrated by photographs. She began
by producing images of seaweed gathered around the coasts of Britain, or
sent to her by friends, moved on to ferns, and then became accomplished
at portraying flowering plants. Her artistic eye and the natural elegance of
her subjects produced works that combined the best in the world of fine
art, natural science and early photography.

Phegopteris connectilis,
beech fern

After her mother died shortly after childbirth, Anna and her father, John Children, became very close and shared the same interests. It was from him that Anna gained a love of science; unusually for the time, he believed that gender was no barrier to success and encouraged her interest in botany. Through his position as a librarian at the British Museum and Secretary of the Royal Society, he encouraged her participation in what were traditionally male-dominated circles. His contacts in the scientific world were useful, too. He had a large, well-equipped scientific laboratory at his home in Tonbridge, and there is an account of a meeting there, in 1813, of 38 leading English chemists (including Humphry Davy), who had gathered to investigate the properties of a large battery that Children had made. Anna was already a member of the Botanical Society of London when her father chaired the February 1839 meeting of the Royal Society at which William Henry Fox Talbot first revealed the details of photography. A few months later, Children wrote to Talbot, 'my daughter and I shall set to work in good earnest 'till we completely succeed in practicing your invaluable process'.

In 1842 Sir John Herschel sent Children a copy of his paper describing his refinement of Talbot's process, an invention he called the cyanotype. Making a cyanotype was relatively simple. A piece of plain paper was coated with light-sensitive iron salts known as 'Prussian blue', in a darkened room; an object was then laid on the paper, exposed to light for around 20 minutes, depending on the strength of the sun, during which time the exposed paper reacted with the light, turning brilliant blue, while the covered parts remained white. The image was then fixed by washing the paper in clean water, to which a little sulphate of soda had been added, creating a 'blueprint'. It was inexpensive, relatively easy to master, and the blue image tone was perfect for plants. Children's laboratory and its giant battery probably also provided a source of the ammonium ferric citrate and potassium ferricyanide needed for the process.

THE POSSIBILITIES OF PHOTOGRAPHY

Anna was a knowledgeable botanist but a skilled illustrator, too. After contributing more than 200 detailed drawings to her father's 1823 translation of Jean Lamarck's *Genera of Shells*, however, she realised that photography could provide a time-saving method of producing illustrations. Botanists had already seen the potential of photography for recording complex scientific specimens, but it was Anna who thought of them in terms of publication.

Anna was so disappointed by the lack of illustrations in William Harvey's 1841 *Manual of the British Algae* that she decided to produce her own, using specimens from her own collections. *Photographs of British Algae: Cyanotype Impressions*, including 398 plates and 14 pages of text, became the first book in the world to be illustrated with photographs. Each was a perfect example of its kind, artistically laid out, showing the contrasting forms among seaweeds such as *Cystoseira fibrosa* (first named by Linnaeus), with its filamentous stems and tiny floatation bladders. For

*Cassia
(America)*

Pteris aquilina

*Spiraea aruncus
(Tyrol)*

Cystoseira granulata

this specimen, the stems were laid out in a graceful arc to illustrate their flexibility. The presentation of *Sargassum bacciferum* was similarly elegant. The book was published in three volumes between October 1843 and September 1853 and distributed to scientific friends and institutions in paper wrappers and unbound – recipients were expected to undertake the binding themselves. Fox Talbot expressed his gratitude for her 'photographing the entire series of British seaweeds, and most kindly and liberally distributing the copies to persons interested in Botany and photography'. Anna likewise wrote in the text accompanying the book: 'The difficulty of making accurate drawings of objects so minute as many of the Algae and Confervae has induced me to avail myself of Sir John Herschel's beautiful process of Cyanotype, to obtain impressions of the plants themselves, which I have much pleasure in offering to my botanical friends'. Based on the number of surviving copies, she produced 13 editions, describing them as 'impressions of the plants themselves'. She used good-quality paper, so the images are still in excellent condition today, and she became adept at judging how long the paper needed to be in sunlight to produce images that were as clear as possible. Every one of the images in her books was produced by her hand. At the time, cyanotypes were more permanent than early photographs, so her work remained in good condition for many years.

Atkins's cyanotypes (clockwise from top left): *Carex* (sedge), *Pteridium aquilinum* (bracken), *Cystoseira granulata* and *Aruncus dioicus* (goat's beard). Her images are still in great condition today as she used high-quality paper and was so careful when judging how long to expose it to sunlight.

FURTHER WORKS

Anna later collaborated with fellow female botanist and childhood friend Anne Dixon (second cousin of the novelist Jane Austen) to produce two more books using cyanotypes. The first was *Cyanotypes of British and Foreign Ferns* (1853), which included specimens such as *Woodwardia virginica*, *Pteris rotundifolia*, *Adiantum serrulatum*, *Polypodium phegopteris* (now known as *Phegopteris connectilis*, pictured on p92), *Polypodium dryopteris* and *Aspidium denticulatum*.

Cyanotypes of British and Foreign Flowering Plants and Ferns followed in 1854 and included ethereal images of the flowers of *Papaver rhoeas*, *Papaver orientale*, *Leucojum aestivum* and *Taraxacum officinale*. Anna also experimented with other objects, such as feathers and pieces of lace. The text was presented as photographic copies of her own handwriting, written on paper with pen and ink. The paper was then coated in oil to make it transparent, laid on the treated paper, then moved into the light. When the paper turned blue, the top sheet was removed.

The works of Anna Atkins were hugely significant events in the world of botany and photography, and originals are now very rare; the last on sale raised 450,000 euros at auction. After a life in which she created at least 10,000 images by hand, Anna died at Halstead Place in Sevenoaks, Kent, on 9 June 1871 and was buried in the local churchyard there.

Anna Atkins:
INSPIRATION FOR GARDENERS

❧ One of the ferns imaged by Anna Atkins was *Woodwardia virginica* (American chain fern) from part-shaded acidic swamps and wetlands in coastal Canada and the eastern seaboard of the United States. The young fronds of this deciduous fern are reddish brown, reaching 90cm long in average conditions, or up to 3m in boggy ground. This creeping fern can be invasive where conditions replicate its native habitat in wet mud or even underwater. It can also be planted in full sun, providing there is sufficient water. Young plants grow quite well in moist

BELOW In 1854, Atkins turned to wildflowers. Her cyanotypes included reliable border plant *Leucojum aestivum* (summer snowflake).

garden soil but generally die during winter. The rhizomes are tender and deep water protects them from severe frost, so a thick mulch of well-rotted organic matter should improve the chances of success.

❧ *Leucojum aestivum* (summer snowflake) carries beautiful heads of white, green-tipped flowers above elegant leaves in spring, just after the daffodils finish flowering. It likes moist soil and is even happy by the margins of a pond. *Leucojum aestivum* 'Gravetye Giant' was introduced by the great gardener William Robinson, probably from around Limerick, in Ireland, where a particularly large-flowered form is known to be found.

❧ Atkins took a cyanotype of *Papaver rhoeas*, the common poppy associated with the fields of Flanders. In 1880, the Reverend William Wilks discovered a single flower with a white margin to the petal, picked the seed capsule, then spent 20 years breeding soft-coloured white, pink, yellow and orange selections, some with dark edges (picotees); he named them 'Shirley' poppies after his Surrey parish. Other forms, collectively known as 'Mother of Pearl', were selected after the Second World War by artist and gardener Sir Cedric Morris, who

searched Suffolk for soft tints like raspberry-pink, blue-grey and soft lilac. Today several similar single strains are available, such as 'Mother of Pearl', 'Cedric Morris' and 'Fairy Wings'; selections of semi-doubles and doubles include 'Angels' Choir' and 'Shirley Double Mixed'.

Georgiana Molloy

DATE	1805–1843
ORIGIN	ENGLAND
MAJOR ACHIEVEMENT	BOTANICAL COLLECTOR

Georgiana Molloy is remembered as one of the first botanists in the
Swan River Colony in Western Australia. As a retreat from the drudgery
of her arduous daily life as an early settler, she spent her time gardening
and collecting botanical specimens in an area scientists now consider to
be one of 25 biodiversity hotspots in the world. What began as a hobby
ended up as a work of great scientific value, and her collections were
regarded as the finest of their day to arrive in Britain.

*Kennedia
carinata*

G eorgiana's early childhood was idyllic. She lived in Crosby Lodge near Carlisle, England, in a country house with a large kitchen garden, surrounded by open countryside, where she became passionate about gardening and pressing wild flowers. Then, aged 14, disaster struck. Her father died after falling from a horse, leaving a widow and five children with considerable debts. When the family relocated to 'horrid Rugby' in Warwickshire, Georgiana broke with the strict traditions of the time, leaving home without the prospect of marriage or employment, and going to stay with friends at Keppoch House in Dunbartonshire. She remained there for 18 months, seeking solace among plants.

While in Scotland, a long-standing friend, the career soldier Captain John Molloy, exchanged his post with another officer, went onto half-pay, was listed as unattached from his regiment, and decided to join the *Warrior*, sailing for southwest Australia. The Swan River Colony (now the city of Perth) was its destination – the first non-convict colony in Australia. Molloy proposed to Georgiana in 1829 and, several months later, they set off on the demanding five-month voyage. Packed in her luggage were plants, seeds and a collection of pressed flowers she had accumulated since 1821.

A PASSION FOR COLLECTING

Life as a pioneer was punishing. At the time, the colony was a collection of tents, crowded huts and livestock, so John and Georgiana (who struggled with the heat, fleas, flies and dysentery) moved 200 miles south along the coast to Augusta. This was, however, the beginning of further hardship and tragedy. Georgiana's first daughter, born in a tent on the beach soon after landing in Augusta, died a few days later; her only son drowned in a well, aged one-and-a-half, and the colony almost starved to death when supplies failed to arrive. In between, Georgiana endured hours of loneliness while her husband worked away from home.

Yet again Georgiana sought comfort among plants, creating a garden with English flowers and seeds from the Cape, but she soon found greater joy in the native wild flowers that bloomed profusely in spring (such as the south-west Australian *Kennedia carinata*, pictured on p98). At first, she pressed and mounted them, sending them to family and friends in her letters. However, her life changed dramatically in 1838 when Lady Stirling, wife of the Governor of Western Australia, suggested to her cousin, Captain James Mangles, that he ask her to send plant material to him – he was particularly interested in seeds.

Georgiana then spent the last six years of her life pressing plants, describing them and collecting seeds; sending seeds and plants to London became her passion. She even persuaded others to collect material for her: her husband, daughters, farm workers – even soldiers walking between the towns of Vasse and Augusta – brought her specimens. But it was Georgiana who dried and labelled them all. Her pressed specimens were mounted with meticulous care, and her plant descriptions were known for their great detail – habitat, flowering time, soil,

and amount of moisture required. Georgiana waited patiently for seeds to ripen, and her samples were renowned for their freshness and careful packing. Each plant was mounted in a book with a corresponding number on the seed packet, and each package contained a detailed explanatory letter. As she wrote on one occasion: 'I have minutely examined every seed and know they are sound and fresh as they have all been gathered in the past five weeks during December and January.' A parcel sent in 1841 contained 100 different species.

In England, James Mangles dispersed the pressed specimens and seeds he received to 15 of the greatest scientists and gardeners of the day – including Joseph Paxton at Chatsworth House, and George Loddiges, whose nursery was famous for its hot-house orchids. In the words of Paxton, Georgiana's collection was 'collectively, the best and contains more good things than I have before received from that interesting part of the world'; he described her 'important collection of seeds' as 'far superior to any we have received at Chatsworth'.

RECOGNITION AT LAST

The botanist John Lindley (see pp86–91), who was fascinated by Australian flora (particularly its orchids), was very impressed by Georgiana's work. In his appendix to the first twenty-three volumes of *Edwards's Botanical Register*, which included a sketch of the vegetation of the Swan River colony, he wrote glowingly of the lady 'enthusiastically attached to the Botany of this remote region'. To Mangles he wrote: '... Mrs. Molloy is really the most charming personage in all South Australia and you the most fortunate man to have such a correspondent. That many of her plants are beautiful you can see for yourself & I am delighted to add that many of the best are quite new. I have marked many with a X.' Yet despite declaring that Georgiana's 'zeal in the pursuit of Botany has made us acquainted with many of the plants of that little known part of the world', her name was omitted from Lindley's list of acknowledgements.

On 6 June 1830, Georgiana collected what is presumed to be *Sollya heterophylla* (bluebell creeper), and placed it in her baby's coffin.

Georgiana and Captain Mangles's shared passion for plants, however, led to a mutually rewarding correspondence. In a letter of 1 February 1840, she wrote: 'Our Acquaintance is both singular and tantalizing, and somewhat melancholy to me, my dear Sir, to reflect on. We shall never meet in this life. We may mutually smooth and cheer the rugged path of the World's Existence, even in its brightest condition, by strewing flowers in our Way, but we never can converse with each other, and I am sincere when I say, I never met with anyone who so perfectly called forth and could sympathize with me in my prevailing passion for Flowers.'

Georgiana died in childbirth in 1843 aged just 37, having compiled around 1,000 collections. Late in her life she wrote to Mangles, 'I have sent you everything worth sending'. This talented botanist-gardener is now commemorated by the beautiful, pink-flowered shrub *Boronia molloyae* (tall boronia).

Georgiana Molloy:
INSPIRATION FOR GARDENERS

❖ A 'British' garden could not survive the long, dry summers and poor soil of southwest Australia, so Georgiana developed her own ideas and style, combining plants – particularly natives – with plants from other parts of the world. The results were the talk of the colony. Assess the conditions, then adapt to achieve success.

BELOW *Boronia molloyae*, named for Georgiana, is also called 'tall boronia'. Molloy's husband once saw it growing 'as high as his head, riding on horseback', according to Sir Joseph Hooker.

❖ Georgiana found ways of adapting, despite the limitations of what was available. When fungus appeared in some seeds, she rinsed it in salt water, using its antifungal properties; as lime was unavailable, she used wood ash, with an alkaline pH instead. Be flexible, resourceful and unafraid to experiment; sometimes this is the only way to create a garden.

❖ At the start, Georgiana didn't really know how to collect, mount or pack herbarium specimens. Lacking a plant press, she dried plant material between sheets of paper and weighted it down. Until Mangles sent her absorbent paper, everything she used would have been a great sacrifice. Bernice Barry, an authority on Georgiana, suggests that she probably used blotting paper, as writing letters and keeping a journal would have been a daily essential for her husband. Georgiana owned few books so it is likely she used rocks as weights. If you want to try pressing flowers, do so at their peak, once the dew has evaporated from the flowers. If you cannot press them immediately, store specimens in a ziplock bag, in the fridge.

❖ Georgiana noted where she had found plants, even marking the plants themselves, then returned later for the seeds. She made bags to keep seeds separate and discarded any that had been entered by even the tiniest insects. She also experimented with ways to prevent infestation – sprinkling seeds with pepper or wrapping them in 'tanner's bark', and later sending living plants in a 'Wardian case'. When collecting seeds at home, cut the capsules just before they ripen and pop them into a paper bag. Put this in a warm, dry place and the shed seed will be easy to collect later.

TOP *Beaufortia squarrosa* (sand bottlebrush) grew where Molloy lived in Vasse, Western Australia. In Britain, this shrub needs a conservatory.

ABOVE Molloy was a fervent collector; she urgently searched for *Nuytsia floribunda* (Australian fire tree) seeds before she died.

Asa Gray

DATE	1810–1888
ORIGIN	UNITED STATES OF AMERICA
MAJOR ACHIEVEMENT	*GRAY'S MANUAL*

Considered to be the most important American botanist of the nineteenth century for what became known as *Gray's Manual*, Asa Gray was a close friend and correspondent of botanist Sir Joseph Hooker, naturalist Charles Darwin and many of the other great scientists of the time. A committed Christian yet also a passionate supporter of Darwin's ideas, his *Darwiniana* – a collection of scientific and philosophical papers – was instrumental in introducing the theory of evolution in North America in a non-controversial and academically reasoned manner.

Lilium grayi,
Gray's lily

One winter, partway through a course at the Fairfield Medical College in New York, Asa Gray read an article in Brewster's *Edinburgh Encyclopaedia*, which fired his interest in botany. The following spring he eagerly watched for the first flower to appear and, with the aid of Amos Eaton's *Manual of Botany for Northern and Middle States*, found it to be *Claytonia caroliniana* (Carolina springbeauty). Gray had discovered his passion. Correspondence with the eminent botanist Dr Lewis C. Beck about plants that he collected led to a meeting with Dr John Torrey, Professor of Chemistry and Botany at the New York College of Physicians and Surgeons, with whom Gray had been corresponding since 1 January 1831. First, Gray became Torrey's assistant and collector. Then in 1836, through Torrey's kindness, Gray became Curator of the New York Lyceum of Natural History. His first botanical papers, entitled 'A Notice of some new, rare, or otherwise interesting Plants, from the Northern and Western portions of the State of New York and A Monograph Of the North American Species of Rhynchospora' were read before the Lyceum in December 1834.

Gray was later appointed botanist on an expedition to explore the South Pacific. However, excessive delays led to him resigning his commission to collaborate with Torrey in compiling *A Flora of North America*. On a visit to Europe, for future volumes, Gray consulted herbaria holding large collections of American plants in seven countries. He also met many eminent botanists and formed lifelong friendships, including one with Sir Joseph Hooker, before returning to America well equipped to continue the work.

In 1842, he became Fisher Professor of Natural History in Harvard University, a position he occupied until his death. He spent his time researching and developing the botanic garden there. When he arrived there was one greenhouse, no herbarium and there had been no curator for eight years. Gray donated his library and specimens to what is now known as the Gray Herbarium and revived the garden.

GRAY'S MASTER WORK

Gray's classic work, first entitled *A Manual of the Botany of the Northern United States from New England to Wisconsin and South to Ohio and Pennsylvania Inclusive*, ran to eight editions and gradually increased its geographical coverage. The single volume was too large to be the portable excursion flora Gray had hoped for (though enthusiasts remained undeterred). In 1845 Gray wrote to Torrey that he was writing an 'imperfect and hasty' botanical manual, to be used alongside his *Elements of Botany* (1836) and *The Botanical Text-book* (1842). Two years later he focused almost all his efforts on the project, putting himself heavily in debt in terms of both time and money. When it was finally published, he wrote in frustrated tones: 'What can you expect from a man who takes up a job in February 1847, to finish in May or June certain; but who, though he works like a dog and throws everything else, does not get it done until February comes round again.' It took Gray just a year to write a 783-page manual, though he intended it to be half

Sequoia sempervirens (coastal redwood). The history of the sequoia was the subject of a lecture given in Iowa by Gray in 1872.

that size. The impact on the botanical world was immediate and lasting, awakening or intensifying the passion of botanists and lovers of plants around the globe.

Gray had many correspondents, the most enduring of these being Charles Darwin, and letters between the pair mostly discussed design in nature and religious belief. Darwin kept Gray well informed about the publication of *On the Origin of Species*; Gray in turn became one of America's most active promoters of evolution while retaining his belief in a Creator. Gray, a devout Christian, believed that natural selection created new species, but that it was not the only cause of variation; he believed that an inherent power had also been imparted in the beginning by God. Gray's many supportive essays in scientific journals, were published as *Darwiniana: Essays and Reviews Pertaining to Darwinism* (1876). As Darwin noted to A. R. Wallace, 'Asa Gray fights like a hero in defence'.

THE FATHER OF AMERICAN BOTANY

Remarkably, the man who described so many new American species did not travel west of the Mississippi River until the age of 62, working instead from herbarium specimens: 'Although I have cultivated the field of North American botany ... for more than 40 years ... yet so far as our own wide country is concerned, I have been to a great extent a closet botanist.'

In 1873 he retired to work on *A Flora of North America*, the last volume having been published 30 years before. He travelled extensively throughout North America, from Mexico to Montreal, including a trip to the Rocky Mountains with Sir Joseph Hooker (see pp116–121), as guests of the United States Geological and Geographical Survey. A photo of 25 July 1877 shows the party camped at La Veta Pass, Colorado, with Hooker on a chair, and Gray kneeling on the ground beside him, holding a full herbarium press, both deep in conversation.

On Gray's 75th birthday, the botanists of North America, led by the editors of the *Botanical Gazette*, presented him with a silver vase, inscribed '1810, November eighteenth, 1885. Asa Gray, in token of the universal esteem of American Botanists', and embossed with flowers relevant to the occasion, including *Grayia polygaloides*, *Lilium grayi* (pictured on p104) and *Notholena grayi*. A silver salver, bearing the cards of the contributors, was also given, marked with the inscription, 'Bearing the greetings of one hundred and eighty botanists of North America to Asa Gray on his 75th birthday, Nov. 18, 1885'.

Upon his death in 1888, having done more than anyone to unify the taxonomic knowledge of North America, Gray was lauded as 'one of the most remarkable men of our country, and as a scientist, the best and most esteemed abroad of any American of our day'.

Sequoiadendron giganteum (big tree), one of the trees seen by Gray during his travels for the Geological Survey.

Asa Gray:
INSPIRATION FOR GARDENERS

❧ Asa Gray and Sir Joseph Hooker visited the Californian redwood forests, where they were shown two genera described as 'the vegetable wonders of the world' – *Sequoia sempervirens* (coastal redwood) and *Sequoiadendron giganteum* (big tree). The latter was introduced by plant collector William Lobb at the height of the gold rush. In 1852, Lobb set out for Calaveras Grove, California, where he found around 80 trees ranging from 71 to 76m tall, and 25 to 30cm in diameter. He packed his saddlebags with seeds and two seedling plants and, gambling on incurring the wrath of his employers at the Veitch Nurseries, yet convinced of the treasure he'd found, cut short his collecting trip and returned home to England with his bounty. He arrived back on 15 December 1853. On Christmas Eve the 'big tree' was given the name *Wellingtonia gigantea* by John Lindley, after the Duke of Wellington who had died the previous year. This angered American botanists (who had proposed the name *Washingtonia gigantea*); they were outraged that the world's largest tree had been named for an English war hero, by a botanist who had not even seen the tree.

BELOW Gray felt that care should be taken over plants' common names, writing that *Clematis virginiana* (woodbine) should be called 'virgin's bower', as it was not fitting for another plant.

BELOW On their travels, Gray and Hooker saw *Sequoiadendron giganteum* (big tree), which was later introduced commercially to Britain from seed and widely planted as status symbols on country estates.

ABOVE *Carex grayi* (mace sedge), named for Gray, is an attractive garden plant for moist soil and works well by the edge of a pond.

Eventually, it was given the generic name *Sequoiadendron*, for Sequoia (George Gist), the son of a German-American merchant and the Native American girl who invented the Cherokee alphabet. The first plantings of these trees are now emerging above the surrounding trees in Britain, just as John Lindley predicted. They are well worth a visit at Killerton Garden, Devon, Sheffield Park and Garden or Penrhyn Castle, Wales. In California, conservationists – notably John Muir – have also ensured these great trees' survival. If a *Sequoiadendron giganteum* is too large for your garden, try *Metasequoia glyptostroboides* (dawn redwood), a deciduous conifer for moist soil. Its leaves are fresh green in spring and bronze in autumn, and it has attractive bark and a pleasing winter silhouette. Avoid locations with late frosts.

RIGHT/CENTRE RIGHT *Diphylleia grayi*, named for Gray and in the Berberidaceae family, is notable for having white petals that become translucent in the rain. Its pretty flowers are followed by dark-purple fruits.

William Colenso

DATE	1811–1899
ORIGIN	ENGLAND
MAJOR ACHIEVEMENT	MISSIONARY, BOTANIST AND EXPLORER

William Colenso, a Cornish missionary to New Zealand, combined preaching with botany. During his lifetime he walked thousands of miles collecting plants as he visited his parishioners. Colenso met and corresponded with many great botanists of the time, including Joseph Hooker, often accompanying him out into the 'bush' to search for plants on his visit to New Zealand. A man of robust physique, an active and retentive mind, and boundless enthusiasm, Colenso visited the spots where Banks and Solander had collected nearly 70 years before and spoke with Maoris who remembered Captain Cook.

Metrosideros excelsa,
New Zealand fire tree

William Colenso showed an early interest in natural history, reading his first paper to the Penzance Natural History and Antiquarian Society when he was 18. First apprenticed to a printer, he then moved to London and later became a missionary/printer at the Paihia missionary station in the Bay of Islands, on New Zealand's North Island.

Once in New Zealand, Colenso benefited from the encounter with two eminent botanists – Charles Darwin in 1835 and Allan Cunningham, the government botanist of New South Wales, in 1838. Cunningham remained in New Zealand for several months, and during this time he guided Colenso's interest in natural science towards botany, teaching him how to collect plants. In a letter to Colenso, Cunningham urged him 'Not to lose sight of the vegetation of the land you live in, and do not scatter to the winds that little you gather'd regarding the peculiarity of those vegetables, when I was with you'.

In 1839 Colenso travelled extensively through the North Island, gathering knowledge of its natural history and discovering two small Australian plants in New Zealand, a sundew (*Drosera pygmaea*) and a club moss (*Lycopodium drummondii*); neither was rediscovered for over 50 years. He also saw *Lobelia physaloides* in the northern part of the North Island, which Sir Joseph Hooker later classified as *Colensoa physaloides*, a blue-flowered, single-species genus found nowhere else in the world.

EXPLORING THE NEW WORLD

Prior to the British Antarctic Expedition spending three months in the Bay of Islands in 1841, Sir William Hooker advised his son Joseph, who was onboard (see pp116–121) to seek out Colenso upon his arrival. Hooker admired the collection of minerals, shells and insects belonging to this 'brisk and active man' and the New Zealand flora growing in his garden; Colenso often acted as Hooker's guide as they explored the native bush together. Hooker wrote to his father: 'Colenso has been extremely kind to me ... He is a very good fellow in every respect, and has shown me the greatest attention ... Of this class of men Mr Colenso is among the most superior.' Afterwards, the two men continued to correspond for over 50 years, further encouraging Colenso's interest in the plants of his adopted home. Colenso sent large shipments of specimens to the Hookers at Kew Gardens for 14 years, and over 800 herbarium sheets at Kew are attributed to him. He also retained a collection in New Zealand.

Colenso collected wherever he went. In the summer of 1841 he travelled to the east coast, and when he reached Poverty Bay, he found *Coriaria kingiana*, a low-growing bush with undulating leaves, and *Metrosideros excelsa*, the red-flowered New Zealand fire tree (pictured on p110), or Pohutukawa tree, usually associated with the seashore, along the edge of the freshwater Lake Waikaremoana, 80km west–southwest of Gisborne. He also found several 'filmy' ferns deep in the forest – some new to science – including *Hymenophyllum pulcherrimum*, or tufted filmy fern, and *Dicksonia lanata*, the stumpy tree fern.

In 1843, a Maori, paid by Colenso, climbed to the bush line on Mount Hikurangi, returning with a collection of alpines, including a large yellow buttercup (*Ranunculus insignis*), a mountain daisy with white woolly leaves (*Celmisia incana*) and North Island edelweiss (*Leucogenes leontopodium*). A year later he saw New Zealand alpines for himself at the summit of the Ruahine Range, which runs parallel with the east coast of the North Island between East Cape and Wellington. He wrote, 'When we emerged from the forest and the tangled shrubbery at its outskirts on to the open dell-like land just before we gained the summit, the lovely appearance of so many and varied beautiful and novel wild plants and flowers richly repaid me the toil of the journey and ascent, for never did I behold at one time in New Zealand such a profusion of Flora's stores. In one word, I was overwhelmed with astonishment, and stood looking with all my eyes, greedily devouring and drinking in the enchanting scene before me ... Here were plants of the well-known genera of the bluebells and buttercups ... daisies, eyebrights and speedwells of one's native land, closely intermixed with the gentians of the European Alps, and the rarer southern and little-known novelties – *Drapetes, Ourisia, Cyathodes, Abrotanella,* and *Raoulia.*'

Colensoa physaloides, originally named for Colenso, is now classified as Lobelia physaloides. A New Zealand native, it was once widely distributed in coastal and lowland forests, but it is now only common on some offshore islands.

Colenso gathered as much as he could, but was unprepared for such bounty, writing, 'But how was I to carry off specimens of these precious prizes, and had I time to gather them? These mental pictures completely staggered me, for I realized my position well. We had left our encampment that morning, taking nothing with us, so we were all empty-handed.... I had no time to lose, I first pulled off my jacket, a small travelling-coat, and made a bag of that, and then, driven by necessity, I added thereto my shirt, and by tying the neck, etc., got an excellent bag; whilst some specimens I also stowed in the crown of my hat.'

When later given an extensive parish, Colenso toured it twice a year, on foot. His most notable discovery on these tours was the shrub *Senecio greyi* (now *Brachyglottis greyi*) on the east coast north of Cape Palliser, long a favourite in gardens. He also published over 50 botanical papers, most in *Transactions and Proceedings of the New Zealand Institute*, of which he was a founder member, and when Hooker produced his *Flora Novae-Zelandiae* in instalments between 1853 and 1855, three botanists, including Colenso, had contributed richly to his knowledge in the field, through herbarium specimens and correspondence.

Colenso was elected a Fellow of the Linnean Society in 1865 and the Royal Society in 1886. To the latter, he wrote of the 'high honour' that had been conferred upon him and of his hope that it 'may serve to stimulate me yet more in pursuing in the paths of science'. He died in Napier on 10 February 1899.

William Colenso:
INSPIRATION FOR GARDENERS

✤ Twenty-six New Zealand plants have been named in Colenso's honour, among them *Hebe colensoi*, with greyish-green leaves, and *Olearia colensoi*, a daisy bush with thick serrated leaves. Both genera are a source of excellent garden plants. Hebes have been bred extensively and are valued for being evergreen, compact in growth and often long-flowering. Among those with the Awards of Garden Merit from the RHS are low-growing *Hebe pinguifolia* 'Pagei', with grey foliage and short spikes of flowers in spring and early summer; *Hebe* 'Sapphire', which has dark green foliage and lavender flowers in summer; and *Hebe* 'Great Orme', found as a chance seedling in north Wales, being compact and rounded, with bright pink flowers fading to white.

✤ Colenso also sent pressed specimens of the genus *Olearia* to Kew. The daisy bush makes an excellent wind- and salt-resistant plant for mild and maritime climates. *Olearia macrodonta*, known as New Zealand holly, has spiny grey-green leaves with a white felted underside and small clusters of white flowers, while *Olearia cheesemanii* produces billowing clouds of white daisy flowers in spring that almost cover the plant. One of the most beautiful of the genus, *Olearia* 'Henry Travers', found in the wild on the Chatham Islands, is medium-sized, with grey-green leaves that are silvery below, and daisy-like flowers with a purple centre and lilac petals in midsummer.

BELOW Colenso collected several species of hebe, which have become a familiar garden plant. *Hebe* 'Sapphire' is a small, rounded evergreen with spikes of flowers in summer.

ABOVE In 1849, Colenso sent a pressed specimen of *Olearia macrodonta* (New Zealand holly) to the Royal Botanic Gardens, Kew, where it still remains.

RIGHT Among the specimens Colenso pressed was *Astelia nervosa* (bush flax). 'Westland' (pictured) is one of the best cultivars for borders or containers.

✤ Two herbarium sheets of *Astelia nervosa* (bush flax) at the Royal Botanic Gardens, Kew, were sent by Colenso. This is a tussock plant with sword-shaped silvery leaves up to 2m long and 4cm wide, forming large colonies at altitude on damp grasslands, fell and herb fields; its flowers are small but sweetly scented. The selection 'Westland' has silvery bronze leaves that often adopt red tints in cold weather. It needs a sheltered position in moist, humus-rich soil, and may need frost protection in winter in cooler climates.

Joseph Dalton Hooker

DATE	1817–1911
ORIGIN	ENGLAND
MAJOR ACHIEVEMENT	BOTANIST AND EXPLORER

Sir Joseph Dalton Hooker was a man of many talents – botanist, plant hunter, phylogeographer, artist and cartographer. Gardeners remember him for the multitude of rhododendrons from Sikkim that he introduced to the grand estates of his homeland, transforming the style of British gardens. He was a close friend and supporter to many, a collaborator to Charles Darwin, and, in his capacity as Director of the Royal Botanic Gardens at Kew, responsible for establishing botanic gardens throughout the British Empire. No wonder, then, that he is regarded as one of the greatest botanists, naturalists and explorers of the nineteenth century.

*Rhododendron
ciliatum*

Joseph Dalton Hooker was born in Halesworth, Suffolk, on 30 June 1817. His father, Sir William Hooker – who would later become the first Director of the Royal Botanic Gardens at Kew – was a botanist and professor at Glasgow University, so the young Hooker spent his formative years in that town. Even as a child he had a keen interest in plants. When aged around 5 and found 'grubbing in a wall in the dirty suburbs of the city of Glasgow', as he later put it, he simply explained that he had found the moss *Bryum argenteum*.

As a boy, Hooker was enraptured by the idea of exploration, avidly reading Mungo Park's *Travels in the Interior Districts of Africa* and an account of Captain Cook's voyages. Then, at the age of 15 he began to study medicine at Glasgow University, during which time he became friends with Charles Darwin, whom he met by chance in Trafalgar Square. Hooker graduated in 1839. In that same year, he learned that Captain James Clark Ross was about to lead an expedition to the Antarctic, and Hooker was determined to be on board.

On 28 September 1839, HMS *Erebus* and HMS *Terror* left England, with the 22-year-old Hooker as Assistant Surgeon (though he preferred the title 'Botanist to the expedition'). Their journey was not without incident. On the night of 13 March 1842, Ross recorded, the ships encountered a tempestuous gale and a giant iceberg. Ross wrote that the two ships became 'entangled by their rigging, dashing against each other with fearful violence ... Sometimes the "Terror" rose high above us, almost exposing her keel to view, and again descended as we in turn rose to the top of the wave, threatening to bury her beneath us whilst the crashing of the breaking upperworks and boats increased the horror of the scene.'

The four-year trip, though, was a complete success. Hooker botanised intensively in Madeira, South Africa, Australia (including Tasmania), New Zealand, Patagonia and the Falkland Islands. He collected and identified over 1,500 species that he then painstakingly documented over the next 20 years, notably in his *Flora Antarctica* (1844–59) and *Handbook of the New Zealand Flora* (1846–67). While travelling, Hooker drew or painted his surroundings and discoveries, including a fish taken from the stomach of a seal, and an active volcano – a sight he said 'surpassed anything that can be imagined'. He later had a sea lion named for him – the now-endangered *Phocarctos hookeri* (Hooker's sea lion). Hooker's habit of meticulously recording the location of plants was the beginnings of his work as a plant geographer, which would become vital to his friend Darwin's theory of evolution.

THE HIMALAYAS

In 1847 Hooker set off again, saying he was intent on 'acquiring a knowledge of exotic botany'. The Scottish botanist Hugh Falconer, who was leaving for India to become Superintendent of Calcutta (Kolkata) Botanic Gardens, and Lord Auckland, First Lord of the Admiralty, independently advised the exploration of the Himalayan region of Sikkim. By taking their advice, Hooker became the first European collector in that region.

On arrival in Calcutta, Hooker was delayed by monsoon rains and political negotiations between the British and the Rajah of Sikkim, so he distracted himself with botanising in Darjeeling, discovering plants such as the ivory-flowered *Rhododendron grande*, the first of his new rhododendrons.

Hooker wrote that he had 'eight thermometers in daily use, 2 barometers, 2 chronometers, a sextant and an artificial horizon'. He also made detailed scientific drawings and painted prolifically, including what is believed to be the earliest Western illustration of Everest. He endured many hardships, including altitude sickness and even arrest. (In November 1849, Hooker and his travelling companion, Archibald Campbell, were arrested by the Dewan of Sikkim in a political manoeuvre against the British government, before eventually being released.) Yet Hooker continued his work assiduously, collecting from 9am to around 5pm every day before returning to his camp to press herbarium specimens and document his collections: 'Large and small moths, cockchafers, glow worms and cockroaches made my tent a Noah's ark by night, when the candle was burning; together with winged ants ... flying insects and many beetles, while a very large species of Tipula, swept its long legs across my face as I wrote my journal or plotted off my map.'

A BOTANICAL HERITAGE

Hooker's efforts were rewarded, not least by the 25 new species of rhododendrons he discovered, including the beautiful *Rhododendron ciliatum* (pictured on p116) and many species named after those who had assisted him: *Rhododendron thomsonii* for Thomas Thompson (Scots Doctor, Surgeon in the Bengal Army and Superintendent of Calcutta Botanic Garden); *Rhododendron dalhousiae* named after Lady Dalhousie (wife of the first Marquess of Dalhousie, Governor-General of India); and *Rhododendron griffithianum* (to commemorate William Griffith, British botanist and medic who collected in India and Afghanistan but died before he could publish his observations). Hooker's notes, edited by his father, were published in *The Rhododendrons of the Sikkim-Himalaya* (1849–51), with paintings by the legendary botanical artist Walter Hood Fitch. Sir William Hooker also transformed Capability Brown's 'Hollow Walk' at Kew into a Rhododendron Dell to accommodate Joseph's Sikkim collections; it was described as the Sikkim of Kew and rated by many as the finest display in Britain.

Magnolia cambellii, from Hooker's The Rhododendrons of Sikkim-Himalaya.

In later life Hooker succeeded his father as Director of Kew. He also continued to write scientific papers and floras, including his collaboration with George Bentham, *Genera Plantarum*, containing over one and a half million words, describing all of the known members of 200 plant families, all individually examined. The work took 26 years to complete. On his retirement, Hooker was one of the most influential scientists in the British Empire, continuing his interest in collecting and classifying plants, and botanising in the Lebanon, Morocco and California. He died peacefully at home in Sunningdale, Surrey, aged 94.

Joseph Dalton Hooker:
INSPIRATION FOR GARDENERS

❖ Joseph Hooker was a keen observer of plants. He looked at them carefully and noted all the details of their appearance that could be seen with the naked eye. Close attention to plants is essential to every gardener. Check plants every day and you will notice pests, diseases and nutrient deficiencies before they become established. You will also see if a plant needs staking or watering. Don't just survey your plants overall – look closely.

❖ Hooker was prepared to travel to search for new plants. Finding treasures often requires inspiration, so don't restrict your own plant-collecting expeditions to the local garden centre – be prepared to travel to specialist shows and plant fairs, where you will discover new plants and obtain advice from the experts who grow them.

LEFT *Primula capitata* (round-headed Himalayan primrose) was raised at the Royal Botanic Gardens, Kew, from seeds collected by Hooker in June 1849, during his time in Lachen, Sikkim.

BELOW *Meconopsis napaulensis* (satin poppy) was collected by Hooker at about 3,000m above sea level in Sikkim, in the Himalayas.

❧ The rhododendrons Hooker collected transformed large country estates with a garden style that re-created natural habitats. Wealthy land owners sought to re-create the Himalayan valleys and forests Hooker described in his journal. Consider the different habitats you can create in your own garden, from ponds and bog gardens to herbaceous borders and alpine troughs. This will provide your own plot with maximum interest.

❧ Hooker kept meticulous records and journals for future reference. Keep a garden book, recording details of your own garden, such as which vegetable varieties are reliable performers and which taste good. You can also note seed sowing dates and keep a plan of borders as a back-up in case labels are lost or moved. Note, too, when plants are fed or harvested. A book of this kind provides an interesting record and is much more reliable than your memory.

❧ Hooker's father, who was Professor of Botany at Glasgow University from 1820 to 1841, noted his son's interest in natural history – and particularly plants – and he nurtured it to fruition. If you have children with a specific interest, do everything you can to encourage their passion. You never know – they may become the next Sir Joseph Dalton Hooker.

TOP RIGHT Hooker named *Rhododendron thomsonii* for his friend Dr Thomas Thomson, who became Superintendent of the Calcutta Botanical Garden.

RIGHT Joseph introduced *Inula hookeri* (Hooker inula) into cultivation from the Sikkim Himalayas in 1849. It's ideal for attracting wildlife; butterflies love the flowers and birds eat the seedheads.

Gregor Mendel

DATE	1822–1884
ORIGIN	SILESIA (MODERN-DAY CZECH REPUBLIC)
MAJOR ACHIEVEMENT	'EXPERIMENTS IN PLANT HYBRIDISATION'

Gregor Mendel was an Austrian monk who later became abbot of his monastery in Brno. As a result of curiosity, intellect and prolonged experiments using pea plants in his monastery garden, he discovered the basic principles of heredity. Although neither Mendel himself, nor his scientific contemporaries, realised the impact of his findings at the time, his observations were confirmed by later scientists. When his research work was rediscovered in the early twentieth century it became the foundation of modern genetics and the study of heredity. He is now revered as the 'Father of Modern Genetics'.

Pisum sativum,
garden pea

Johann Mendel was born on the family farm on 22 July 1822, in Heinzendorf bei Odrau, a small village in what is now in the Czech Republic but in his day was part of the Austrian Empire. As a child Mendel worked in the garden, studied beekeeping and developed a great love and fascination for biological sciences.

When he was 11, his schoolmaster, impressed with his aptitude for learning, recommended he be sent to secondary school to continue his education. The move was a financial strain on his family, and often a difficult experience for Mendel, but despite the challenges he excelled in his studies and graduated with honours in 1840.

Mendel then enrolled in a two-year course at the Philosophical Institute of the University of Olmütz, where yet again he excelled, this time in maths and physics, graduating in 1843. His father expected him to take over the family farm, but instead he joined the Augustinian Order of monks, at St. Thomas Abbey in Brno, where he was given the name Gregor.

STUDIES WITH PEA PLANTS

In 1849, when work in the monastery drove him to the point of exhaustion, Mendel was sent to become a temporary teacher in Znaim (now Znojmo in the Czech Republic), which was part of his monasterial duties. However, the following year, Mendel failed the exam for his teaching certificate, so was sent to the University of Vienna to continue his scientific studies. While there he studied mathematics and physics under Christian Doppler (who first described the Doppler effect of wave frequency) and botany under Franz Unger, who had begun using a microscope in his studies and theorised that the cells contained hereditary information, inspiring Mendel to begin his own experiments in this field.

Mendel began experimenting with pea plants (*Pisum sativum*, pictured on p122) in 1854, and continued until 1864, publicising his results in 1855. He selected 34 varieties of pea because they were easy to grow in large numbers, and produced two generations per year, growing tens of thousands of plants in total. Pollination was also easy to manipulate; Mendel either self-pollinated or cross-pollinated the plants himself, ensuring that they were protected from insect pollinators. For his experiments, Mendel selectively cross-pollinated purebred plants with selected traits, then observed the characteristics of their progeny over many generations. The results became the basis for his conclusions about genetic inheritance. Mendel had noticed seven traits in pea plants, which remained consistent over the generations: flower colour (either purple or white), flower position (axil or terminal), stem height (short or tall), seed shape (round or wrinkled), seed colour (yellow or green), pod shape (inflated or constricted) and pod colour (yellow or green). He then cross-pollinated plants with contrasting characteristics so he could examine the characteristics of the offspring. His discovery was that there was never any blending of parental characteristics – one characteristic would simply become dominant and the other would become recessive.

THE LAWS OF INHERITANCE

Mendel delivered two lectures on his theories to the Natural Science Society in Brno on 8 February and 8 March 1865, and the results of his studies were published in 1866 under the title 'Versuche über Plflanzenhybriden' ('Experiments in Plant Hybridisation'). Mendel did not promote his discoveries, so they created little impact in his day, and the few contemporary references to his work reveal that the complex and detailed work he produced was not understood, even by influential people in his field. The importance of variability and its implications on genetics and evolution were usually overlooked, and his findings were not believed to be widely applicable – even by Mendel himself, who wrongly believed that they only applied to certain species or traits.

It was not until 1900, after the rediscovery of his paper, that the results of his experiments were understood. His paper was translated into English by the botanist William Bateson in 1901, and its contents eventually became known as Mendel's Laws of Inheritance. The laws are as follows: the Law of Independent Segregation, which states that inherited characteristics (such as the stem length of Mendel's pea plants) exist in alternative forms, such as tallness and shortness; the Law of Independent Assortment, which states that specific traits operate independently of one another; and the Law of Dominance, which states that for each characteristic, one factor is dominant and appears more often, while the alternative form is recessive – a mathematical formula at a constant ratio of 3:1. For example, when Mendel cross-bred true-breeding purple-flowered peas with white-flowered peas, all of the offspring bloomed purple. When he cross-bred the offspring, three quarters bloomed purple and a quarter bloomed white. Scientists later discovered that Mendel's results not only applied to pea plants but to most plants, animals and humans.

Many inherited characteristics in *Zea mays* (sweet corn) are controlled by genes that follow Mendel's laws of inheritance – among these are the crop's shape and the colour of its kernels.

Gregor Mendel died on 6 January 1884 at the age of 61, after suffering from kidney problems, and was buried at the monastery; all of the paperwork relating to his research was burned by the abbot, and it would be another 16 years before his results resurfaced. Three scientists all discovered Mendel's principles independently at around the same time – the Dutch botanist and geneticist Hugo de Vries, who had suggested the concept of genes; the Austrian botanist Erich Tschermak; and the German botanist and geneticist Carl Erich Correns. As Correns admitted: 'I thought that I had found something new. But then I convinced myself that the Abbot Gregor Mendel in Bruno, had, during the sixties, not only obtained the same result through extensive experiments with peas, which lasted many years, as did de Vries and I, but had also given exactly the same explanation, as far as that is possible, in 1866.' As a result of their recognition, Mendel, who had the priority of discovery, was posthumously hailed as the 'Father of Modern Genetics'.

Gregor Mendel:
INSPIRATION FOR GARDENERS

✤ Gregor Mendel's crop of choice was peas. In his day, varieties would have grown taller but modern varieties have been selectively bred for mechanical harvesting and growing in gardens. Garden peas are listed according to the timing of their harvest – early, second early (or early maincrop) and maincrop varieties – and some descriptions refer to the pea itself or the pod. Varieties with wrinkled seeds tend to be less hardy and are generally sweeter, although breeding has blurred the boundaries. Petit pois are small and tasty; semi-leafless have more tendrils than leaves, and intertwine as they grow, becoming self-supporting; sugar peas, or mangetout, are grown for their sweet pods.

BELOW These *Begonia semperflorens* Cultorum Group (wax plant) flowers demonstrate Mendel's Law of Segregation: the red flowers have been inherited from one parent, the white from another.

✤ Mendel's experiments had to span many years, due to the time it takes from sowing to harvest. Earlies mature in around 12 weeks, early maincrops take one or two weeks longer, and maincrops another one or two weeks longer again. Sow in succession for continued cropping and grow some as 'sprouting' seeds for their leaves.

✤ The number of crops Mendel could sow per year was also restricted by the local climate, as peas do not germinate in soil temperatures below 10°C. Gardeners can start them off in pots under glass or in the greenhouse. Early peas can also be sown in guttering. At planting time, make a trench of a similar profile in the vegetable plot, water the seedlings in the guttering and slide the row into the trench.

✤ Seed companies offer F1 hybrids. Plant breeders cross plants with different desirable features to produce one plant incorporating both. These are again crossed, creating inbred lines of offspring that are true to type, as Mendel discovered. F1 hybrids are usually annuals and vegetable cultivars and are selected for uniformity – usually height of growth, timing of cropping and flavour; they are also larger and more robust, and more able to overcome difficult growing conditions. F1 seed is more expensive to produce; if you save the seed for sowing the following year, they do not come 'true' to the parent. Due to the high cost of maintaining these lines, they are regularly replaced.

TOP If, like Mendel, you want to grow peas, try the easy-to-grow, pretty 'Golden Sweet'. Pick mangetouts regularly to encourage cropping.

ABOVE 'Santonio' F1 hybrid plum tomatoes, an enhanced version of 'Santa' tomatoes, maintain consistency of their characteristics, as predicted by Mendel.

Marianne North

DATE 1830–1890

ORIGIN ENGLAND

MAJOR ACHIEVEMENT MARIANNE NORTH GALLERY, KEW

At the age of 40, after spending many years caring for her father, Marianne North decided to realise her dream of travelling the world and painting plants. Between 1871 and 1885 she visited 17 countries on six continents, producing well over 800 botanical paintings. She mostly depicted plants in the context of their natural habitats, providing glimpses of a world that was inaccessible to most, and introducing several new plants to botanists. A gallery at the Royal Botanic Gardens, Kew, houses hundreds of her paintings, which are still in the positions where she placed them.

Amherstia nobilis,
orchid tree

Marianne North was born on 24 October 1830, in Hastings, East Sussex, into a wealthy, cultured, well-connected family; the Norths counted William Holman Hunt, Edward Lear, Charles Darwin, Alfred Wallace, and William and Joseph Hooker among their friends. As a young woman, North received lessons in flower painting, and she became an enthusiastic gardener, often visiting the RHS gardens at Chiswick House and the Royal Botanic Gardens, Kew, where she was given flowers to paint. On one visit, Sir William Hooker gave her the exotic flowerhead of an orchid tree (*Amherstia nobilis*, pictured on p182), the very first to bloom in England. This intensified North's desire, held since childhood, to visit the tropics.

The North family travelled extensively, visiting Europe every summer, and Marianne always took a diary and sketchbook with her. She first used watercolours on a trip to Spain, but it was lessons in oil painting, in 1867, that changed her life. She wrote, 'I have never done anything else since, oil painting being a vice like dram-drinking, almost impossible to leave off once it gets possession of one.' Oils were the ideal medium for the humid conditions she was later to encounter, and one reason why her work has lasted so well.

A TRUE EXPLORER

North had taken over the care of her beloved father after her mother died in 1855, but on a trip to the Alps in 1869 he became ill, and died upon their return. North was devastated, later writing: 'He was from first to last the one idol and friend of my life – apart from him I had little pleasure and no secrets.' She painted to overcome her grief. Aged 40, she sold her Hastings home, devoted herself to botanical art and realised her dream of 'going to some tropical country to paint its peculiar vegetation on the spot in natural abundant luxuriance', as she later wrote. She travelled alone, accompanied only by hired servants to carry her easel and paints.

Between 1871 and 1885, she visited America, Canada, Jamaica, Brazil, Japan, Singapore, Malaysia, Indonesia, Sri Lanka, India, Australia, New Zealand, South Africa, the Seychelles, Chile and Tenerife (where some of the plants she painted still remain at the Sitio Litre orchid garden in Puerto de la Cruz).

In Boston, in the United States, North was overcome by the sight of so many new plants – scarlet lobelias, white orchids and ferns – while in Jamaica, she rented a house in a derelict botanical garden, hanging a bunch of bananas from the ceiling instead of a chandelier, and describing herself as being 'in a state of ecstasy' at the view of palms, orchids and passion flowers from her veranda. Rising at daybreak, she painted *en plein air* until midday, spent rainy afternoons working indoors, and in the evening went out to explore, returning after dark. On her next trip, North visited Brazil, where she wrote that 'every rock bore a botanical collection fit to finish any hothouse in England.' Here she was 'received with much distinction by the Emperor', staying for eight months and completing more than 100 paintings, working from a hut in the rainforest.

Visiting Yosemite on the US West Coast, North witnessed the felling of giant redwoods: 'It broke one's heart to think of man, the civiliser, wasting treasures in a few years to which savages and animals had done no harm for centuries.' Then in a forest on the other side of the world, the Rani of Sarawak described her as having 'skirts kilted up to the knees and heel-less wellington boots, as though born for Borneo jungles'. It was here that North discovered a new species, the *Nepenthes northiana*. This pitcher plant was not the only plant to be named after her; the names of one new genus, *Northea*, and three other species – a feather palm (*Areca northiana*), a red-hot poker (*Kniphofia northiana*) and a poison bulb (*Crinum northianum*) – pay tribute to her achievements. Many species North painted have sadly now disappeared, through what botanist Sir Joseph Hooker described as 'the axe and the forest fire, the plough and the flock'.

Marianne travelled around India for almost 18 months, returning with over 200 paintings. Her diaries ignore the arduous conditions she endured. She wrote that she 'started at four in the afternoon in a big cabin boat ... reached Quilon about 12 the next day ... thence on to Nevereya, where we left the boat and crossed the boundary in a bullock cart. We went on in another canoe, hollowed out of one long tree, for twelve hours more...' She was often forced to pack her paintings while they were still wet, making the final touches on her return to London.

THE GALLERY AT KEW

In 1879, thousands flocked to an exhibition of North's work in London. Later that year, while waiting for a train at Shrewsbury station, she wrote to Joseph Hooker, asking whether he would accept her paintings as a gift to Kew, to hang in a gallery that she would finance. Marianne chose the location, hiring her friend James Fergusson, a well-known architectural historian, as architect, and he designed the gallery in a classical style.

Nepenthes northiana from Sarawak, Malaysia, painted by North around 1876, and later named in her honour by Sir Joseph Dalton Hooker in 1881.

North spent a year designing and painting friezes for the gallery, arranging her paintings – which famously cover the interior like vibrantly coloured wallpaper – and positioning the 246 different types of wood she collected on her travels. When Hooker declined her request to allow refreshments to be served in the gallery, she painted tea and coffee plants over the doors instead.

Shortly after the gallery opened in 1882, as her health began to deteriorate, North travelled to South Africa. Her diaries expressed her frustration that she could not paint faster. After her last trip (to Chile, where she painted the monkey puzzle tree, or *Araucaria araucana*), North added her final paintings to the gallery, which now housed 832 works representing over 900 plant species, ranging in size from a few square inches to a life-size painting of a flower head from Chile, with hundreds of florets. In 1886, she retired to Alderley in Gloucestershire, where she entertained visitors, filled her garden with botanical treasures and died on 30 August 1890, aged 59.

Marianne North:
INSPIRATION FOR GARDENERS

✤ One of Marianne North's paintings portrays a group of North American carnivorous plants, including two pitcher plants – *Darlingtonia californica* and *Sarracenia purpurea* – and the Venus fly trap, *Dionaea muscipula*. All of these can be grown in a shallow tray of rainwater or distilled water, around 1–2cm deep, on a sunny windowsill, or in a conservatory or greenhouse that is frost-free or unheated. Do not feed the plants; put them outside for a few days in summer and let them catch their prey naturally. Remove the flowering spike, as flowers weaken the plant. Towards the end of autumn, when some of the foliage will blacken and die back, keep the compost slightly damp and remove the darkened foliage. They need a cold winter rest, so move plants that are growing indoors to a cooler position like an unheated greenhouse or porch where the minimum temperature is no lower than 0°C. The plants will come back into growth in late winter.

Repot annually in early spring, into carnivorous plant compost in a small 12cm pot, and return them to their growing position and their tray of water.

✤ *Darlingtonia* and some species of *Sarracenia* can also be grown outdoors in a bog garden – the best suited for this kind of planting are *S. flava*, *S. purpurea* subsp. *purpurea*, *S.* × *catesbaei* and *S.* × *mitchelliana*.

✤ In Brazil, North painted angel's trumpet flowers (*Brugmansia arborea*) being visited by hummingbirds. *Brugmansia* are large shrubs with hanging bell-like flowers, renowned for their sumptuous fragrance. They are not hardy but make a wonderful feature plant for the greenhouse or conservatory, to stand outdoors in summer. Grow them in John Innes Compost No 3, in a large container in a sunny position. Keep the compost moist and feed with general fertiliser once a month, while in active growth. Water sparingly in winter, maintaining night temperatures of 7–10°C and day temperatures of 10–12°C. In autumn, cut back the plants so they fit comfortably in the greenhouse, maintaining a height of 1.2–1.8m.

LEFT *Darlingtonia californica* (California pitcher plant), found next to streams and bogs, was among several North American species Marianne painted.

TOP RIGHT North painted *Brugmansia arborea* (angel's trumpet) during her trip to Brazil. It is now classified as extinct in the wild.

RIGHT *Sarracenia purpurea* (common pitcher plant) was included in a painting by Marianne of three North American carnivorous plants.

133

Luther Burbank

DATE	1849–1926
ORIGIN	UNITED STATES OF AMERICA
MAJOR ACHIEVEMENT	*NEW CREATIONS IN FRUITS AND FLOWERS*

Luther Burbank, the maverick 'Plant Wizard', worked his magic to create hundreds of new plants through rigorous hybridisation and selection. Producing over 800 different kinds of plants during a 55-year career, his creations encompassed fruits, flowers, grains, grasses and vegetables. Not all were successful – there was only one 'pomato', and the 'white blackberry' was a short-lived novelty crop – but one 'sport' of his 'Burbank Seedling', named the Burbank russet, has achieved long-term fame in commercial catering and is now the favoured potato of McDonald's.

Abutilon vitifolium,
Chilean tree mallow

Born on 7 March 1849, on a farm near Lancaster, Massachusetts, the thirteenth of 18 children, Burbank had little more than a high-school education, yet he showed great imagination and creativity from an early age, inventing such objects as a steam whistle made from a willow stem and an old kettle. He also showed great enthusiasm for the plants in his mother's garden.

Early on in life he was inspired by two books: *The Variation of Animals and Plants Under Domestication* by Charles Darwin, and *Gardening for Profit: A Guide to the Successful Cultivation of the Market and Family Garden* by Peter Henderson. On the death of his father, Burbank moved to a small farm in Groton, Connecticut, where he bought 17 acres of land with his inheritance and began breeding plants. He believed that all plants could be improved through selection, hybridisation and grafting, and he selected the best products to breed the best varieties he could.

THE PLANT WIZARD

In 1871 Burbank chanced upon the Early Rose potato and planted 23 seeds. One at maturity proved to be high-yielding, well flavoured and smooth-skinned, with oblong tubers that stored well. Three years later, in 1874 he sold the rights of 'Seedling no 16' – later to become the 'Burbank Seedling' – for 150 dollars (instead of the 500 dollars he'd asked for), kept ten tubers and, soon after, used the money to finance a move to Santa Rosa, 60 miles north of San Francisco, where three of his brothers had settled, eking out a living from a small nursery. Burbank's fortunes changed and he proved himself a skilled horticulturist, when he took an order for 20,000 Agen plum trees. He germinated almond seedlings in the field, inserting buds of Agen into the growing shoots, and fulfilled the order in nine months. He then sold his nursery to concentrate on plant breeding.

Such was Burbank's brilliance that he created over 800 fruit, flower, vegetable and grain varieties. A showman, who became known as the 'Plant Wizard', he loved 'playing with plants' and pushing the boundaries, creating, among other things, spineless cacti (mainly for cattle food) and the 'plumcot' (by crossing apricots and plums). Some of Burbank's best-known creations include the fire poppy, the Shasta daisy, and the 'Burbank July Elberta' peach.

For Burbank it was mass production on an industrial scale. At any one time he would have around 3,000 experiments in progress, involving millions of plants; when working on plums, for example, he tested around 30,000 varieties. Burbank bought plants in from abroad, hybridised, and demonstrating a keen eye, instantly spotting desirable characteristics and making every selection himself.

Burbank wrote several books explaining his work, among them *Luther Burbank: His Methods and Discoveries and Their Practical Application* (1914–15), published in 12 volumes and prepared from his notes of over 100,000 experiments, and *How Plants Are Trained to Work for Man* (1921) in 8 volumes.

SHOWMAN AND INVENTOR

Spurred on by favourable postal rates, Burbank entered the mail-order business, creating his own descriptive catalogue of horticultural wonders. *New Creations in Fruits and Flowers*, published between 1893 and 1901, and the excitement of happy customers, bewitched by his prowess in plant breeding and the many wonderful varieties he created, propelled Burbank to fame and fortune and greater success. By the turn of the century, interest in Burbank was so great that a stream of distinguished personalities visited him in Santa Rosa. These included two other self-made men of genius – Henry Ford and Thomas Edison (with more than 1,000 patents of his own) – who paid Burbank a joint visit on 22 October 1915. Burbank also received the scientist Nikolai Vavilov (see pp170–175) as a guest. (In an obituary, Vavilov would praise Burbank for his creativity, but find weakness in his understanding of genetics.)

In all, along with his famous potato, Burbank introduced 113 plums (many using stock imported from Japan), including his 'stoneless' plum, 10 apples, 16 blackberries (including the Himalayan giant), 13 raspberries, 10 strawberries, 35 fruiting cacti, 10 cherries, 2 figs, 4 grapes, 5 nectarines, 8 peaches, 4 pears, 11 plumcots, 11 quinces, 1 almond, the Wonderberry (which is now back in favour as a 'superfood'), 6 chestnuts,

BELOW 'Rainbow corn' (left) and a selection of plumcots (right) are classic examples of novelty plants raised by Burbank. The latter, a hybrid between a plum and an apricot, has the best flavour when home-grown.

3 walnuts, 9 different kinds of grasses, grains and other forages, 26 kinds of vegetables and around 1,000 ornamental plants, from *Abutilon* (such as *Abutilon vitifolium*, pictured on p134) to *Zinnia*, including various species of *Amaryllis*, *Hippeastrum* and *Crinum*, followed by *Lilium*, *Hemerocallis*, *Watsonia*, *Papaver* and *Gladiolus*.

Burbank was often criticised by the scientific community for not keeping meticulous records of his work, but he was more interested in results than in how they were achieved. In 1904, he received a large grant from the Carnegie Institution ($10,000 annually) to promote the scientific study of plant breeding, although this was withdrawn after five years when the reviewer decided that Burbank's methods were more art than science, attributing his success solely to his abilities as a selector.

However, Burbank was undoubtedly a brilliant inventor, a skilful self-publicist in the spirit of P. T. Barnum, and a well-intentioned man who gave generously to others and contributed funds to education, possibly because he felt the lack of an education himself. In 1940 his face appeared on a stamp (in the 'Famous Americans' series) and he was inducted into the National Inventors Hall of Fame in 1986, where he is numbered alongside the Wright Brothers and Steve Jobs.

Burbank died in Santa Rosa on 11 April 1926, and in 1930 the Plant Patent Act in the US was amended to ensure breeders were financially rewarded for their efforts, as an incentive to other growers to continue plant breeding (an early example of plant breeders rights). Edison commented at the time, 'This will, I feel sure, give us many Burbanks'. But there was only one Luther Burbank.

Luther Burbank:
INSPIRATION FOR GARDENERS

✤ Burbank wanted to create the ultimate daisy, his favourite flower. He grew oxeye daisies (*Leucanthemum vulgare*), selected the best, then crossed these with English daisies (probably *Leucanthemum maximum*). He then chose the best hybrids and crossed those with Portuguese oxeye daisies (*Leucanthemum lacustre*), refining these over five or six generations. Deciding that the flowers were not white enough, he cross-pollinated the hybrids with Japanese field daisies (*Nipponanthemum nipponicum*), finally selecting a single plant that had everything he desired – it was long-flowering, with large, white flowers. The Shasta daisy, named for the snow-capped mountain near his home, took 17 years to create and was introduced in 1901. Vigorous and full of flower, it may need staking with brushwood or canes in exposed positions.

BELOW Burbank selected an unusually perfumed *Zantedeschia* (arum lily) and named it 'Fragrance'. Plant arum lilies in moist, rich soil or in water.

✤ The plumcot, a plum–apricot hybrid, was relentlessly selected until Burbank had created a fruit with a plum-like flesh and apricot fragrance. Grow this in a sheltered, sunny position, protected from cold winds, or under glass in colder climates.

✤ One night, Burbank was walking among his arum lilies when he detected the scent of violets. He knew that arum lilies are not fragrant, so he began crawling around in the dark until he discovered the source. He named the selected plant 'Fragrance'. Grow arum lilies in moist soil or in up to 30cm of water, in sun or part shade.

✤ Burbank spent two decades trying to breed the spines out of a cactus. He wrote, 'For five years or more the cactus blooming season was a period of torment to me both day and night.' He hoped he could transform deserts into productive grazing. Initially his experiments appeared to be a success, but the plants he bred did not like the cold and needed regular watering. Some cacti, such as *Lophophora williamsii* (dumpling cactus) and *Pachycereus schottii* f. *monstrosus*, are naturally spineless and make interesting additions to collections in glasshouses and gardens.

TOP RIGHT *Prunus domestica* (plum) plants, ready to be harvested to make Agen prunes. Burbank called prunes 'educated plums' due to their extraordinary health-giving properties.

RIGHT Burbank wanted to breed a daisy that was longer-flowering, larger and whiter than the rest; the result was the Shasta daisy.

Henry Nicholas Ridley

DATE	1855–1956
ORIGIN	ENGLAND
MAJOR ACHIEVEMENT	*THE FLORA OF THE MALAY PENINSULA*

Henry Ridley was born into a family whose ancestors included
Nicholas Ridley, sixteenth-century Bishop of London, who was burnt
as a heretic; William Penn, founder of Pennsylvania; and John Stuart,
third Earl of Bute, botanical advisor to Princess Augusta, founder of the
Royal Botanic Gardens, Kew. Ridley is remembered for his developments
in tapping rubber trees, his enthusiasm for them as an economic crop,
his intensive botanical collecting and discovery of new species,
and his numerous scientific papers and books on relationships
between animals and plants.

Hevea brasiliensis,
rubber tree

A s a boy, Henry Nicholas Ridley was interested in nature, particularly birds and insects, publishing his first paper while at school. On leaving Oxford University he searched for work among the subjects he enjoyed, but after applying and failing to get a zoological post at the Natural History Museum in London, he tried again for a job in the botany department and was successful. Although botany was not high on his list of interests, he threw himself into it with great energy and enthusiasm. While at the museum he published a series of papers on plants from Madagascar, West Africa, Timor and New Guinea, plus two monographs, and in 1887, visited the island of Fernando de Noronha, off the coast of Brazil and published papers on its botany, zoology and geology. In 1888 he was appointed Director of Gardens and Forests in Singapore's Straights Settlements. Travelling at every opportunity, he created a large herbarium of Malayan plants, bringing many to the Singapore Botanic Gardens for further cultivation and study. Ridley also collected information and published a series of reports after a survey of timber trees, rattan palms and other economic plants, rapidly amassing knowledge of the country and its economic products.

RUBBER RIDLEY

While Sir Joseph Hooker (see pp56–61) was Director at Kew, he encouraged the exchange of plants among tropical countries of the empire, highlighting to the India Office the potential importance of many plants, among them, the rubber tree (*Hevea brasiliensis*, pictured on p188). Twenty-two seeds from Henry Wickham's collection in Brazil had been planted by his predecessor, so on his way to Singapore in 1888, on the advice of Hooker, Ridley broke his journey in Ceylon, where there were plantations, to learn more about their cultivation. On arriving in Singapore, Ridley nurtured a plantation of young trees and began tapping experiments on older specimens. His experiments on tapping living trees, without affecting their life span or vigour, and revealing an increase in latex flow when a recent cut was reopened, as Ridley had suspected. These discoveries were pivotal to the future success of the industry.

Such was Ridley's zeal for the tree, he spoke to coffee planters at every opportunity, ignoring their lack of interest and urging them to change their crop. His habit of always carrying a *Hevea* fruit in his pocket, ready to talk about it at any moment, gaining him the nickname 'Mad' (and later 'Rubber') Ridley. Convinced of the crop's potential, and sensing the opportunity to establish a rubber industry in Malaya, Ridley continued his experiments with tapping techniques and increased the size of his plantation to be ready with seeds and advice for other plantation holders when that opportunity arose. After the first was planted by Tan Chay Yan in 1896, an epidemic of 'Coffee Rust', which wiped out the Malaysian plantations, was followed by Ridley's predicted rubber boom. Ridley provided a large volume of seeds for the new plantations and shipped them overseas, having improved Wickham's methods of packing. Around the time the plantings matured,

Henry Ford was beginning mass production of cars, which led a growing demand for rubber for tyres. On Ridley's retirement in 1911, he received a gift of £800 from the Malaysian rubber planters, the only financial gain he received for his work. The rubber produced by him was sold to help pay for maintenance of the gardens.

RIDLEY THE BOTANIST

Ridley was also an outstanding field botanist, with a keen eye and vast knowledge. Whenever he travelled, he collected plants. Many species he found were new to science, including 200 orchid species, 73 ginger species and 50 in the genus *Didymocarpus*. He also made several trips to the east coast of Malaya up the Pahang River, and unsuccessfully tried to reach Gunung Tahan, the isolated highest mountain of the peninsula because his food supplies failed, forcing him to return. He also visited Borneo, Sumatra, Christmas and the Keeling Islands, Sarawak and Indonesia. He was also fascinated by plant–insect relationships and wrote on the control of the coconut beetle, pollination of orchids by insects, the habits of the caringa ant, and was the first to report on the white snakes living in the limestone caves of Malaya, and mosquito lavae in pitcher plants.

In 1893, Ridley examined a cross between the Burmese *Papilionanthe teres* (pictured) and the Malayan *P. hookeriana,* describing it in the *Gardeners' Chronicle.*

Ridley produced a great wealth of written material, publishing 38 separate papers and notes in 1906 alone. His *Flora of the Malay Peninsula* in five volumes appeared between 1922 and 1925, and *Dispersal of Plants Throughout the World* in 1930. The final tally of his botanical publications numbers around 350, plus 68 on zoological subjects, 8 on geology and mineralogy, 12 on medical issues, 5 on ethnological matters and 14 biological notes.

Days were not long enough for Ridley to do all that he wanted. Imperfections in his *Flora* were partly due to illness during much of its compilation, and he feared he would not live to complete the work. On his retirement Ridley went to live in Kew, and was publishing new species descriptions in his 91st year. He kept a diary of his travels, his daily life in Singapore and beyond until his lost his sight. He became a Fellow of the Royal Society in 1907, was awarded the Gold Medal of the Linnean Society in 1950, aged 95, making a speech in reply to the president, and from 1892 to 1912 *Curtis's Botanical Magazine* contained at least one of his plants. A 1906 issue, dedicated to him read: 'To Henry Nicholas Ridley, who with untiring generosity has surpassed all recent contributors, enriching the Kew collections with rare and novel plants.' Ridley died at 101 on 24 October 1956, after a monumentally energetic and productive life.

Didymocarpus malayanus

Henry Nicholas Ridley:
INSPIRATION FOR GARDENERS

❧ Henry Ridley found 73 new species in the ginger family, Zingiberaceae. Several in this family make good exotics for cool temperate gardens, being hardier than is often realised, although they dislike waterlogging in winter. Hardy gingers can be grown in large containers and overwintered under glass and encouraged into growth before planting out once the danger of frost has passed. Plant them in an open, hot, sunny position, or in light shade, and improve the soil by incorporating well-rotted organic matter before planting. Protect with a layer of organic matter over winter. Left outdoors, they are often late to appear in spring. *Hedychium densiflorum* is one of the hardiest: 'Assam Orange' produces spikes of rich orange flowers; *Hedychium greenii* has leaves that are green above and maroon below, with orange flowers later in the growing season; *Hedychium forrestii* grows at altitudes of 200 to 900m and produces beautifully fragrant white flowers.

❧ Although Ridley collected tropical orchids, and native species can naturalise in lawns or areas of grassland, there are also garden-worthy cultivars for shady borders. *Cypripedium* hybrids are ideal for moist, rich, free-draining soil that never dries out, with a pH of 6.5 to 7.0. They must be placed in a sheltered, shady position, away from scorching sunshine. Lighten heavier soils with well-rotted organic matter and sharp sand or grit to improve drainage. Plant in autumn or, if not possible, in early spring, taking care not to damage the roots. Day temperatures should not exceed 30°C, or fall below 5°C in winter. Mulch with pine needles or similar as protection, if needed. Do not dig up plants from the wild. *C. kentuckiense* is dark purple with a creamy yellow pouch; *C.* 'Gisela' is pink-purple with venation on the pouch; *C. reginae* has white flowers and a deep candy pink pouch, and grows well in gardens, coming into growth late in spring. The genera *Pleione*, *Bletilla*, *Epipactis* and *Calanthe* are also suitable for garden borders.

TOP LEFT Ridley collected 73 new species of Zingiberaceae (the ginger family), including *Hedychium forrestii*.

LEFT The richly coloured *Hedychium densiflorum* 'Assam Orange' (ginger lily) was one of the hardiest ginger plants that Ridley collected.

TOP Ridley collected tropical orchids, but *Bletilla striata* (hyacinth orchid) is one of many hardy orchids that would suit a cool, temperate garden.

ABOVE Since Ridley's day, *Cypripedium reginae* (showy lady's slipper orchid) has been extensively hybridised to make it suitable for cooler climates.

145

Charlotte Wheeler-Cuffe

DATE	1867–1967
ORIGIN	ENGLAND
MAJOR ACHIEVEMENT	MAYMYO BOTANIC GARDEN

A prolific plant collector, painter and letter writer, Charlotte Wheeler-Cuffe travelled extensively in Burma (now Myanmar) with her husband, often to remote, inhospitable places. The first botanist to visit Mount Victoria, she painted plants, found new species and, on the summit of Mount Victoria, discovered what she described as 'a crimson rhododendron brandishing defiance to the four winds of heaven'. With no previous experience she oversaw the design, construction and development of the Maymyo Botanic Garden, proving that strength of character and passion can transform challenges into pleasures.

Rhododendron cuffeanum

C harlotte Williams (nicknamed 'Shadow' following a serious childhood illness) was born in Wimbledon, London, to a family that had a strong Irish connection – her maternal grandfather was the Reverend Sir Hercules Langrishe, 3rd Baronet of Knocktopher, in County Kilkenny.

Charlotte was taught by a governess at home, studied painting and became adept at 'tinkering' with clocks, French polishing and wood carving. On 3 June 1897 she married Otway Fortescue Wheeler-Cuffe, a civil engineer with the Public Works Department in Burma, whom she had known since childhood. Charlotte confessed in a letter to her aunt, 'I can't help but seeing the comical side of it all! The idea of Otway and me, after jogging along all these years, ending in matrimony'. Two weeks later the couple set off for Burma, from where Charlotte wrote to her aunt: 'I delight in the life out here, it is so full of interest, and the freedom and unconventionality of it suits me down to the ground'. Charlotte created a garden and menagerie there, which at various times included a bear, a leopard and a cockatoo; 'his perch is brought in sometimes as a treat at dinner time.... He loves potatoes & beans and such like, but goes quite silly over milk pudding'!

Charlotte regularly accompanied her husband on official inspection tours, often to remote regions, setting up her easel and painting plants in their native habitat. She produced hundreds of botanical sketches and illustrations, mainly of orchid and rhododendron species, collecting plants as she travelled. She also chronicled her adventures in weekly letters to her mother, and then, after the death of her mother in 1916, to her husband's cousin – over 1,000 in all. Charlotte also corresponded regularly with Sir Fredrick Moore, the Keeper of the Royal Botanic Gardens in Glasnevin, Dublin, exchanging ideas, plants and seeds.

AN EXPEDITION TO MOUNT VICTORIA

In early 1911 Charlotte accepted what she called 'a most tempting invitation' from her friend Winifed Macnabb to spend part of the warm season on Mount Victoria. They were the first botanists to visit the area and to sketch and paint there, and Charlotte returned with a large collection of plants and seeds. She later showed these to the plant explorer George Forrest (see pp74–79), when he was in Burma en route to Yunnan, reporting to Sir Fredrick Moore that, 'Mr. Forrest, a botanical collector who is now in Yunnan tells me that the yellow rhododendron is new.... The white rhododendron grows epiphytically on other trees of any sort, including pines – between 6-8500'....The yellow is a bush & does not grow more than 8' high & flowers like the white one, when quite small'. A parcel duly arrived at Glasnevin containing 12 rhododendrons, 2 orchids, 2 *Selaginella* and 1 fern, along with accompanying paintings. The plant she had labelled 'blue buttercup' was dead, but the seeds were sown carefully, and once they had germinated and flowered, they were identified at Kew as *Anemone obtusiloba* f. *patula*. One of the orchids became *Ione flavescens* (now *Sunipia flavescens*); the yellow-flowered rhododendron was named *Rhododendron burmanicum* and the white-flowered

epiphyte became *Rhododendron cuffeanum* (pictured on p68), in honour of its collector. On a later visit to Glasnevin, Charlotte also met Augustine Henry, an Irish botanist and tree expert who had explored China: 'he & Sir Fredrick Moore waxed quite enthusiastically over my Mt Victoria things & say I must go there again & collect more.'

THE GARDEN AT MAYMO

On 9 November 1917, Charlotte was visited by the Head of the Forestry Department, Charles Rogers, and William Keith, the Burmese Secretary, who proposed that she design and oversee the construction and initial management of a new botanic garden at Maymyo. She wrote, 'The idea is to have a garden of all the beautiful indigenous flowers, trees & shrubs, with a few imported things ... there are a lot of beautiful things in the area now, including a small patch of primeval forest (rich in native species), a marsh, some rocks ... & weeds.' Charlotte approached the task with relentless zeal, describing it as 'an even more fascinating job than I expected'. Contacts sent seeds from remote areas: rhododendrons, 'a black arum', 'wild flower seeds from the Karind Valley', 'a curious plant from Mansi forest', the coffin juniper (*Juniperus recurva*) *Codonopsis*, bamboo seeds, a small pink *Lilium* (*Nomocharis* species) and three orchids, including *Vanda coerulea*, were among the items from which a garden gradually emerged.

Anemone obtusiloba f. patula was collected by Charlotte at an altitude of 3,800m, from Mount Victoria, Burma, according to a 1915 edition of *Curtis's Botanical Magazine.*

In February 1920, plant collector Reginald Farrer visited the garden, while Charlotte was supervising the installation of the water pipes and metalling of the roads. He later waxed lyrical in *The Gardeners' Chronicle*: 'in a few seasons ... it will rank with Buitenzorg [in Java] and Peradeniya [Sri Lanka; Charlotte later set up a plant exchange between the two gardens] as an object of pilgrimage ... it may even be lovelier ... because a particularly beautiful piece of ground has been chosen ... a winding shallow vale, full of diversities ... and a lake as blue as gentians ... I have no doubt that the Maymyo garden will be paradise.'

In 1921, Otway retired and the Wheeler-Cuffes left Burma. The garden that Charlotte had created was left in the hands of new superintendent R. E. Cooper: 'he is keen & enthusiastic & delightful to work with – so I am handing over my beloved garden to him with great confidence.' Cooper later sent seeds of a beautiful white rambling rose growing in the garden to Glasnevin. Its origin was shrouded in mystery for many years until it was found to have been collected by Charlotte, as she wrote, 'at Kutkai on the limestone plateau of the North Shan States ... about 4,300 ft up and near streams'. It was fittingly named *R. laevigata* 'Cooperi'.

After returning to Europe, they settled in the Cuffe family home at Leyrath, outside Kilkenny, Ireland. Shadow, so weak as child, survived Otway by thirty-three years and died in Kilkenny on 8 March 1967 - eleven weeks short of her one hundredth birthday.

Charlotte Wheeler-Cuffe:
INSPIRATION FOR GARDENERS

❖ Charlotte sent 20 Shian lily bulbs (*Lilium sulphureum*) for her mother and family friends and to Glasnevin in exchange for apple scions, informing Sir Fredrick Moore: 'I believe they are not quite as hardy as *Lilium candidum* … there are four here which thrive splendidly in a cold house in winter, and stood out all the summer.' Since the plant hadn't taken well to being repotted, Charlotte helpfully recommended renewing a bit of the topsoil instead and earthing up the stems an inch once they have grown 30cm high. She added, 'You said you had found them difficult, so this may be of interest'.

❖ An Indian horse chestnut (*Aesculus indica*), the only plant left at Glasnevin collected by Charlotte, dates from October 1913. This species is part of a group, including *A. pavia*, *A. flava* and *A. chinensis*, which are resistant to the leaf miner that is currently affecting the horse chestnut. Species from the resistant group should now be planted instead.

❖ John Besant, successor to Sir Fredrick Moore at Glasnevin, wrote in *The Gardeners' Chronicle* in 1926 about *Anemone obtusiloba* f. *patula*, as it was then in flower blooms for most of the summer. He recommended ordinary soil and a half-shady position for this plant, and also mentioned a white variety called '*Anemone potentilloides* [now *A. obtusiloba* subsp. *potentilloides*], like the last named, introduced by Lady Wheeler-Cuffe. It has not proved so successful in the open, due more to the ravages of slugs than it being tender.'

❖ Charlotte said that when approached to design and construct the Maymo garden, she 'knew nothing about botany. But they insisted and I had to admit I had collected plants all over Burma', adding, 'if it is not well done, I can only plead that I undertook to do my best'. Charlotte undertook the project with great enthusiasm and determination – and succeeded. Never underestimate your potential.

LEFT Contacts sent seeds of *Juniperus recurva* to Charlotte to grow in her botanical garden. This elegant tree thrives in a cool, moist climate.

RIGHT Of all the plants Charlotte originally brought to the National Botanic Gardens of Ireland, Glasnevin, *Aesculus indica* (Indian horse chestnut) is the only one that remains there.

George Forrest

DATE 1873–1932	
ORIGIN SCOTLAND	
MAJOR ACHIEVEMENT PLANT HUNTER AND EXPLORER	

George Forrest was a robust man and lover of the great outdoors
– perfect attributes for a career as a plant hunter. During seven
expeditions to China over 28 years – mainly to Yunnan, a province
rich in flowers – he introduced 1,200 new species. Among them were
509 rhododendrons, over 50 primulas and thousands of seeds, to the
excitement of botanists and gardeners alike. Most of his 30,000
herbarium specimens, plus his letters and artefacts, are stored in
the archives at the Royal Botanic Garden in Edinburgh.

Primula malacoides,
fairy primrose

As a young man working in a chemist's shop, Forrest produced herbarium specimens, later moving to the herbarium of the Royal Botanic Garden, Edinburgh, where he learned about plants and their classification. He walked six miles to work each day, stood while working, then walked back home again. This idiosyncrasy was noted by Keeper of the Herbarium, Sir Isaac Bayley Balfour, so when Arthur Bulley, a wealthy Liverpudlian cotton broker, wrote asking Balfour to recommend someone to collect plants for his garden from the mountains of Yunnan, Balfour recommended Forrest: 'the head of the herbarium speaks very highly of him. He is a strongly built fellow and seems to be of the right grit for a collector.' Forrest's first expedition amply illustrated that fact.

THE FIRST CHINA EXPEDITION

A year into his time in China, Forrest had been lodging at a Catholic mission, preparing to explore the region near Tibet, when violence broke out; Tibetan lamas had become intent on slaughtering all foreigners in the area. Forrest's group was forced to flee for their lives, and Forrest – having raced down a narrow track and leapt from the path to escape his pursuers, was forced to scramble a few hundred feet down a slope and hide. That first night, in an attempt to escape, he climbed to around 600 metres where it was 'very steep, precipitous in parts ... the footing was so precarious, it took me nearly five hours to gain the summit'. When he did, a line of sentries prevented his escape, so he climbed down again and spent the day 'hiding in a hollow under a rock'. The second evening, when he realised the lamas were following his boot prints, he buried his boots, 'descended to the stream, entered the water and waded ... for nearly a mile, taking the utmost care when I got out to leave no track', then carried on barefoot. The journey took all night. On the third night, Forrest ascended a ridge, again blocked by sentries, but found some ears of wheat 'all the food I had for eight days'; 'Once, while lying asleep behind a log in the bed of a stream, I was awakened by a sound of laughing and talking, and on looking up I discovered thirty of them in the act of crossing the stream about fifty yards above my hiding place.'

Throughout this ordeal, it rained heavily. 'By the end of eight days I must have presented a most hideous spectacle, clothes hanging in rags, and covered in mud, almost minus breeches, face and hands scarred and scratched with fighting my way through scrub in the dark, feet ditto, and swollen almost beyond the semblance of feet, shaggy black beard and moustache, and, I have no doubt, a most terrified, hungry and hunted expression on my countenance.' Forrest finally had no choice; he gave himself up at a nearby village with 'only strength to murmur the one word "tsampa" before I collapsed. Fortunately, I had fallen amongst friends'. His trek to safety was arduous, too. 'Most of the time we had to cut our way through rhododendron and cane brake, and then, when we reached the summit of the range, had two days frightful travelling at an elevation of from 14,000 to 17,000ft over snow, ice, and wind-swept tip-tilted strata, which literally cut my feet to

pieces and shreds and even played havoc with the hardened hoofs of my guides. Bitterly cold it was, sleeping out at such an elevation without covering of any sort. One night it rained so heavily that we had no fire, and had to content ourselves with only a very small quantity of rain water caught in a piece of pine bark. How I scraped through all the hardships I cannot tell.' However, Forrest still managed to take note of the plants he saw along the way: 'The flowers I saw were really magnificent, in fact, so fine were they, that I have decided to run the risk of going back next year if Mr Bulley gives his consent to the arrangement. There was several species of *Meconopsis*, all of them surpassingly lovely, acres of primulas, of which I noted nearly a dozen species in flower, ditto rhododendrons, many of which I had never seen before, and which may probably be new species, besides numberless other flowers.'

Pieris formosa var. *forrestii* was first described from a plant that was raised by seed Forrest collected in the Yunnan mountains, in south-west China.

Despite the trials of his first trip, Forrest returned to China six more times, collecting many iconic plants. Chinese gentian (*Gentiana sino-ornata*) from 'the summit of the Mi Chang Pass between the River Yangtze and the Chungtien Plateau at altitudes between 14-15 000 feet', was granted an RHS Award of Merit in 1915. *Camellia saluenensis* was crossed with *Camellia japonica* by J. C. Williams at Caerhays Castle, Cornwall, to become the first of many *Camellia* × *williamsii* hybrids. When *Rhododendron sinogrande* first flowered in Arisaig, Invernesshire, the garden owner John A. Holmes cut a stem with leaves and flowers, then travelled to Edinburgh and marched towards the Botanic Garden, as later biographer Dr J. MacQueen Cowan put it, 'carrying shoulder high the huge truss, supported by huge leaves, like a magnificent umbrella'. He was stopped, questioned and mobbed before reaching the garden in triumph! The cerise pink-flowered *Rhododendron griersonianum* (pictured right), named for R. C. Grierson Esq. of the Chinese Maritime Customs at Tengyueh, yielded over 150 hybrids, almost one third receiving an AGM or First Class Certificate from the RHS. Among the many primulas Forrest introduced to the world were the hugely popular *Primula malacoides* (pictured on p152) and another that Bulley was so pleased with that he would introduce himself as *Primula bulleyana*.

Rhododendron griersonianum

On 5 January 1932, Forrest died from a heart attack while shooting game. He was buried in a small graveyard at Tengyueh, among the plants and scenery he loved, his legacy as a great plant hunter secured.

George Forrest:
INSPIRATION FOR GARDENERS

✤ *Pieris formosa* var. *forrestii*, a popular plant for gardens with shade and acidic soils, needs shelter, moist soil, and protection from frost when young. According to Forrest, the seeds came from the Tali Range in Yunnan, and the original specimen still exists at Liverpool's Ness Botanic Gardens. Once owned by A. K. Bulley, these gardens are now part of the University of Liverpool.

BELOW *Primula bulleyana* (Bulley's primrose) was grown from seed collected by Forrest and named for his employer, A. K. Bulley. It needs moist soil.

BELOW RIGHT *Abies forrestii* var. *forrestii* (Forrest fir) was discovered by Forrest in Yunnan, China, in 1910. It is fast-growing and sensitive to drought.

✤ When Forrest saw *Magnolia campbellii* subsp. *mollicomata* in the distance in snowdrifts 3 metres deep, he was determined to collect the plant, eventually gathering seeds from it near the Burmese frontier in 1924. The three seedlings raised were named after the gardens where they were planted. The cultivar 'Lanarth' was originally known by the Williams family who own that garden as 'the Magnolia with the telephone number' after its collection number – 25655 (British phone numbers had five digits at the time). It is highly prized, with a flower colour that was described by G. H. Johnstone in *Asiatic Magnolias in Cultivation* as 'like that of vintage port'. The original plants can still be seen at Lanarth Gardens on Cornwall's Lizard Peninsula.

ABOVE Forrest observed that *Magnolia campbellii* subsp. *mollicomata* took half as long to flower as other forms of *M. campbellii*.

✤ Forrest demonstrated incredible fortitude and resilience, and overcame huge challenges on his journeys. However tough your gardening conditions or unsuccessful your attempts to propagate a plant you should never give up. If you continue, even against the odds, there is always a chance that you will succeed.

✤ Forrest's *Journal of Botany* obituarist wrote: 'It is probable that in quality and richness his herbarium material has never been surpassed. He had developed the technique of plant-drying to a fine point.' The key to his successful collection and preparation of specimens was that he trained local tribespeople to work with him. Having helpers makes a job more pleasant, increases the work rate, and brings other skills to a project. Although gardeners are traditionally possessive of their own plot, offers of skilled help are always worth accepting.

ABOVE The autumn-flowering *Gentiana sino-ornata* (showy Chinese gentian), ideal for rock gardens, is one of many special plants introduced by Forrest.

Ernest Wilson

DATE	1876–1930
ORIGIN	ENGLAND
MAJOR ACHIEVEMENT	PLANT COLLECTOR

A brown plaque on a terrace house at one end of Chipping Campden High Street in Gloucestershire marks the birthplace of Ernest Henry Wilson, 'plant hunter in China and the East'; at the other end is the Ernest Wilson Memorial Garden. Both commemorate a man who introduced more 'garden worthy' plants into cultivation than any other and is regarded by many as the most successful plant hunter of all time. Wilson introduced over 1,000 new plants, took over 800 images on a full-plate camera and collected over 100,000 herbarium specimens.

Ceratostigma willmottianum,
Chinese plumbago

On leaving school, at 13, Wilson became an apprentice at the nurseries of Messrs Hewitt of Solihull. Three years later, he became a gardener at Birmingham Botanical Gardens, while he studied in the evenings at Birmingham Technical College and won the Queen's Prize for Botany. His next move, aged 21, was to become a student on the diploma course at the Royal Botanic Gardens, Kew, where he won the Hooker Prize for his essay on Coniferae. Wilson was about to enter the Royal College of Science, intent on teaching botany, when he was recommended by the Director of Kew, W. T. Thiselton-Dyer, to Harry Veitch, head of the James Veitch and Sons nursery. Veitch wanted to send a plant hunter to China who would collect seeds of the handkerchief tree (*Davidia involucrata*, pictured on p161). Veitch's objective was clear: 'the object of the journey is to collect a quantity of seeds of a plant the name of which is known to us ... do not dissipate time, energy, or money on anything else.' Herbarium specimens from a tree found in the Yangtze Gorges had been sent to Kew by Augustine Henry, who was working for the Chinese Maritime Customs Service. Veitch, who had an eye for a good garden plant, had noted their beauty.

IN SEARCH OF THE HANDKERCHIEF TREE

Wilson embarked on his first trip on 11 April 1899, travelling via the United States, and stopping briefly at Harvard University's Arnold Arboretum, before arriving in Hong Kong on 3 June 1899. He then headed to Simao, a town in southwest Yunnan, to receive directions from Henry as to the tree's location. Travelling up the Red River, Wilson's boat nearly capsized and lost masts and a sail while negotiating a dangerous rapid. He then joined a mule train to trek 17 days to Simao. Here he finally met Henry, who sketched an area of around 140,000 square kilometres on a page torn from a notebook, on which he marked where he had discovered the tree, in the 'high mountains ... bordering the upheh and Szechwan provinces'. After a long, arduous journey Wilson 'reached the hamlet of Ma-huang-po and the house where Dr Henry stayed when he found the "Davidia" tree on 17th May 1888'. Did they remember Dr Henry? Yes. Did they know of the tree? Yes. Sould someone guide Wilson to the tree? Certainly. After walking for a couple of miles he arrived at the spot, and was confronted by a new house and a *Davidia* stump nearby. 'I did not sleep during the night of 25th April 1900', Wilson wrote in *Aristocrats of the Garden*. Undeterred, he continued 1,500 kilometres west to where it was first discovered, and less than a month later (19 May) he 'suddenly happened upon a "Davidia" in full flower! It was about fifty feet tall ... and with its wealth of blossoms, was more beautiful than words can portray'. Wilson collected fruits, too.

AN INTREPID TRAVELLER

After two trips to China, for Veitch, Wilson began collecting for the Arnold Arboretum. On his second expedition, in 1910, Wilson discovered the king's lily (*Lilium regale*) in the arid Min River valley in Sichuan, where he saw them in 'hundreds, in thousands, aye in tens of thousands ... the air in the cool of the

evening is laden with delicious perfume exhaled from every blossom ... its beauty of blossom and richness of fragrance had won my heart and I was determined it should grace the gardens of the Western World'. After returning the following October and gathering the 6,000 bulbs he had previously marked for collection, he was walking along a narrow mountain track, when 'Suddenly I noticed the dog ceased wagging its tail, recoil then rush forward as a small piece of rock hit the path and bounced into the river some 300 feet below'. He shouted to the bearers to put down his sedan chair just as a rock smashed into it, propelling it over the side of the cliff. Another rock then bounced over his head and knocked off his hat. He was just a few yards from safety in the lee of some rocks, when he 'felt as though a hot wire had passed through my leg'. Having been knocked over, he tried to get up but realised his leg was useless; his leg had been broken in two places, and the rock had ripped off his boot and big toenail. Remarkably, Wilson remained conscious and ordered his men to make a splint from his camera tripod. As he lay helpless, a mule train, unable to retrace their route, walked over him, but not one of them stood on him. It was then he 'realised the size of a mule's hoof'. He was carried in a sedan chair to Chengdu, and although infection had set in and amputation looked likely, Dr Davidson, operating for more than an hour, saved and set the leg, leaving him with what he later called his 'Lily Limp'.

Clematis montana var. rubens; this Chinese variety was introduced by Wilson to the nursery of Messrs John Veitch and Sons in 1900.

Wilson made further trips for the Arnold Arboretum (where he became Assistant Director), including one to Japan to collect the Kurume azaleas, and wrote several books, including *Plantae Wilsonianae*, a summary of the woody plants collected in western China for the Arnold Arboretum in 1907, 1908 (when he collected *Ceratostigma willmottianum*, pictured on p158) and 1910. The book was edited by the Director of the Arnold Arboretum, Charles Sprague Sargent.

Davidia involucrata, handkerchief tree

Wilson's life was cut short when his car skidded on wet leaves and crashed into an embankment after visiting his daughter in the United States. His wife died at the scene and Wilson died a week later, on 15 October 1930; both requested to be buried on British soil so were laid to rest at Montreal's Mount Royal Cemetery in Canada.

Ernest Wilson:
INSPIRATION FOR GARDENERS

✤ Wilson found *Clematis armandii* on trees and growing over thickets and bushes. Wilson wrote that this strong-growing, evergreen climber is great for a garden where a 'genial climate prevails' and counted it 'among the most desirable and beautiful of plants I have been privileged to introduce into cultivation.' It has white, fragrant flowers in spring.

✤ *Clematis montana* var. *rubens*, with purple-tinted leaves and vanilla-scented, rose-mauve flowers is hardier than many and, as Wilson wrote, 'acclaimed by garden lovers to be one of the most beautiful of all the clematis'. Flowering, from mid- to late June, *Clematis montana* var. *wilsonii* has small white flowers with a fragrance of hot chocolate. Wilson said this was the most common species in west Sichuan.

✤ *Ceratostigma willmottianum* (Chinese plumbago) is an attractive shrub, boasting azure blue flowers from midsummer to early autumn, when the foliage develops red tints. This is a native of west Sichuan, where Wilson found it in 1908 in the semi-arid regions of the Min River valley. Ellen Willmott raised two plants from seed, sent to her by the Arnold Arboretum; one

TOP LEFT A native of central China, a *Clematis montana* var. *wilsonii* plant (named for Wilson) first flowered in Britain in July 1909. It produces large white flowers and likes rich, moist, alkaline soil.

LEFT *Kolkwitzia amabilis* (beauty bush) was found by Wilson in Hupeh, China, at about 3,000m, at the watershed of the Han and Yangtse rivers.

was grown in her garden at Warley Place in Essex and the other at her sister's garden at Spetchley, Worcestershire. It is best to prune this beautiful plant hard, early in spring, and place it in a sunny spot. It will grow well in chalky soils.

✤ Although *Actinidia chinensis* is commonly known as the kiwi fruit, the alternative name of Chinese gooseberry is more applicable, since seeds were sent from China by Wilson, who collected it in Hubei province: 'The handsomest of all the Actinidias and one of the most beautiful of all climbers.'

✤ Wilson wrote of *Lilium regale* (king's lily), 'The discoverer is fearful lest its admirers undo it with kindness'. He noted that it has certain requirements, and that loam, leaf soil, good drainage and full exposure to sun are absolute essentials. He added, 'Do not give it fertiliser in any form any more than you would give an infant in arms beef-steak.'

BELOW *Actinidia chinensis*, famous for its kiwi fruits (although not as popular as *Actinidia deliciosa*), was collected by Wilson in China in 1900.

BOTTOM *Lilium regale* (king's lily) was collected by Wilson on his first expedition for the Arnold Arboretum in America, just before he and his party were hit by an avalanche.

Francis Kingdon-Ward

DATE	1885–1958
ORIGIN	ENGLAND
MAJOR ACHIEVEMENT	PLANT COLLECTOR, AUTHOR OF 25 BOOKS

The doyen of plant collectors in his day and a noted geographer, Francis Kingdon-Ward devoted his whole life to collecting plants. Over almost 50 years he undertook 22 expeditions, mainly to the Sino-Himalayan region, returning with a host of new species, particularly primulas and rhododendrons. His experiences are recorded in detail in 25 books and innumerable journals, written in his vivid, appealing style. On his last five expeditions Kingdon-Ward was accompanied by his wife, Jean, a resilient and able companion, who is notable as one of an elite group of female plant hunters.

Trollius pumilus, dwarf globeflower (yellow) and *Trollius chinensis*, Chinese globeflower (orange)

K ingdon-Ward was the only son of Harry Marshall Ward, Professor of Botany at Cambridge. Kingdon-Ward went to Christ's College, Cambridge, to study natural sciences but partway through the course his father died, forcing him to finish his degree in two years. Kingdon-Ward then became a junior schoolmaster at a public school in Shanghai. En route in Singapore, he headed out to the rainforest, later writing, 'That was my night out: fireflies and bullfrogs ... I just wanted to steep myself in an atmosphere, to revel in the scents, and to see with my own eyes all the exuberance of life that the warmth, humidity, and equinoctial time-sequence of the tropics produces...'

THE URGE TO TRAVEL

With little enthusiasm for teaching Kindon-Ward joined an American zoological expedition, to Western China, sponsored by the Duke of Bedford, and made a small collection of herbarium specimens. Shortly after his return, Arthur Bulley, who had just lost George Forrest (see pp152–157) to J. C. Williams of Caerhays Castle in Cornwall, was looking for a replacement. Again he wrote to Isaac Bayley Balfour at the Royal Botanic Garden in Edinburgh. 'There is a good man in China now ... with a good knowledge of botany and of plants' was the reply he received. Kingdon-Ward accepted the offer immediately: 'travel had bitten too deeply into my soul and I soon began to feel restless again, so that when after four months of civilised life something better turned up, I accepted it with alacrity', he later recalled. 'Bulley's letter decided my life ... for the next forty-five years.'

Kingdon-Ward's most successful expedition, in 1924, to Bhutan and southeast Tibet, was with Lord Cawdor, where they solved 'the Riddle of the Tsangpo Gorge', one of the deepest gorges in the world. The upper section of the Brahmaputra River, close to Lhasa, is at 3,600 metres above sea level, yet where it emerges from the Himalayas and pours into the Assam Valley it is only at a height of 300 metres. It had been believed to step down in a series of magnificent cataracts, including the mythical Falls of Brahmaputra, said to be 45 metres high; Kingdon-Ward and Lord Cawdor found it to be a series of smaller falls. On this trip they also collected Tibetan cowslip (*Primula florindae*), dwarf globeflower (*Trollius pumilus*, pictured on p164 with *Trollius chinensis*, another garden-worthy member of the genus), *Berberis tsangpoensis*, several rhododendrons and, among what Kingdon-Ward called 'the wooded hills east of sacred Lhasa', the blue poppy (*Meconopsis betonicifolia*). He wrote, 'among a paradise of primulas the flowers flutter out from amongst the sea-green leaves like blue and gold butterflies'.

A CLOSE SHAVE

Kingdon-Ward faced many challenges on his travels, including battling a fear of heights, suffering bouts of malaria, getting lost in the 'jungle' and surviving by eating rhododendron blossoms, being impaled on a bamboo spike, and escaping when a tree fell on his tent. His greatest escape, however, came on 15 August 1950,

in the Lohit Valley, when he and his second wife, Jean, were caught near the epicentre of the 1950 Assam earthquake, which was 8.6 on the Richter scale, and killed around 4,800 people. Jean recorded the traumatic event in her book *My Hill So Strong* (1952), describing the night when she felt her camp bed give 'a sharp jolt. In a split second it jerked again, more violently and I was dragged roughly from the very brink of sleep back to full consciousness.' She wrote that Francis Kingdon-Ward 'methodically put the cap on his pen' before picking up his lantern and following his wife outside, where they found themselves thrown to the ground, unable to stand or even sit due to the violent shaking of the ground. Jean described the colossal sound they heard as a 'deafening roar that filled all the valley. Mixed with it was a terrifying clatter as though a hundred rods were being drawn over corrugated iron.' As the earthquake continued, Francis, Jean and their porters lay together, face-down in the sand, holding hands as they waited 'in indescribable terror for the enraged earth to open beneath us and swallow us whole.' Miraculously, every member of the group survived this savage ordeal and managed to make their way back to safety.

A LASTING LEGACY

As a botanist, Kingdon-Ward was known for his meticulous scientific approach – his detailed notes were published after each trip by his sponsors. He also had an excellent knowledge of several genera. Between expeditions he worked on identifying plants he had collected, sometimes with other specialists, notably Harry Tagg at Edinburgh's Royal Botanic Garden, an authority on rhododendrons. Kingdon-Ward collected and catalogued over 23,000 plants during his life, and described 119 new species, including 62 rhododendrons, 11 *Meconopsis* and 37 primulas. Several were named after him in later years, including *Rhomboda wardii*, in 1995, from one of his herbarium specimens. In 1956, at the age of 71, he climbed Mount Victoria (3,053 metres) in southwest Myanmar. A herbarium specimen indicates he collected an *Impatiens*. When it was rediscovered in 2002 in the same location, it was named *Impatiens kingdon-wardii*, because Kingdon-Ward had been the first to collect the species.

Meconopsis betonicifolia (blue poppy) was one of Kindon-Ward's finest introductions; he described its collection in his book, *Land of the Blue Poppy*.

Kingdon-Ward was honoured with the Founder's Gold Medal and an Honorary Fellowship by the Royal Geographical Society, and received the Victoria Medal of Honour and Veitch Memorial Medal from the RHS. While planning another trip at the age of 72, he had a stroke and died in hospital on 8 April 1958. He was buried in the churchyard at Grantchester, Cambridge, just behind the church. On 10 February 2016, Jean's ashes were buried with him and *Rosa* 'Frank Kingdon Ward' was planted against the churchyard wall in his memory, in the presence of admirers and three generations of the Kingdon-Ward family.

Francis Kingdon-Ward:
INSPIRATION FOR GARDENERS

❧ Kingdon-Ward commissioned Lady Charlotte Wheeler-Cuffe to paint *Meconopsis speciosa* in 1917; the painting was lost and the plant died, too. Not every introduction is successful – even for Frank Kingdon-Ward – but his passion made him keep trying.

❧ Kingdon-Ward wrote of *Meconopsis betonicifolia*: 'The finest flowers hid themselves … along the banks of the stream. Here among the spiteful spiny thickets of Hippophae, barberry, and rose, grew that lovely poppy'. He noted that several Himalayan poppies do as well in humid climates as in parts of Scotland, Wales and Ireland, but they will not grow just anywhere, and need a good deal of attention.

❧ Kingdon-Ward was adamant about how Tibetan cowslip (*Primula florindae*, named after his first wife) should be grown. He advised that a single plant is 'big and bold' enough to stand alone if its surroundings are big and bold enough, but he felt that *P. florindae* looks its best growing 'in a crowd,

BELOW LEFT *Rhododendron wardii* var. *puralbum*, a white-flowered variety of the species named for Kingdon-Ward that flowers in mid- to late spring

BELOW *Rosa* 'Kingdon Ward', bred by Girija and Viru Viraraghavan in India, in 2012. One parent is *Rosa gigantea*, a species collected by Kingdon-Ward and his wife Jean in the mountains of Rajasthan.

as nature intended it to grow'. He thought that it was the 'forest of stems rising above the cured leaves, like frail masts from a rough green sea which is the attraction; not in a lone specimen.'

✤ After the Second World War, Kingdon-Ward worked for the US government searching for wrecked aircraft over the eastern Himalayas ('The Hump'). During one search he discovered *Lilium mackliniae* (named for his second wife's maiden name) on Mount Sirohi in Manipur. 'That the Manipur lily grows on both sides [of the ridge] – that is to say, in full sun and in half shade – in itself suggests a certain degree of adaptability'. He warned that it will not stand drought or near-drought in the growing season, though, and noted that even slight sunlight bleached the flowers. The plant had grown best on a north-facing slope.

✤ After George Forrest (see pp152–157) met Kingdon-Ward on a ship returning to Southampton, Forrest wrote: 'I must admit much of my prejudice regarding him has gone by the board. He is rather keen we should arrange an expedition together to the country NE of Putao.' Disappointingly nothing materialised, but it is well worth any gardener looking up the huge range of Asian species discovered by these two great botanists.

TOP RIGHT Kingdon-Ward found *Primula florindae* (giant cowslip) growing in the Yarlung Tsangpo basin in northeast Tibet, and named it for his first wife, Florinda Norman-Thompson.

RIGHT Kingdon-Ward discovered *Lilium mackliniae* (Manipur lily) in 1946, in the Manipur region of northeast India, and named it for his second wife, Jean Macklin. It received an RHS Award of Merit when exhibited for the first time in 1948.

Nikolai Vavilov

DATE	1887–1943
ORIGIN	RUSSIA
MAJOR ACHIEVEMENT	*ORIGIN AND GEOGRAPHY OF CULTIVATED PLANTS*

Soviet botanist, geneticist and geographer Nikolai Vavilov was a man of vigour, intellect and charisma, and with one ambition – to end famine in Russia and the world. Knowing this could be achieved by plant breeding and selection, he and his teams combed the world for economic crops and their wild relatives, collecting and preserving genetic diversity. Despite his extraordinary achievements in creating the world's first seed bank and penning a groundbreaking work (*Origin and Geography of Cultivated Plants*) he died an untimely death and became a global martyr for science.

Daucus carota,
wild carrot

As a child, Nikolai Vavilov liked the natural sciences, creating his own herbarium. After studying at the Moscow Agricultural Institute (writing his BA diploma essay on snails as pests) he left Russia and visited the key research laboratories in Europe, meeting many great scientists. Those who influenced him most, with their ideas on genetics, were Rowland Biffen, an agricultural botanist, Director of the Plant Breeding Institute at the University of Cambridge and an authority on wheat rusts and cereal breeding; and William Bateson, Director of the John Innes Horticultural Institution and the first person to use the term 'genetics'. Vavilov also met Charles Darwin's son Francis.

Vavilov realised that the principles of plant geneticist Gregor Mendel and the theories of Darwin could be used in breeding programmes to increase productivity and resistance to drought and disease, but only if the widest possible range of genetic material was available. With this in mind, he and his researchers scoured the world to select as many different kinds of crops and their wild relatives as they could find. These would then be stored in a seed bank in Leningrad for future use.

ESTABLISHING A SEED BANK

Believing that the greatest diversity would be found near the centres of origin, between 1923 and 1931, Vavilov organised, or undertook himself, 115 expeditions to 64 countries over 5 continents. These included Afghanistan, Iran, Spain, Taiwan, Algeria, Eritrea, Bolivia, Korea, Peru and the United States. The goal was to collect seeds on a 'mission for all humanity', creating a seed bank containing over 60,000 seed and plant samples, including around 26,000 varieties of wheat. They not only collected essential crops (wheat, oats, rice and rye) but also forage plants such as clover, fruit, vegetables (like *Daucus carota*, pictured on p170), and plants that produced resins, dyes, textiles and medicines – any plant of use to humankind. On analysis of the data, Vavilov proposed eight Centres of Diversity: I. China, II. India and Indo-Malaya, III. Central Asia, IV. the Near East, V. the Mediterranean, VI. Abyssinia, VII. South Mexico and Central America, and VIII. South America (Peru, Ecuador and Bolivia). The number was modified several times as his research progressed, eventually numbering seven.

The seeds were deposited in the seed bank of the All-Union Institute of Plant Industry in Leningrad, where Vavilov was director. He was honoured for this work with the Lenin Prize, and named as a foreign member of the Royal Society of London and many other venerable institutions. Vavilov had transformed this organization into a network of 400 experimental stations and laboratories, employing some 20,000 people. His seminal work, a selection of his academic papers entitled *Origin and Geography of Cultivated Plants*, was published in 1926 and translated into English in 1992, revealing his findings. As a result, he became a celebrated academic, and travelled the world, meeting other geneticists including Luther Burbank (see pp134–139).

ENEMY OF THE STATE

Despite his heroic achievements, Vavilov made enemies, notably Stalin's favourite scientist, T. D. Lysenko, once Vavilov's student and 'a young man with green fingers, ruthlessness and boundless ambition', as noted by Vavilov's biographer, Peter Pringle. Famine, drought and Stalin's collectivisation of private farms had led to reduced yields across the Soviet Union. Vavilov, the perfect scapegoat, was held responsible for the famines because his breeding programmes took too long, and the principles of genetics, founded on Western research, were deemed offensive to Communist ideology and branded 'reactionary, bourgeois, and capitalistic', according to Pringle. Lysenko publicly denounced Vavilov at several plant-breeding congresses. Vavilov was then removed from his position, his beliefs on genetics were rejected (and outlawed in 1948) and his reputation was destroyed.

Vavilov was arrested by the NKVD, Stalin's secret police, on 6 August 1940 while on a plant hunting expedition to Ukraine. His 'charges' included sabotaging agriculture, maintaining links with émigrés, belonging to a rightist conspiracy and spying for England. He was subjected to brutal interrogations, then sentenced to death, commuted to 20 years in prison, 'having failed in his duties of apply genetics to practical problems of crop improvement', and for having sent 'worthless expeditions' to gather material for his collection instead of concentrating on local varieties and being unsympathetic to the ideas of Lysenko and Ivan Michurin (a Russian 'Luther Burbank'). The man who had famously stated, 'We shall go into the pyre, we shall burn, but we shall not retreat from our convictions', and had committed his life to eradicating world famine, died in prison of starvation on 26 January 1943. His name was expunged from the Soviet Academy of Sciences' list of members in 1945.

Red flowered *Gossypium arboreum* (Ceylon cotton) and *Gossypium herbaceum* (Levant cotton) – both collected by Vavilov.

Vavilov's staff continued his work at the Institute. Even during the 28-month siege of Leningrad in the Second World War – which resulted in one million casualties – nine members of staff guarding the collections chose to sacrifice their lives and die of starvation, surrounded by thousands of packets of seed, in order to preserve the material for future use, rather than save themselves.

Vavilov was posthumously pardoned, absolved of his 'crimes' and 'rehabilitated' after Stalin's death in 1953. The organisation he worked for was renamed the N. I. Vavilov Research Institute of Plant Industry and awarded the Order of Lenin in 1967 and the Order of Friendship of Peoples for its scientific achievements. After Stalin's death, hundreds of books and articles on Vavilov's life and accomplishments were published and memorial displays were opened in Moscow, St Petersburg and Saratov, where he died. The Vavilov Institute in St Petersburg is now one of the largest and most varied stores of plant germplasm in the world.

Vavilov was often quoted as saying, 'Time is short, and there is so much to do. One must hurry.' When it comes to conserving genetic diversity, the work he started remains a priority today.

Nikolai Vavilov:
INSPIRATION FOR GARDENERS

❧ Vavilov recognised that 'genetic erosion' endangered human survival. If we lose plants, in the wild or old varieties in gardens, what will be left for future breeding? Gardeners can maintain genetic diversity by growing heritage varieties and supporting 'seed saver' groups like the Irish Seed Savers Association, the Seed Savers Exchange in the US, Seed Savers in Australia, and Garden Organic's Heritage Seed Library and Seedy Sunday events, both in Britain. Old ornamental varieties need saving, too, through organisations like Plant Heritage in the UK.

❧ Create your own collections of 'heritage' varieties to preserve the genetic diversity of your area. They may be apples from the county where you were born, or the county where you now reside – or possibly apples recommended by others, such as specialist local nurseries, or by the notable Edwardian pomologist and gastronome Edward Bunyard.

❧ Heritage varieties are usually selected for taste and suitability to local conditions rather than their ability to be transported great distances to supermarkets. You will find them very tasty but not always highly productive – they do not always store well.

❧ Scientists have bred disease resistance into garden crops to reduce the need for chemicals. Some of the most disease-resistant potatoes, for example, are the Sarpo varieties bred in Hungary – particularly Axona, which has excellent resistance to potato blight. However, resistance can always be overcome by a massive attack.

❧ The Svalbard Global Seed Vault opened on 26 February 2008. It is housed in an old copper mine, 120 metres inside a mountain in Norway, and has enough space for four and a half million seed samples; seeds can be stored for future use, from 2,000 to 20,000 years. The Seed Vault contains duplicate specimens of genetic strains from seed banks around the world, including material collected by Vavilov. The N.I .Vavilov Research Institute of Plant Industry has deposited 5,278 seed samples of 112 species originating from 96 different countries in the vault. In a domestic setting, if you are saving seed for use next year, use an airtight labelled container in the fridge, together with a packet of calcium oxalate crystals to control humidity.

LEFT Vavilov and his researchers collected *Avena sativa* (cultivated oat); it is widely used by humans but most commonly eaten by livestock.

TOP Vavilov thought that *Prunus armeniaca* (apricot) originated in China. Cultivars have now been bred to tolerate various climates.

ABOVE *Colocasia antiquorum* (Arabian cocoa root) is a staple crop in the tropics. Vavilov identified central and western China as its potential centre of origin.

175

Carl Rudolf Florin

DATE	1894–1965
ORIGIN	SWEDEN
MAJOR ACHIEVEMENT	*THE EVOLUTION OF THE CONIFER CONE*

Florin spent his entire professional career at Stockholm University and later became Director of the Royal Swedish Academy's Bergius Botanic Garden. A life in academia that began with works of practical botany on fruit pollination and ended as a global authority, renowned for his outstanding contribution to knowledge on the evolution of conifers, marks him as one of the greatest palaeobotanists of the twentieth century. Florin was one of the first to make the link between *Ginkgo biloba* (the maidenhair tree) and fossilised plants.

Cephalotaxus harringtonii,
cow's tail pine

C arl Rudolf Florin (also known as Rudolf Florin) was born at Solna, near Stockholm, on 5 April 1894. The fact that his father was head gardener at Hortus Bergianus, the University of Stockholm Botanic Gardens, influenced his two sons greatly; Rudolf became a palaeobotanist and, his brother, a garden designer. The family link with the garden remained strong for decades, Rudolf lived there until he was married in 1922, then returned as Professor in 1944.

When Florin took his degree, his professors included several outstanding scientists, such as Gustaf Lagerheim, a pioneer of pollen analysis, and cytologist Otto Rosenburg. Florin gained valuable experience and training in microbiological technique in his laboratory, which bore fruit in his work on chromosome numbers of several *Ephedera* species and *Welwitschia*.

Early papers on pomology, including one co-authored with his father describing a new apple, 'P. J. Bergius', found in the University Botanical Garden, indicate an attraction to practical botany; he and his wife, Elsa, also undertook research on sterility and compatibility in orchard fruit after the First World War.

LIVING AND ANCIENT PLANTS

In 1918 Florin was appointed Assistant Keeper of the Paleobotanical Department of the Swedish Museum of Natural History, having impressed with his knowledge of liverwort ecology. The director at the time was Thore G. Halle, and the founder of the department, A. G. Nathorst, was still working there. It was he who suggested Florin research the cuticles (the waxy layer on the leaves) of some living conifers, to discover if there were any distinguishing characters between leaf-bearing shoots of *Taxodium* and *Sequoia*, two genera thought to have a rich record in the flora of the Antarctic. Nathorst, who had come to plants via geology, thought they might be distinguished by variation in the leaf margins, but Florin, a talented botanist, discovered that it was through the arrangement of the stomata (or breathing pores) of the leaves.

This discovery prompted Florin to make a wider study of fossilised conifers; he placed fossilised relatives of *Cephalotaxus harringtonii* (pictured on p176) in a new genus he named *Thomasiocladus*. It was the start of what became a lifetime's research on the epidermal structures of conifers. He realised that before he began, he would have to learn about living conifers, an area poorly covered by systematics, so began working on his PhD on this subject, including some genera in the fossil record, too. His analytical research covered 600 pages, following the stomatal development of 25 genera and 36 species, demonstrating that the epidermis – particularly the stomatal structure – can be used to distinguish between species of living and fossil members in each group. One of his early discoveries established a link between the stomata of the extinct order Bennettitales and the living genus *Welwitschia*. He also began work on *The Ginkgophytes of Franz Joseph Land*, published in 1936, described by Halle as 'without counterpart in Palaeobotanical literature with regard to the technical methods employed'. Florin was not satisfied with the

results produced by serial sectioning so dissolved the rock in hydrofluoric acid and extracted the carbonised remains. His findings added six new genera to Ginkgoales and established several taxa as members of the group. The success of his investigation depended on comparing fossilised remains with the external morphology of a *Ginkgo biloba* leaf – not just the characteristics of the epidermis but the anatomy and physiology, too. His paper became a key factor in later identification of past members of the *Ginkgo* genus.

Florin researched and published prolifically, writing papers on the pollen grains of Cordaitales – an extinct order of woody plants that were either early conifers, or may have given rise to the conifers (*Pinophyta*), ginkgos (*Ginkgophyta*) and cycads (*Cycadophyta*) – complemented by photographs of wonderfully preserved nuclei and studies of fossil *Salvinias* (a genus of floating ferns) and, in 1940, 'The Tertiary Fossil Conifers of South Chile and their Phytogeographical Significance'. The latter paper supported the view that the differences between characteristics of conifers in the northern and southern hemispheres were already established in the Palaeozoic period.

FLORIN'S GREAT MONOGRAPH

All of these works are overshadowed by *Die Koniferen des Oberkarbons und des unteren Perms* (*The Evolution of the Conifer Cone*) a monumental eight-part monograph that Florin worked on between 1938 and 1945, aiming to discover whether the cones of conifers were flowers or inflorescence. It contained 729 pages, 126 plates and text figures, taken from material from 75 collections throughout Europe and America.

Florin was the first to link *Ginkgo biloba* (maidenhair tree) with fossilised plants.

The project was too great for the Swedish Academy printers, so it was completed in Stuttgart (despite the interruption of the Second World War), by a company who specialised in palaeontological work. The fact that many of the collections Florin studied were destroyed by military action increased the value of this work. In 1942 he became Professor of Botany at Stockholm University, and two years later Director of the Bergius Botanic Garden.

Florin published around 125 scientific papers. He also established over 25 new genera of fossil plants, three of which took his name – *Florinites*, *Ruflorinia* and *Rufloria*. Florin was a member of several academic institutions and, at the time of his death, was President of the Swedish Botanical Society. He received the Linnaeus Gold Medal of the Royal Physiographic Society of Lund, and was one of 20 biologists in the world who received the Darwin-Wallace commemorative medal from the Linnean Society in London in 1958.

Florin's greatest legacy is arguably *Die Koniferen des Oberkarbons und des unteren Perms*. As one reviewer wrote: 'This work of Florin's is the greatest contribution ever made to Conifer morphology. It makes progress in giant strides and it eliminates many errors. Never before has such wealth of fact been assembled with such profuse illustration, nor indeed has so much been written.'

Carl Rudolf Florin:
INSPIRATION FOR GARDENERS

❧ The leaves of *Ginkgo biloba*, a 'living fossil', have been found in the fossil record of every continent. Introduced into the West in the mid-eighteenth century, one of the oldest specimens, dating from at least 1762, grows near the main gate at the Royal Botanic Gardens at Kew. It was planted there shortly after a small botanic garden was established in what were then the Royal Pleasure Grounds, by Princess Augusta. At the time its hardiness was unknown, so it was planted against a hot house; when the hot house was demolished, the tree remained. Genetic analysis has shown this to be three trees in one: two males bundled together as saplings and one female, grafted onto the pair in an attempt to produce fruit. It produced pollen cones in 1795, and was the first male tree in Europe to do so. Males are often planted as street trees due to their pollution resistance; females produce small, waxy, rancid-smelling fruit with edible seeds. If you take care over selecting and planting a *Ginkgo biloba*, it can live well over 100 years.

❧ Chile, whose conifers were studied by Florin, is home to nine conifer species, five of them threatened with extinction. It would be tragic to lose the mighty *Fitzroya cupressoides* (Patagonian cypress), the second-oldest living thing on Earth, or the charismatic *Araucaria araucana* (monkey puzzle), which, after being introduced by plant hunter William Lobb, helped to stoke Victorian fervour for tree planting. These are just two of the 216 conifer species threatened due to unprecedented habitat loss. The International Conifer Conservation Programme (ICCP), based at the Royal Botanic Garden Edinburgh, is responding by planting trees of known origin to broaden the genetic material held in cultivation. As a result, there are now 400 fitzroyas and almost 2,000 araucarias planted in a network of conservation sites throughout Britain and Ireland, which could be used to replant native populations. For the garden, *Araucaria araucana* is a hardy tree and *Fitzroya cupressoides* is hardy for moist climates; both grow very large, so will need lots of space.

BELOW *Araucaria Araucana* (monkey puzzle), one of the more iconic Chilean conifers studied by Florin, was widely planted on Victorian estates.

TOP *Taxodium distichum* (bald cypress) is an attractive deciduous conifer. Florin believed the genus to have strong links with Antarctic flora.

ABOVE *Taxus baccata* (English yew) is a conifer renowned for its longevity. Fairly fast-growing, it can be used for dense, clipped hedges.

E. K. Janaki Ammal

DATE	1897–1984
ORIGIN	INDIA
MAJOR ACHIEVEMENT	PIONEERING CYTOLOGIST AND PLANT BREEDER

Janaki's achievements were astonishing for a woman of her era.
Born into a low-caste family, she was highly educated at a time when
women were expected to stay at home, went abroad to study and work
when it was taboo for Indian men or women to do so, and became a
leading cytologist and plant breeder. Despite her focus, the 'woman
who sweetened India's sugar cane' also retained an interest in
ethnobotany, plant geography and 'all plants', remaining humble
and dedicated to her life of science until the end.

Nicandra physalodes,
shoo-fly plant

Geeta Doctor once described her Aunt Janaki as a 'tall and commanding presence in her prime. She tied her lustrous long hair into a loose bun at the nape of her neck. In her later years, she took to wearing brilliant yellow silk sarees with a long loose blouse or jacket in the same colour. Her statuesque presence reminded people of a Buddhist lady monk ... she took a vow of chastity, austerity and silence for herself, limiting her needs to the barest minimum.'

Janaki Ammal was born on in Tellichery, Kerala, on 4 November 1897, the tenth of 19 children of Dewan Bahadur E. K. Krishnan, a sub-judge. Her father corresponded regularly with academics, maintained descriptive notes about his developing garden, took a keen interest in the natural sciences and wrote two books on birds. The family was cultured and open-minded and Janaki was encouraged to engage in intellectual pursuits at a time when most Indian girls did not even attend school, let alone develop a career.

Ammal displayed an early passion for botany and fulfilled her potential with extraordinary speed. On leaving school, she moved to Madras, obtained a BA from Queen Mary's College, and then a BSc (Hons) from the Presidency College in Chennai in 1921, where she became interested in cytogenetics. She then won the Barbour Scholarship from the University of Michigan, where she gained her master's degree and became the first woman to obtain a PhD in botany in the United States – for her 1931 thesis, 'Chromosome Studies in *Nicandra physalodes*' (the shoo-fly plant, the focus of this paper, is pictured on p182).

A CAREER ABROAD

Between 1934 and 1939, Ammal worked as a geneticist at the Sugarcane Breeding Institute at Coimbatore in Tamil Nadu, founded to develop sweeter hybrids for the Indian sugarcane industry. Her research played a vital role in selecting the best varieties for a breeding programme. She succeeded in creating several high-yielding strains that thrived in Indian conditions, reducing the need for imports and turning India into a major sugar-cane producer. She also identified *Saccharum spontaneum* as an Indian variety and produced hybrids between related plants, and was the first to cross sugar cane with other members of the grass family like *Zea*, *Sorghum*, *Imperata* (including *Imperata cylindrica*, pictured on p185) and bamboos.

Yet despite her brilliance, Ammal's status as a single female scientist created problems among her male peers, so she left for England just after the beginning of the Second World War and became Assistant Cytologist at the John Innes Horticultural Institution in London. She would often dive under her bed during night-time bombing raids, returning to work the following day to brush broken glass from the shelves and continue her research. Her studies on chromosome numbers traced the evolution of many species and varieties, and she detailed much of this work in her *Chromosome Atlas of Cultivated Plants*, written with C. D. Darlington, Director of the Institution. Her staff file also noted 'she smuggled a Palm Squirrel into the country and it was kept at J.I.I. for many years. Its name was "Kapok".'

Ammal then became Cytologist at the Royal Horticultural Society at Wisley, where she analysed chromosomes of a wide range of garden plants, lectured, created new hybrids and answered questions from gardeners. She also authored several articles in the *Journal of the Royal Horticultural Society*, reflecting her interests, including 'Chromosomes and the Evolution of Garden Philadelphus', 'Chromosomes and Horticulture', 'The Chromosome History of the Cultivated Nerines' and 'The Story of Primula Malacoides'. Ammal examined a Plymouth strawberry plant sent by plantsman E. A. Bowles during her research on the origins of cultivated strawberries and corresponded with him about the identity of a crocus. On 7 November 1949 she wrote: 'I am glad to confirm from chromosome counts your doubts about the Crocus distributed as *C.karduchorum* being only an unspotted variety of *C.zonatus*. The bulb you sent was 2n=8 ... the true *C.karduchorum* is 2n=20.'

Ammal also investigated the effects of colchicine (a chemical found in autumn crocus, or *Colchicum autumnale*) on the cell division of a number of woody plants. Applying it in solution to the growth tip of seedlings once the seed leaves have expanded doubles the number of chromosomes. Ammal treated several *Magnolia kobus* seedlings and one was selected and named after her. 'Janaki Ammal' is a vigorous, multi-stemmed tree, over 6 metres tall and wide, producing masses of white flowers, with varying numbers of petals, over several weeks, and heavily textured leaves. The original specimen can still be admired on Battleston Hill at Wisley. In 1951 Ammal returned to India at the invitation of the Prime Minister, to reorganise the Botanical Survey of India (BSI), eventually becoming Director General.

Ammal experimented by hybridising one of the world's major crops, *Saccharum officinarum* (sugar cane), with other genera and species.

Not only was Ammal a brilliant cytologist, she was also a great thinker. She proposed that the Chinese and Malaysian influence on the flora of northeast India had led to natural hybridisation between them and the native Indian plants, leading to greater plant diversification, while she attributed the higher rate of plant speciation in the cold and humid northeast Himalayas, compared to the cold and dry northwest, to polyploidy, creating greater variation in plants.

Imperata cylindrica, cogon grass

Even after retirement, Ammal continued her research at the Centre for Advanced Study in Botany field laboratory, creating a garden of medicinal plants and rearing of a large family of cats to study their subtle differences. She died at work of natural causes on 7 February 1984.

Ammal was a woman of humility and an early follower of Gandhi, who even when Director of the BSI was often seen sweeping the road outside. She refused to speak about her career, saying: 'My work is what will survive.' It remains a lasting testament to one of the most remarkable cytologists and women of her generation.

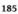

E. K. Janaki Ammal:
INSPIRATION FOR GARDENERS

✤ In an article entitled 'The Origin of the Black Mulberry' for the *Journal of the Royal Horticultural Society*, Ammal wrote: 'The black mulberry has the highest chromosome count of any flowering plant … the origin of this species therefore presents a problem of special interest.' She noted that this plant had not been recorded in the wild and had been a cultivated plant from 'very ancient times'. She linked the development of the species with its increasing chromosome numbers. Long-lived and often seen as very old trees in gardens, there are also dwarf varieties of the black mulberry plant, such as *Morus* Charlotte Russe 'Matsunaga', which are ideal options for containers and small gardens, and are also highly productive.

✤ Ammal also studied triploid *Kniphofia snowdenii* (now *Kniphofia thompsonii* var. *snowdenii*), taken from Colonel F. C. Stern's garden at Highdown, which she found to have more chromosomes than the other species. It had been discovered by Mr Snowden of the Department of Agriculture, growing in short grass and scrub at 2,400–3,000m up on Mt Elgon, Uganda, in 1916. Knowledge of a plant's native habitat allows gardeners to put the right plant in the right place, so that it will flourish. This approach was first presented

BELOW Ammal wrote about the genetics of *Morus nigra* (black mulberry), which is noted for its large number of chromosomes.

by Andrew Chatto, and was the basis for the choice of plants at Beth Chatto's garden. It is a recommended principle for your own garden, too.

✤ In 'Chromosomes in Horticulture', Ammal used the strawberry as an example, and quoted from Shakespeare's *Richard III*, when the Duke of Gloucester urges his host, the Bishop of Ely, to send for some home-grown strawberries. These would have been *Fragaria vesca* (woodland strawberries). When Sir Isaac Newton ate strawberries, he would have eaten *Fragaria elatior* (musk strawberries), introduced from Europe, before his death. *Fragaria chiloensis* (beach strawberries) and *Fragaria virginiana* (scarlet strawberries) were introduced from the New World. Fifty years later these were hybridised to produced 'Royal Sovereign', a regular Chelsea gold-medal winner for the great gardener Beatrix Havergal, and the strawberries of today.

TOP *Kniphofia thomsonii* var. *thomsonii* (Thomson's red-hot poker), grown by great gardener Fredrick Stern, was analysed in detail by Ammal.

ABOVE Ammal described the origins of garden strawberries using *Fragaria virginiana* (scarlet strawberries). These were first reported in 1766.

William Stearn

DATE	1911– 2001
ORIGIN	ENGLAND
MAJOR ACHIEVEMENT	*DICTIONARY OF PLANT NAMES FOR GARDENERS*

Professor William Stearn, a polymath of immense academic brilliance, was a kindly, modest man. Denied a university education, he was almost entirely self-educated and published his first scientific paper while working as a shop assistant. During a career based first at the library of the Royal Horticultural Society, then later at the Natural History Museum, he wrote around 500 books, articles and monographs, ranging from detailed studies of plant genera, through histories and biographies, to books on botanical taxonomy, many of them becoming standard works of reference for both botanists and gardeners.

Hosta plantaginea,
August lily

Willam Thomas Stearn was born in Chesterton, Cambridge, on 16 April 1911, the eldest of four sons of a coachman. He gained a scholarship to Cambridgeshire High School for Boys, where he was inspired by an outstanding biology teacher and became secretary of the Natural History Society. While still at school, Stearn attended an evening course in palaeobotany taught by Professor of Botany A. C. Seward, who recognised his potential and gave him access to the herbarium and library at the University of Cambridge Botany School, where the young man spent most of his evenings and weekends. John Gilmour, curator of the herbarium there, soon realised the extraordinary ability and enthusiasm of his assistant.

Stearn's father had died when Stearn was 11, and his widowed mother lacked the means to support him through university, so he became a shop assistant and cataloguer at Bowes and Bowes, university booksellers in Cambridge. It was during this time that he published his first scientific paper in 1929, after finding a campanula with a distorted corolla in a garden – 'A new disease of *Campanula pusilla* (*Peronospora corollae*)' – thereby documenting its first known appearance. This was followed by several papers on several genera of garden plants, among them *Poncirus*, *Mimulus* and *Vinca* – 24 papers in all – followed several years later by his first major monograph on *Epimedium* and *Vancouveria*, which he worked on while studying the genus *Allium*, writing 'A Bibliography of the Books and Contributions to Periodicals Written by Reginald Farrer', and making a significant contribution to the catalogue of the Cambridge herbarium.

THE MOVE TO LONDON

In 1933, after a recommendation to the Royal Horticultural Society by the gardener E. A. Bowles, Stearn was made assistant librarian at the Lindley Library in London; he was later promoted to Chief Librarian. While there, Stearn began to teach himself Swedish, the language of the eighteenth-century botanist Carl Linnaeus (see pp56–61), and started to travel to botanical centres throughout Europe. He served in the RAF Medical Service during the Second World War, then returned to the RHS, moving into the library while searching for somewhere to live.

Just before the war, the Director of Wisley, Frederick Chittenden, had become Editor-in-Chief of a new *RHS Dictionary of Gardening*; when war broke out and many botanists were called up for active service, Chittenden ended up writing much of the text himself. When he died in 1950, Stearn completed the task, compiling entries on more than 500 plants, writing the fourth volume in just six months and becoming, as he often recalled, 'a peculiar authority on plants from "So-" onwards'. In 1950, he also co-authored *The Art of Botanical Illustration* with Wilfrid Blunt, the standard authority on the subject.

After attending the International Botanical Congress in Stockholm in 1950, Stearn drafted the first edition of the *International Code of Nomenclature for Cultivated Plants*, governing the naming of garden plants. This was published in 1952, the same year that Stearn moved to the Natural History Museum, where he eventually

became Senior Principle Scientific Officer. He remained there until his retirement in 1976, and around 200 publications date from this period.

In 1976 Stearn was awarded the Gold Medal of the Linnean Society for his 176-page introduction to the facsimile of Linnaeus's *Species Plantarum* (1957). It was later written in his *Daily Telegraph* obituary that 'No other botanist had the knowledge of botanical history and the linguistic ability in Latin, German, Dutch and Swedish needed to write what is regarded as a classic study of the great naturalist'. Much the same was said of another of his outstanding works, *Botanical Latin: History, Grammar, Syntax, Terminology and Vocabulary* (1966), which could only have been written by a unique individual with a diverse knowledge of botany, taxonomy and the construction of Greek and Latin; it was a book that many thought could never be written. Although designed to help students, it became a standard work for plant taxonomists and remains so to this day.

LATER LIFE

Visits to the Cambridge Botanic Gardens, gardening at home and his work with the Royal Horticultural Society gave Stearn a lifelong interest in horticulture, amply reflected in his *Dictionary of Plant Names for Gardeners* (1992), revealing the fascinating stories behind the Latin names of popular plants (including *Hosta plantaginea*, pictured on p188 – *plantaginea* meaning 'resembling a plantain').

After retirement Stearn continued his research at the herbarium and library of the Royal Botanic Gardens near to his home at Kew, in his final years, returning to the genus *Epimedium*, the subject of his first monograph, examining specimens in his hospital bed, many of them new to science, until shortly before he died.

Stearn wrote about *Poncirus trifoliata* (Japanese bitter orange), the only member of its genus. It is a fragrant but viciously spiny plant.

Stearn received many honours and accolades but the one that gave him most pleasure was his first honorary doctorate from Leiden University in 1960. He also became an honorary professor of Reading University and a visiting professor at Cambridge University's Department of Botany, and received the RHS's Victoria Medal of Honour in 1965.

At one time Stearn's entry in 'Who's Who' listed his recreations as 'gardening, walking', until his family changed it to 'gardening, talking'. Dr Max Walters wrote in his obituary in the *Guardian* in 2001: 'I am not the only inquirer to have benefited from his affable, patient care, which was sometimes positively uncanny. I recall an international botanical gathering in Cambridge some 20 years ago; we had set out in a coach for some local nature reserve, and I took the opportunity of asking William about cultivated varieties of cannabis, the illegal growing of which was just becoming a problem. He answered my question adequately, and we proceeded on our outing. But, on the return journey – before any of us had been back to Cambridge – he presented me with a copy of his [scientific] cannabis paper, which he "thought I might like to have". I never learned how he did that trick.'

William Stearn:
INSPIRATION FOR GARDENERS

✤ William Stearn had a brilliant mind, but without the traditional opportunities for formal education, he educated himself. He read, absorbed, reasoned, questioned and analysed, mixed with intellectual fellow enthusiasts, went to evening classes, and used all of the facilities available to him. It is perfectly possible to educate yourself as a gardener or botanist – there are many people who have done so, and this should be an inspiration to us all.

✤ Stearn wrote his first major monograph on the genus *Epimedium* and pubished a revised and greatly enlarged edition in 2002. His first mongraph published in 1938 included 21 species; the revised monograph included 54. These low-growing woodland plants are

evergreen or decidous. Most prefer shade in moist, humus-rich, well-drained soil and are clump or mat forming. New leaves are often patterned, and the delicate spidery flowers, held on thin, wiry stems just above the foliage, appear from mid-April or early May to June. There are many choice varieties, including *Epimedium* 'Amber Queen', with heart-shaped leaves and amber flowers; *Epimedium ogisui*, an evergreen with white flowers, and leaflets that are spashed coppery red when young; and *Epimedium* 'William Stearn', a hybrid with mauve-pink flowers, produced by Robin White of Blackthorn Nursery, in Hampshire.

✤ Stearn became inspired by epimediums when browsing through plant hunter Reginald Farrer's *The English Rock Garden*. Farrer, who was renowned for his descriptive prose, characterised the blooms as 'Columbines of waxy texture, and in any colour, from white, through gold, rose and violet'.

✤ Stearn's monograph encompassed 'other Berberidaceae including the genus *Podophyllum*'. The latter enjoys the same 'woodsy' soils as *Epimedium*. One selection that has gained considerable popularity is the hybrid *Podophyllum* 'Spotty Dotty'. This has large, lobed parasol-like leaves, which are chartreuse green, marked with chocolate-brown spots. Under these hang large beetroot-coloured flowers, followed by plump red fruit. The fruits, though attractive, are poisonous and should not be eaten.

LEFT Stearn was a globally respected authority on the *Epimedium* genus. Try growing the lovely, hardy *Epimedium* 'Amber Queen' (barrenwort).

ABOVE Stearn explained in accessible terms how plants got their Latin names. *Rosa farreri* f. *persetosa* (Farrer's threepenny-bit rose) honours plant collector Reginald Farrer.

LEFT The colouring of *Mimulus guttatus* (monkey flower) is described in its Latin name; the translation of *guttatus* is 'with spots'.

Richard Evans Schultes

DATE	1915–2001
ORIGIN	UNITED STATES OF AMERICA
MAJOR ACHIEVEMENT	*PLANTS OF THE GODS*

Professor Richard Evans Schultes, considered by many to be the 'Father of Ethnobotany', spent much of his life in Amazonia, wrote the rainforest herbal *The Healing Forest*, and was an authority on hallucinogenic plants. His encyclopaedic knowledge of his subject led him to rebuke his Harvard colleague Timothy Leary for misspelling botanical names, and as a serious researcher and scientist, he showed little patience with those who indulged in mind-altering drugs. When William Burroughs described a trip as a 'mind-opening metaphysical experience', Schultes responded: 'That's funny, Bill, all I saw was colours'.

Lophophora williamsii,
dumpling cactus

From the age of six, Richard Evans Schultes became passionate about plants, travel and South America, after his parents read him the travelogue of Richard Spruce, a nineteenth-century plant hunter in the Amazon and Andes while he was ill in bed with stomach problems for a considerable length of time.

On leaving school in 1933, he won a full scholarship to study medicine at Harvard but he soon swapped courses to pursue his first love – plants. Professor of Botany at the time, Oakes Ames, encouraged him to study ethnobotany, a field that Ames described as having 'tremendously important human implications'. As an undergraduate, Schultes read *Mescal: The Divine Plant and Its Psychological Effects* by German psychiatrist Heinrich Kluver, about a small grey-blue, hallucinogenic cactus *Lophophora williamsii* (also known as the dumpling cactus, or peyote – pictured on p194) and he set off for Oklahoma to study its use by Kiowa Indians. For his post-graduate thesis, he headed south to Oaxaca in Mexico, studying the native peoples' use of sacred plants such as the ololiuqui (*Rivea corymbosa*) and the hallucinogenic mushroom teonánacatl (*Panaeolus campanulatus* var. *sphinctrinus* and *Psilocybe cubensis*); later, compounds extracted from the fungi led to the manufacture of the first beta-blockers.

After completing his doctorate in 1941, Schultes received a grant from the National Academy of Sciences to study curare, a rainforest drug used in surgery, whose properties as a muscle relaxant avoided the need for deep anaesthesia and was used as a treatment for tetanus. The exact composition of curare had been a mystery but by living with tribes in the Columbian Amazon, Schultes identified over 70 plant species involved in its production; several of them are now known to contain active alkaloids, notably *Chondrodendron tomentosum*. Schultes also discovered that the combination of species varied according to the effect being sought , and that what was once thought to be a primitive cocktail of poisons was in fact a complex indigenous pharmacopeia.

FOLLOWING IN SPRUCE'S FOOTSTEPS

Schultes travelled the Amazon's tributaries in an aluminium canoe, sometimes alone, and at other times accompanied by a native guide. On one journey up the river he hit some rapids and his canoe overturned; he scrambled back inside but lost his guide and all his equipment. Weakened by malaria and beriberi he paddled for ten days before finding help at a remote outpost. All he carried on his trips was a change of clothes, notebooks and pencils, a pith helmet, a hammock, a machete and a small medicine case containing vitamins, antibiotics and morphine – in case he broke a limb and had to be transported for days before receiving proper treatment. He went native with his diet apart from regular supplies of instant coffee and baked beans, preferring to rely on food offered by his indigenous friends. This included ground manioc roots, fish, wild game, insect grubs, fruit and chicha, a drink made from fruit that is chewed and fermented in spittle. Schultes also carried a pair of secateurs, harvesting up to 90 specimens a day, and a camera

and film to photograph the tribes he lived among. Some of the images were published in 1988 in his book *Where the Gods Reign*. He did not believe the indigenous people were hostile, stating instead: 'All that is required to bring out their gentlemanliness is reciprocal gentlemanliness.'

His friendships with local shamans gave him a great understanding of the rainforests as their larder, laboratory and medicine cabinet. Many plants they showed him were unknown to science, and over 3,000 were named after him. *Hiraea schultesii* is used to cure conjunctivitis, *Piper schultesii* treats tubercular coughs, *Schultesianthus* is a genus in the potato family, and *Pourouma schultesii* treats ulcers and wounds. When taxonomists ran out of ways to use his name they resorted to using his initials, naming a new genus in the African violet family, *Resia*. However, Schultes wore the honour lightly, and the only one he ever spoke about was the firefly cockroach (*Schultesia lampyridiformis*) and he carried a picture of it around in his wallet.

Schultes identified *Strychnos toxifera* (curare) as a source of a muscle relaxant, so this species contains both potent arrow poison and medicine.

On hearing of the Japanese attack on Pearl Harbor, Schultes headed off through the rainforest for Bogotá to enlist, but on arrival was told he was needed elsewhere. The Japanese occupation of Malaya had deprived the Allies of their main source of rubber, originally an Amazon rainforest tree. With an intimate knowledge of the forest and its people he was perfectly placed to investigate alternative sources. He set up a rubber plantation that was managed and tapped by Indians and collected thousands of specimens of *Hevea*, selecting them for disease resistance and yield, and remaining in the Amazon until 1953, apart from a few visits home.

THE HARVARD PROFESSOR

Schulte's explorations yielded over 24,000 plant specimens, and of these, 2,000 had practical uses, ranging from medicines to clothing and contraceptives. He was one of the first campaigners to fight for the rainforest and its people, racing to record as much of their knowledge as possible before 'civilisation' arrived.

Returning to Harvard in 1953, Schultes became Curator of the Oakes Ames Orchid Herbarium, then the Curator of Economic Botany, later becoming Executive Director of the Harvard Botanic Museum and Edward C. Jeffrey Professor of Biology, posts he held until he retired in 1985. He also received the Gold Medal from the World Wildlife Fund and another from the Linnean Society. Columbia awarded him its highest honour and named a 22.2-million-acre area of protected rainforest 'Sector Schultes'.

Richard Evans Schultes often described himself as 'just a jungle botanist', yet he could read, write or speak ten languages, including two Amazonian languages – Witoto and Makuna – and when lecturing at Harvard, he taught his students to shoot a dart into a target on the other side of the lecture hall, using a blowpipe.

Richard Evans Schultes:
INSPIRATION FOR GARDENERS

❧ Before Richard Evans Schultes confirmed that ololiuqui was *Rivea corymbosa*, nineteenth-century botanists had believed it to be *Ipomoea sidaefolia* (now known as *Turbina corymbosa*), the genus that includes morning glory. Several are grown in gardens as climbers that can be grown as perennials in warmer climates, or half-hardy annuals in a cooler location. Morning glory behaves like its relative bindweed when hot summers or warm climates remind them of their native habitat.

❧ Speed of growth makes morning glory useful for new gardens, providing temporary screening or covering unsightly buildings. If the micro-climate allows for overwintering outdoors, the cumulative effect can be spectacular. *Ipomoea indica* was planted at least 20 years ago by the side of a building in the courtyard at Lambeth Palace in London. Protected from frost, it has now reached the top of the wall and is around 20m tall.

❧ Best planted where it is backlit by the sun, morning glory needs a sheltered sunny spot and room to roam. Soak seeds for 24 hours before planting, then sow at 20°C in small pots or modules, to avoid root disturbance when transplanting. Grow them on in cooler

TOP LEFT In 1941, Schultes documented the use of *Ipomoea* by native Americans in Mexico, which he traced back to Aztec times. *Ipomoea purpurea* 'Grandpa Ott' is a vivid cultivar for the garden.

LEFT Vibrant *Aphelandra aurantiaca*, used by the South American Ticuna to treat deafness, was in *The Healing Forest* (1990) by Schultes and Robert Raffauf.

conditions, 'hardening off' when temperatures rise – they are particularly sensitive to cold when young and show their disapproval with checked growth and pale yellow or white leaves; they often never recover.

❖ Schultes charted the native-American use of *Ipomoea* from Aztec times to the present day. All plants from the genus are colourful plants for the summer garden; a lovely option is dark-purple-flowered *Ipomoea purpurea* 'Grandpa Ott'. This was given to Kent and Diane Whealy (née Ott) in 1972 by her grandfather, Baptist John Ott. His parents were Bavarian immigrants who sailed to America in 1867, bringing seeds of morning glory that they had grown in their garden in Germany. It grew over the porch on their 40-acre farm near St Lucas, Iowa, and on what proved to be their final visit, Grandpa Ott gave Diane some seeds. These (and those of a heritage tomato) were the catalyst for her interest in heirloom varieties, and the beginning of Seed Savers Exchange in the USA.

TOP Schultes studied the use and effects of *Psilocybe mexicana* (hallucinogenic mushroom). Related species can appear with other fungi on damp lawns.

ABOVE *Strychnos usambarensis* has the same use as the *Strychnos* arrow poison plants Schultes studied in the Amazon, but this species is a native of Africa.

Mikinori Ogisu

DATE	BORN 1951
ORIGIN	JAPAN
MAJOR ACHIEVEMENT	*TRADITIONAL FLORICULTURE IN JAPAN*

Mikinori Ogisu, a botanist, horticulturist and plant explorer, is renowned
for his introductions of new or long-lost plants. He has travelled extensively
in China, covering hundreds of thousands of kilometres, particularly in
Sichuan, and has visited plant-rich Mount Omei many times. Taxonomic
botanists have benefited greatly from his work and introductions of new
plants; *Epimedium* and *Mahonia*, in particular, have enriched our gardens.
He is also an authority on Japanese horticulture and ornamental plants,
and has achieved the status of 'national treasure' in his home country,
in recognition of his work.

Iris laevigata,
Japanese iris

Mikinori Ogisu was born in Owari, Aichi Prefecture, Honshu Island. He revealed a passion for plants when he was only 7; received private tuition from experts in the propagation, production and cultivation of traditional Japanese ornamental plants at 10; and by 15 he had set his mind on a career in horticulture and landscape design. His guru, Kazuo Anami, taught natural sciences at his high school, had seen most of the 5,500 species of Japanese native plants, was a talented botanical illustrator, and authored several books on the Japanese flora.

On leaving school, Ogisu broadened his knowledge and experience with a year at the Keisei Rose Research Institute, studying genetics and plant breeding. At the age of 20, he went to Europe to study at the Kalmthout Arboretum in Belgium, and then the Royal Botanic Gardens, Kew, and the RHS garden at Wisley, before enrolling on a postgraduate course in the department of biology at Sichuan University. There he became an honorary research scholar, and like Professor Fang, his tutor, developed an affection for Mount Emei and its flora. Ogisu has made well over 30 visits to the mountain, maintaining a checklist of its flora, confirming early records and adding new finds; his knowledge of the flora of Sichuan, and particularly of Mount Emei, is unrivalled.

MASTER OF JAPANESE HORTICULTURE

In 1977 the publication of *History and Principles of Traditional Floriculture in Japan*, an account of 33 groups of traditional ornamental plants from the Edo period, secured Ogisu's reputation as one of the most remarkable botanists in Japan. In 1978, the late Seizo Kashioka, founder of the Kansai Tech Corporation, wanted to make a contribution to Japan's horticultural heritage. Inspired by Ogisu's passion for traditional Japanese ornamentals, and aware of the threat to their survival, he established the Japanese Iris Garden at Yamasaki Shiso-gun, west of Osaka. Under Oguisu's guidance, the garden was filled with 1,000 cultivars and hybrids of *Iris ensata* var. *spontanea*, and later expanded to include *Iris laevigata* (pictured on p200), hydrangeas, evergreen azaleas and *Phlox subulata*. In 1986 a research institute was established on the site and collections expanded to include *Hosta*, *Asarum*, *Nandina*, *Epimedium* and many other genera, a collection of well over 3,000 different species and cultivars. Ogisu was retained as special advisor.

Since 1980, Ogisu has made annual visits to China (sometimes five or six a year), travelling many hundreds of thousands of kilometres, often to remote, little botanised areas, discovering new species and rediscovering rarities. In the early 1990s, Professor William Stearn (pp188–193), pondering an update of his 1938 monograph on *Epimedium*, was eager to discuss the taxonomic status and distribution of Chinese species with him. When Ogisu, who had already discovered and introduced several undescribed species, presented Stearn with several beautifully described specimens and an album of colour photographs displaying dissections of the flowers of a dozen or more taxa, the decision became easy. Stearn revised his early work,

described the new species, and new plants were introduced into cultivation, including *Epimedium fangii*, *Epimedium franchetii* and *Epimedium leptorrhizum*. Stearn wote of him: 'no man has made a greater contribution to the knowledge of the genus *Epimedium*, notably in the province in Sichuan by introducing live plants for study in cultivation and collecting herbarium specimens, and photographing plants in their habitats, together with their floral parts than Mikinori Ogisu.'

NOTABLE REDISCOVERIES

Ogisu's wide-ranging interests led to a host of introductions and reintroductions into cultivation. In 1983 Graham Thomas challenged him to rediscover the legendary wild rose, *Rosa chinensis* var. *spontanea*, unseen by Western botanists since plant explorer Joseph Rock collected herbarium specimens early in the twentieth century. In autumn that year, Ogisu was driving his jeep at dusk along treacherous winding roads in a mountainous area of southwest Sichuan, when out of the corner of his eye he spotted some late-flowering roses. Despite being tired, despondent and unwell, he parked his jeep precariously on the verge and climbed 200m uphill to investigate. His instinct was rewarded – it was the long-lost plant.

Epimedium plants (left to right): *E. hybridum*, *E. versicolor* and *E. sulphureum*. Ogisu greatly increased the choice for gardeners within the genus.

In March 2005 he discovered a daphne, again from his car. A broken flowering stem with yellow flowers lying on the roadside alerted him to plants on the slopes above. Convinced it was a new species he took the specimen back to Japan, checked existing literature and on consultation with Li Zhenyu of the Beijing Institute of Botany at the Chinese Academy of Sciences, it was named *Daphne ogisui*.

In 1989, Ogisu accepted yet another challenge: to find Tibetan hellebore (*Helleborus thibetanus*). First discovered by nineteenth-century French missionary and plant explorer, Père David, it was little known to anyone except local people who used its roots in herbal medicine. Using David's writings as a guide, Ogisu arrived in Moupin (now Baoxing) in west China. On showing a dried specimen to farmers, he was met with a blank, but when he described 'a big pinkish flower, growing straight out of the snow', several people immediately responded and led him to rocky ground where they were growing, quite possibly in the same site David found 120 years before.

In 1994 Ogisu was awarded the K. Matsushita Expo'90 prize for his work in botany and horticulture. In 1995, he received a Veitch Memorial Medal from the RHS, and the Yoshikawa Eiji Cultural prize recognising his botanical achievements in China. He also wrote about his explorations in a 2002 book published in Japan called *In Search of Long Lost Plants*.

Ogisu remains respectful of people, plants and nature, and, in turn, highly respected by his peers. An ardent defender of Japanese horticultural traditions and garden plants, with a keen eye for detail, he more than lives up to his sobriquet, the 'Green Samurai'.

Mikinori Ogisu:
INSPIRATION FOR GARDENERS

✤ Plants named after Mikinori Ogisu, his family and associates include several garden-worthy members of the *Epimedium* genus, among them *E. mikinorii*, with dainty rose-purple and white flowers; *E. ogisui*, boasting large white flowers; and *E. leptorrhizum* 'Mariko', with pale magenta-and-white flowers, which was named by Ogisu after his wife. There is also *E. sternii*, with caramel-and-pink flowers, and *Epimedium* 'William Stearn', with dark red and scarlet flowers with yellow spurs, named after Ogisu's great friend and collaborator. In Sichuan, Ogisu discovered what is now *Cotoneaster ogisui*, with white flowers followed by large red fruits; the branches of the small tree bend under the weight of the display and are followed by attractive autumn colour. There is also *Prunus incisa* 'Mikinori' (cherry 'Mikinori'), named after him by Harry van de Laar in 1989. This is an early flowering shrub, covered in spring with semi-double flowers, white to pale pink, with leaves that turn to shades of yellow, purple and red in autumn. And from southern Sichuan there is the attractive and distinctive honeysuckle *Lonicera subaequalis* 'Ogisu', with yellow flowers in tubular clusters, surrounded by a hooded green cup.

✤ Ogisu has also focused on mahonia species, adding *Mahonia ogisui* (boasting large, glossy leaflets on long leaves, and stout spikes of yellow flowers), *M. sheridaniana* (bearing long, finger-like spikes of bold yellow flowers) and a hybrid found in the wild and cultivation, *M. x emeiensis* (which varies in leaf shape and the density of waxy coating on the leaf underside).

BELOW *Epimedium ogisui*, a perennial with bright white flowers, was named by botanist William Stearn to honour Ogisu's contribution to the genus.

BELOW *Epimedium mikinorii* was collected by Ogisu in Hubei, China, and then named for him. It is evergreen except in severe winters.

❧ *Bergenia emeiensis* is found on limestone cliffs, often under overhangs where water seeps through the rock. First collected in 1935, it was introduced to cultivation in the West by Ogisu, who collected it on Mount Emei in 1982. When first introduced it was regarded as tender and grown in pots under cover, to protect and encourage the flowers and to keep its attractive dark green leaves undamaged through winter, but the plant itself is completely hardy. This elegant species can be grown outdoors in a protected position.

TOP *Mahonia bodinieri*, introduced to cultivation by Ogisu in 1997, can be found growing in the Queen Elizabeth II Temperate House at the Savill Gardens in Windsor, where it is used to add winter colour.

RIGHT Ogisu found *Bergenia emeiensis* growing on cliffs in China. Although hardy, it prefers a shady, protected spot outdoors and humus-rich soil.

Bleddyn & Sue Wynn-Jones

DATE	BLEDDYN BORN 1948; SUE BORN 1952
ORIGIN	WALES
MAJOR ACHIEVEMENT	PLANT COLLECTORS

A twist of fate led Bleddyn and Sue Wynn-Jones into horticulture, but now their nursery, Crûg Farm Plants in North Wales, with its reputation for rarities (including *Holboellia latifolia*, pictured below), has become the focal point for anyone with a passion for desirable plants. Their plant-collecting exploits around the world have created a catalogue full of new introductions and discoveries, particularly those that tolerate cool temperate climates. Their work is benefiting not just gardeners, who like to collect and grow them at home, but government agencies, taxonomists and conservation organisations, too.

Holboellia latifolia

Bleddyn and Sue Wynn-Jones changed from beef farming to plants with the impending arrival of BSE in 1990. As Bleddyn had been a keen vegetable grower and they loved travelling, they began producing hardy geraniums, exporting *Tropaeolum tuberosum* var. *lineomaculatum* 'Ken Aslet' and *Tropaeolum speciosum* to the Dutch, then turned to plant hunting after deciding to specialise in selling unusual plants. Most of the locations where they collect have a climate similar to northern Europe, where the greatest killer is winter wet.

Their first venture, a three-month trip to Taiwan, in 1992, was aided by a Taiwanese friend whose husband worked for the National Park Service. He organised permissions to collect in their target areas, including Taroko National Park, in the eastern part of the country where mountains rise above 3,000m. Before leaving on their trip the Wynn-Joneses visited Treborth Botanic Gardens, at Bangor University, to learn techniques for collecting, recording and taking herbarium specimens; Sue also made 200 cloth bags to take with them (they now use paper and plastic zip-lock bags). Most of the 1,500 seeds and plants they collected grew successfully, including a new species, *Actaea taiwanensis*, with spikes of scented white flowers. The area where they collected later disappeared in an earthquake; it is not unusual for whole mountainsides to drop away, and with that, their flora is lost forever.

VETERAN COLLECTORS

The Wynn-Joneses have now visited over 30 countries, among them Laos, Guatemala and Colombia and many others that have been poorly botanised. The couple share their knowledge with scientists and government agencies in these countries, who cannot afford to send out botanists of their own, and as part of their policy of giving back to the community, they always employ local guides.

Their collaboration with the Vietnam Environment Agency has been particularly rewarding. In 2003 Bleddyn discovered a botanical 'hot spot' but had little time to collect. Returning three years later, the couple found an epiphytic lily, growing in moss on vertical trunks and horizontal branches of large forest trees, well above the ground, at altitudes of 1,900 to 2,000m. Many thought it to be long-lost *Lilium arboricola*, introduced by Francis Kingdon-Ward (see pp164–169) in 1953 but lost to cultivation. However, Bleddyn believed it was something different, and he was right; it turned out to be a new species of lily (later named *Lilium eupetes*), with maroon-purple flowers. They also discovered what is believed to be a new genus, a tree with pink flowers in the family Hamamelidaceae, which has been incorrectly named *Disanthus ovatifolius* by an overzealous Russian collector. Conservation has become a massive part of the Wynn-Joneses' work, since it is a race against time to save plants like these – the Vietnamese government is encouraging people to settle in these habitats and they are rapidly being cleared of understory plants to grow black cardamom. Plants are being lost before being described, so Bleddyn and one of their employees are now making more freqent, shorter trips to Vietnam.

Days are long, and climbing steep mountains or travelling through dense jungle is physically demanding. At the end of each day, collections are recorded, photographs are captioned, often in tents battered by unforgiving weather. Plants are pressed and given an accession number, then as much detail as possible is written in a book and keyed into a laptop – soil type, altitude, location in sun or shade. GPS positioning provides exact locations and a mobile phone, laptop and Google Earth combine to reveal routes in remote locations. The Wynn-Joneses also use their phones to show people pictures of the plants they are seeking.

The Wynn-Joneses have made over 18,000 different collections to date. They began by looking mainly for herbaceous plants for shade, then woody plants, learning much from American plantsman and gardener Dan Hinkley when they collected together in the early days. The Wynn-Joneses taught Hinkley about herbaceous plants, and Hinkley taught them about woody plants. They then focused on the Araliaceae family, and genera like *Schefflera*, in a quest for plants with impact, discovering architectural *Schefflera taiwaniana* in the mountains, with up to 11 oval to oblong long, leafleted leaves and elegantly long purple leaf stalks, and *Fatsia polycarpa* in woodlands, with large, many-lobed, matt green leaves. Both look exotic and tender, but are actually tough plants.

THE CONTINUING QUEST

Since 2017, the couple have explored for plants in Georgia, looking for *Ruscus colchicus*, a highly suitable species for British horticulture. Working alongside botanists and taxonomists from the Moscow State University and the Batumi Botanical Garden in Georgia has allowed the Wynn-Joneses to collect previously unseen forms and varieties. Some Georgians are wild harvesting this plant for the cut-flower trade and flying them out to Moscow, a practice that is in the process of being regulated, since *R. colchicus* is rare in Georgia.

Bleddyn and Sue Wynn-Jones collected *Echeveria bicolor* in the Colombian Andes at 3,600m above sea level, at El Cocuy, in February 2015.

The Wynn-Joneses have been threatened by Maoist guerrillas in the Himalayas, spent the night in an old paddy field infested by thousands of leeches (only dissuaded from streaming into the tent by an application of insect repellent to the vents), have eaten anteater and have endured many of the hardships experienced by the early plant explorers. The latest challenge is legislation – the Convention on Biodiversity (CBD) has not only increased the amount of bureaucracy, but many countries also try and use it to generate 'additional' income.

Nevertheless, the couple find their travels extremely rewarding, and both enjoy experiencing different cultures. But it is the plants that matter above all. As Bleddyn has explained: 'There is no point in bringing back plants that are already in cultivation, unless they are new forms, but the pleasure is returning with surprises and bringing back plants with impact, that are of benefit to science, conservation and gardeners.'

Bleddyn & Sue Wynn-Jones:
INSPIRATION FOR GARDENERS

✤ One of Bleddyn Wynn-Jones's favourite finds is *Pachysandra axillaris* 'Crûg's Cover', collected in Sichuan in 2000 with Dan Hinkley after a trip with the Alaskan chapter of the North American Rock Garden Society. It was found on the lower slopes of Longzhoushan, in saturated ground under a small colony of *Hydrangea chinensis*. Very different from the well-known *P. terminalis,* it has scented flowers, like *Sarcococca,* on short, dense, upright spikes,

RIGHT The Wynn-Joneses collected *Acer amoenum* on Mount Matsuo in western Honshu, Japan, in the autumn of 2005. It is easy to grow and can be 4m tall.

BELOW *Pachysandra axillaris* 'Crûg's Cover', collected by Bleddyn, has proved to be very popular with gardeners. Resembling a *Sarcococca*, it has fragrant flowers, attractive glossy leaves and pink-red fruit.

and polished, undulating leathery leaves on short flexible, suckering stems. It performs very well as vigorous ground cover in moisture-retentive, fertile soil, in light to deep shade.

✤ Patrick Blanc (see pp212–217) fell in love with *Schefflera taiwaniana* when he visited Crûg Farm Plants. Arriving in the dark, he opened the shutters the following morning and could not believe what he saw. He was so excited about its structure he ran straight out into the garden to take a closer look. This small and elegant evergreen tree or large shrub, reaching 3 to 4m tall, was one of the Wynn-Joneses' first wild collections, from the high mountain forests of central Taiwan. Each long purple leaf stalk bears 7 to 11 oval to oblong leaflets. Green-tinted flowers are followed by purple fruit in winter.

✤ One of Sue's favourites is *Dahlia excelsa* 'Penelope Sky'. When she suggests to visitors they buy dahlias they sometimes turn up their noses, but when they see this plant they cannot believe its lovely foliage, beautiful flowers, and the height and structure of its bamboo-like stems. It was discovered on the moist mountains to the east of Oaxaca, southern Mexico, at around 2,500m and named for their youngest granddaughter. The upper parts bear bronzy pinnate foliage and large lilac-purple flowers from July to the first frost. It is ideal for a warm, sunny spot in moist, fertile, well-drained soil, protected from severe frost.

TOP RIGHT *Heloniopsis umbellata* is a rare clump-forming woodland perennial, introduced by the Wynn-Joneses and now prized in gardens.

RIGHT *Dahlia excelsa* (giant dahlia). Sue often recommends 'Penelope Sky', a cultivar of this species; it grows to 3m and it flowers from midsummer until the first frosts.

Patrick Blanc

DATE	BORN 1953
ORIGIN	FRANCE
MAJOR ACHIEVEMENT	VERTICAL-GARDEN PIONEER

Patrick Blanc is a left-field genius and a modern innovator of the 'green wall'. Usually dressed in green, with green hair and green nail varnish – on one long nail – he is part artist, part scientist, part landscape architect, and his ideas have revolutionised urban architecture. As a research botanist specialising in tropical forests, he has travelled worldwide, studying plants and habitats to develop his style. From shop fronts to high-rise dwellings and a *Robe Végétal* for Jean Paul Galtier, this horticultural icon has brought nature to the city.

Iris japonica,
fringed iris

Patrick Blanc became hooked on botany as a teenager and began experimenting with plants. At the age of 12, he created a rudimentary version of a plant wall, planting flowers on a mesh frame along the walls of his parents' garden and, after reading how rooting plants in water purifies them of nitrates, he created a biological water-filtration system for his aquaria and grew philodendrons up the wall. Fascinated by plants that flourish without soil and grow in low light, Blanc went on to study this phenomenon at the Pierre & Marie Curie University in Paris, dedicated himself to studying tropical plants and travelling to Malaysia and Thailand for the first time in the 1970s to observe first-hand how plants grow on rocks or in the forest understory. One day, when a hideous new wall was constructed in front of his living room, he was inspired to develop the concept of a frost-resistant evergreen wall, so immersed himself in the flora of the temperate zones. With a PhD in natural sciences, he has been a professor and researcher at the National Center for Scientific Research in Paris for over 25 years. His living laboratory is his home – indoors and out, its walls are home to an ecosystem of birds, lizards, frogs and over 250 plant species.

THE GREEN WALL

Blanc is inspired by nature and vertical habitats such as the rocks, cliffs and karst in rainforests and other moist habitats he visits on research trips. Here, plants grow on a thin layer of moss, or attach themselves directly onto rocks and trees by their roots, fed by a constant flow of nutrient-rich water. Soil, therefore, is not essential to their growth. Blanc has found that there are various other plants that can grow this way, such as drought-tolerant lavender and moisture-tolerant *Iris japonica* and *Nandina domestica* (pictured on p212 and p215, respectively).

The *mur végétal* (plant wall) structure that Blanc patented in 1988 after creating his first installation at the Cité des Sciences et de l'Industrie in Paris, used a simple system of hydroponics. Two 3mm layers of polyamide felt, mimicking the mosses into which the plants naturally root, were stapled onto a 10mm PVC plate attached to a metal frame. A network of pipes at the top of the wall automatically drip-fed the plants with a nutrient solution, which flowed down the wall, soaking the capillary matting. Excess liquid was then collected in a gutter at the bottom of the wall and recycled through the system. Blanc's extensive experiments and encyclopaedic knowledge of plants and ecosystems enabled him to select plants that would thrive in this habitat and at each different point on the wall.

Each of Blanc's planting plans is drawn up on paper – a wavy design, usually from top right to bottom left, that reflects the formations he has seen on precipices and screes in the wild, where plants often spread out in smooth diagonals along water channels. As he explains, 'My scientific approach is essential for designing the whole system and for selecting the plant species for each peculiar location'. The rainforest bears similarities with an urban environment, and the height of city buildings reflects the ecological niches in a rainforest.

INTERNATIONAL SUCCESS

Blanc's work has taken him beyond France – his vertical gardens can now be seen in Spain, the United States, India, Japan, Malaysia, Poland, Germany and Hong Kong, gracing embassies, shopping malls and hotels, and his portfolio continues to grow. His installation at the Musée du quai Branly, created in 2005, includes 15,000 plants from 150 species growing on the outer walls, along with vertical gardens in the museum's administration offices. He has also created the tallest garden in the world – at One Central Park in Sydney, Australia, where vegetation reaches 116m into the sky. These hanging vertical gardens are planted with 35,000 green wall plants from 350 different species, the 23 green walls covering a total of 1,200sq m.

Boehmeria macrophylla, a Himalayan perennial herb in the nettle family, is one of many striking foliage plants grown in Blanc's home.

His wall at the Shin-Yamaguchi station in Japan was planted with 100 different species of native plants collected on expeditions in 2012 and 2013; at 103m, his rainforest Chandelier at EmQuartier in Bangkok is the longest free-standing structure to be covered by plants; and with around 200 different species of climbing plants, the installation at Le Nouvel in Kuala Lumpur features the highest vine biodiversity on a high-rise building. As an artist, all of Blanc's works are copyrighted, unique and never replicated.

Maintenance of his walls is minimal; with careful plant selection, green walls do not need to be trimmed, and the density of the planting prevents weeds from germinating. At the time of writing, a wall that Blanc designed for the Cartier Foundation for Contemporary Art in Paris has never been pruned.

Nandina domestica, sacred bamboo

Blanc and the green walls he has created have won many accolades, including a botany award from the French Academy of Sciences, a top 50 best invention of the year from *Time* magazine, and an Honorary Fellowship from the Royal Institute of British Architects. His international profile has brought the idea of vertical planting to a wider audience, but a lifetime dedicated to the acquisition of knowledge and perfecting his art mean that his is often copied but never bettered: 'the horizontal is finished ... but the vertical is still free'.

Patrick Blanc:
INSPIRATION FOR GARDENERS

❧ Patrick Blanc discovered a new species, which was named *Begonia blancii*, near the Bulalakaw Falls in Palawan, Philippines. It has distinctive triangular leaves with rounded corners. The leaves may be green, mottled with darker green, dark green with slightly paler veins, or blackish green. Only known from one location, this plant grows attached to the sides of small boulders that are almost devoid of soil and moss. The plant roots grow directly onto the surface and the fleshy leaves remain on the plant during the dry season. Now available commercially, it should be grown in organic, rich, moisture-retentive and free-draining

compost, with added perlite, or similar, for drainage. It must be kept in moderate to low light, and watered with soft, tepid water at 15 to 30°C. Stand it on a tray of pebbles filled with water to the bottom of the pot, to increase atmospheric humidity, or lightly mist around the plant with soft water, but do not wet the foliage. Feed it with general fertiliser while in active growth.

❧ Blanc's work demonstrates the impact and importance of foliage in design. Flowering in a garden may ebb and flow, but it is foliage, with its varying shapes and textures, that provides a constant backcloth to the floral displays. Flowers are not the only way of bringing colour to a garden; variegated or coloured leaves have the same effect.

❧ Every one of Blanc's planting schemes is a celebration of diversity – even smaller works include around 100 different varieties. This is not just to create changing textures and colours in the design but because biodiversity keeps pests and diseases away. This reflects a technique used in traditional cottage gardens, where vegetables were dotted among the flowers, encouraging natural predators for pests, while ensuring that if one group was affected, the problem would not decimate the whole crop because there was a good chance that other clumps scattered elsewhere around the garden would stay healthy and problem-free.

BELOW Blanc uses hellebores on his green walls for their texture and colour. On the ground, *Helleborus argutifolius* (holly-leaved hellebore) is an evergreen perennial for alkaline to neutral soil.

RIGHT Blanc's breathtaking green walls, which can use thousands of plants from hundreds of different species, should prove to every gardener that there is more than just ivy for covering walls.

Bibliography

Sources consulted during research include books, scientific papers, websites and journals, primarily obtained through JSTOR, the Biodiversity Heritage Library and Hertfordshire libraries. Among the sources: the *Dictionary of National Biography*, the Royal Horticultural Society magazine, *The Garden*, *Curtis's Botanical Magazine*, *The Gardeners' Chronicle*, *The Plantsman*, *Garden History*, *Transactions of the Linnean Society*, *Transactions of the American Philosophical Society*, *Transactions and Proceedings of the Royal Society of New Zealand*, *Gardens Illustrated* and *Agricultural Bulletin of the Straits and Federated Malay States*.

Books include:

Barry, Bernice (2016) *Georgiana Molloy: The Mind That Shines*. Picador.

Bartram, William (1791) *Travels Through North and South Carolina, Georgia, East and West Florida*. James & Johnson.

Bellairs, Nona (1865) *Hardy Ferns: How I Collected and Cultivated Them*. Smith, Elder and Co.

Blunt, Wilfrid (2004) *Linnaeus, The Compleat Naturalist* (revised edition). Frances Lincoln.

Burbank, Luther (2004) *Some Interesting Failures: The Petunia with the Tobacco Habit and Others* (facsimile of 1914 edition). Athena University Press.

Dampier, William (2007) *A New Voyage Round the World* (facsimile of 1703 edition). 1500 Books.

Dandy, James (1958) *The Sloane Herbarium: An Annotated List of the* Horti Sicci *Composing it; with Biographical Details of the Principal Contributors*. British Museum.

Desmond, Ray (1999) *Sir Joseph Dalton Hooker: Traveller and Plant Collector*. ACC Art Books.

Desmond, Ray (2007) *The History of The Royal Botanic Gardens, Kew* (2nd edition). Royal Botanic Gardens.

Faulkner, Thomas (1813) *An Historical and Topographical Account of Fulham; Including the Hamlet of Hammersmith and Fulham*. J. Tilling.

Fuchs, Leonard (2016) *The New Herbal of 1543* (facsimile of 1543 edition). Taschen.

Gunther, Robert W. T. Ed. (1928) *Further Correspondence of John Ray*. Ray Society.

Hayavadana Rao, C. Ed. (1915) *The Indian Biographical Dictionary*. Pillar & Co.

Kingdon-Ward, Francis (1913) *The Land of the Blue Poppy: Travels of a Naturalist in Eastern Tibet*. Cambridge University Press.

Kingdon-Ward, Jean (1952) *My Hill So Strong*. Jonathan Cape.

Lazenby, Elizabeth Mary (1995) *The* Historia Plantarum Generalis *of John Ray: Book I – A Translation and Commentary.* Newcastle University.

Linnaeus, Carl (1737) *Genera Plantarum.* Conradum and Georg. Jac. Wishoff.

Linnaeus, Carl (1737) *Hortus Cliffortianus.* Amsteldami.

McLean, Brenda (2009) *George Forrest: Plant Hunter.* ACC Art Books.

Nelson, E. Charles (2014) *Shadow Among Splendours: Lady Charlotte Wheeler-Cuffe's Adventures Among the Flowers of Burma.* National Botanic Gardens of Ireland.

North, Marianne (1893) *Recollections of a Happy Life: Being the Autobiography of Marianne North.* Macmillan & Co.

Oliver, Francis. Ed. (1913) *Makers of British Botany.* Cambridge University Press.

Pavord, Anna (2005) *The Naming of Names: The Search for Order in the World of Garden Plants.* Bloomsbury.

Pringle, Peter (2008) *The Murder of Nikolai Vavilov.* Simon & Schuster.

Pulteney, Richard (1790) *Historical and Biographical Sketches of the Progress of Botany in England* (volume two). T. Cadell.

Raffauf, Robert and Schultes, Richard Evans (1990) *The Healing Forest: Medicinal and Toxic Plants of the Northwest Amazonia.* Dioscorides Press.

Smith, James Edward (1825) *The English Flora.* Longman, Hurst, Rees, Orme, Brown and Green.

Stearn, William T., (2002) *The Genus* Epimedium *and other Herbaceous Berberidaceae* (revised edition). Royal Botanic Gardens.

Stearn, William T. (1999) *John Lindley, 1799–1865: Bi-centenary Celebration Volume: Gardener – Botanist and Pioneer Orchidologist.* Antique Collectors' Club.

Stearn, William T. (1992) *Stearn's Dictionary of Plant Names for Gardeners.* Cassell Illustrated.

Turner, William (1548) *The Names of Herbes.* The English Dialect Society.

Turner, William (1995) *A New Herball: Parts I* (facsimile of 1551 edition). Cambridge University Press.

Wilson, Ernest H., (1917) *Aristocrats of the Garden.* Doubleday, Page & Company.

Index

Image credits

5, 166 © Lyubov Tolstova | Shutterstock. 8, 16 (bottom), 17, 26 (right), 56 (right), 68 (right), 74 (right), 86 (right) © Wellcome Collection. 12 © Ligak | Shutterstock. 13 (top) © VicW | Shutterstock. 13 (bottom) © nadtochiy | Shutterstock. 18 (top) © Sealstep | Shutterstock. 18 (bottom) © IanRedding | Shutterstock. 19 (top) © Niwat.koh | Shutterstock. 19 (bottom) © Olga Miltsova | Shutterstock. 20 © alex74 | Shutterstock. 23, 34, 74 (left), 106, 122 (left), 158 (right), 164 (right) © RHS | Lindley Library. 24 © blickwinkel | Alamy Stock Photo. 25 © Sophie Davies | Alamy Stock Photo. 30 (left) © Rob Whitworth Garden Photography | Alamy Stock Photo. 30 (right) © Ole Schoener | Shutterstock. 31 (top) © Gary K Smith | Alamy Stock Photo. 31 (bottom) © Elena Koromyslova | Shutterstock. 36 © FarOutFlora | Flickr Commons. 37 (top) © alybaba | Shutterstock. 37 (bottom), 42 © REDA &CO srl | Alamy Stock Photo. 43 (top) © Vladimir Gjorgiev | Shutterstock. 43 (bottom) © J Need | Shutterstock. 48 © haris M | Shutterstock. 49 (top) © Casliber | Creative Commons. 49 (bottom) © Geoff Derrin | Creative Commons. 52, 64 © The Natural History Museum | Alamy Stock Photo. 54 © Paul Asman and Jill Lenoble | Flickr Commons. 55 (top) © Graham Prentice | Shutterstock. 55 (bottom) © Ariel Bravy | Shutterstock. 60 (left) © Wonderful Nature | Shutterstock. 60 (right) © Anastasios71 | Shutterstock. 61 (top) © ncristian | Shutterstock. 61 (bottom) © A. Barra | Creative Commons. 66 © adaptice photography | Shutterstock. 67 (top) © John Richmond | Alamy Stock Photo. 67 (bottom) © RM Floral | Alamy Stock Photo. 72 © aniana | Shutterstock. 73 © haris M | Shutterstock. 78 (top) © Anna Gratys | Shutterstock. 78 (bottom) © Auscape International Pty Ltd | Alamy Stock Photo. 79 (top) © Martin Fowler | Shutterstock. 79 (bottom) © Eileen Kumpf | Shutterstock. 84 (left) © Gl0ck | Shutterstock. 84 (right) © RHS | Carol Sheppard. 85 (both) © Del Boy | Shutterstock. 90 © Sharon Day | Shutterstock. 91 (top) © Tamara Kulikova | Shutterstock. 91 (bottom) © Old Man Stocker | Shutterstock. 96 © skyfish | Shutterstock. 97, 169 (bottom) © Avalon/Photoshot License | Alamy Stock Photo. 102 © Universal Images Group North America LLC |

DeAgostini | Alamy Stock Photo. 103 (top) © anastas_styles | Shutterstock. 103 (bottom) © Jessika Knaupe | Shutterstock. 107 © De Agostini Picture Library | De Agostini | Getty images. 108 (left) © Kathy Clark | Shutterstock. 108 (right) © ZayacSK | Shutterstock. 109 (top) © Steffen Hauser | botanikfoto | Alamy Stock Photo. 109 (middle) © sarintra chimphoolsuk | Shutterstock. 109 (bottom) © Alpsdake | Creative Commons. 114 © RHS | Herbarium. 115 (top) © BENCHA STEWART | Shutterstock. 115 (bottom), 192, 204 (left), 210 (bottom) © RHS | Tim Sandall. 120 (left) © DGSHUT | Shutterstock. 120 (right) © J Need | Shutterstock. 121 (top) © RukiMedia | Shutterstock. 121 (bottom) © Steve Cordory | Shutterstock. 126 © ntdanai | Shutterstock. 127 (top) © Kathy deWitt | Alamy Stock Photo. 127 (bottom) © Julie Fryer pics | Alamy Stock Photo. 128 (right) © Paul Fearn | Alamy Stock Photo. 132 © RHS | Graham Titchmarsh. 133 (top) © ahau1969 | Shutterstock. 133 (bottom) © Alice Heart | Shutterstock. 136 (both) © Biodiversity Heritage Library | Flickr Commons. 138 © Jack Hong | Shutterstock. 139 (top) © sylviane decleir | Shutterstock. 139 (bottom) © Kenneth Keifer | Shutterstock. 144 (top), 211 (top) © Garden World Images Ltd | Alamy Stock Photo. 144 (bottom) © Peter Turner Photography | Shutterstock. 145 (top) © tamu1500 | Shutterstock. 145 (bottom) © Edgar Lee Espe | Shutterstock. 150 © Nature Photographers Ltd | Alamy Stock Photo. 151 © Rex May | Alamy Stock Photo. 152 (right) © RHS. 156 (left) © Layue | Shutterstock. 157 (top) © RHS | Rodney Lay. 157 (bottom) © HHelene | Shutterstock. 162 (top) © asdfawev | Flickr Commons. 162 (bottom) © Alexandra Giese | Shutterstock. 163 (top) © kukuruxa | Shutterstock. 163 (bottom) © Nate Allred | Shutterstock. 168 (left) © KirinX | Creative Commons. 168 (right) © Girija and Viru Viraraghavan. 169 (top) © travelview | Shutterstock. 174 © mpetersheim | Shutterstock. 175 (top) © Irina Borsuchenko | Shutterstock. 175 (bottom) © 271 EAK 7 Images. 216 © Sample Stars | Shutterstock. 217 © flowerphotos | Alamy Stock Photo. Portrait sketches on pp50, 92, 146, 182, 194 and 200 by Ian Durneen © The Bright Press. All other images are in the public domain.

Acknowledgments

I would like thank the following for their help during the preparation of this book: James Evans, Associate Publisher, and Lucy York, Senior Editor, at The Bright Press; Katriona Feinstein, Project Editor, for her endless patience and good humour; Lindsey Johns, for selecting such wonderful images; Julia Nurse, Collections Researcher at the Wellcome Library, for being so generous with her time and knowledge; Bernice Barry, expert on Georgiana Molloy, for her constant help and prompt replies to my many emails; Jessica Biggs, for her research and transcription; Jack Seddon and Hertfordshire Libraries, for facilitating library access; the RHS library: Fiona Davison, Crestina Forcina and Susan Robin, for providing books and texts; Dr Stephen Harris, Druce Curator (Herbaria), and Serena Marner, Herbarium Manager of Oxford University; Dr Isabelle Charmantier, Deputy Collections Manager and Librarian at the Linnaean Society; Michael Marriott, Senior Rosarian; rose

breeders Calvin and Heather Horner; Deborah Jordan at Middleton Hall Trust; Dr Martin Gardner MBE, for his text on conifer conservation; Chris Lane of the RHS Woody Plant Committee; Tony Hall, Arboretum and Gardens Manager; Miranda Janatka, Collections Horticulturist at RBG Kew, and Leonie Paterson Archivist, at RBG Edinburgh; Oliver Tooley, for information on Frank Kingdon-Ward; Robert Vernon of Bluebell Nursery and Arboretum, for the story of *Liquidambar styraciflua* 'Lane Roberts'; Sorrel Everton and Mike Grant, for their help while researching Mikinori Ogisu; John Anderson, Keeper of the Gardens, and Harvey Stephens, Deputy Keeper of the Gardens, at Windsor Great Park; Hannah Newton, Dan Cocker and Laurence Bassett at Somethin' Else Productions; Martin and Nikki at The Local; Dan Wilson, Bill and Joy Parkin, Gill, Jessica, Henry and Chloe, for their help and support.